To
John Wesley and Lennie Priser
From
Your Christian Friend,
Henry Beer,
1-12-'59.

HYMNS OF ZION

A Selection of Sacred Songs and
Hymns for Devotional Use

†

PUBLISHED BY
Apostolic Christian Publishing Company
MILFORD, INDIANA

FOREWORD

Next in importance to the ministry of God's word is the worship of God in song by true believers. The aspiration of the souls of men and the adoration of God is often best expressed in hymns and songs of praise. The blessings of joy and peace found in God through a born-again experience moves men and women to express themselves in the God-given gift of song.

The consoling and mellowing influence of worship in song has often constrained the unconverted man to turn to God and through faith in Him find salvation for his soul.

HYMNS OF ZION is presented to the Church and Sunday School for worship and devotional use. This new hymnal is made up of a selection of hymns found in the hymnal, "Songs and Hymns of Zion," combined with the hymns found in "Songs of Praise and Worship," together with numerous other meaningful hymns adapted for devotional use. The wide range of topics should make it especially suited to the needs of Sunday School children.

The past, present, and future is portrayed in song. Suitable hymns are presented for Christmas, Good Friday, Repose in the Grave, Easter, Resurrection, Ascension, The Millennial Reign, and The Glories Around the Throne.

In HYMNS OF ZION are found many old favorites which the older brethren will be happy to have brought into use; also, such hymns not often found in present day hymnals, and new songs recently set to music. Each hymn has been chosen from the standpoint of its spiritual worth and scriptural meaning. The sweet melodies and tender words should have a strong appeal to children, to young Christians, as well as to those who are older and more matured in faith.

HYMNS OF ZION is sent forth trusting that it will prove a great blessing wherever it is used.

THE PUBLISHERS

Printed and bound by
THE RODEHEAVER COMPANY
Winona Lake, Indiana

HYMNS OF ZION

A Selection of Sacred Songs and

Hymns for Devotional Use

1 BEFORE THE MEETING

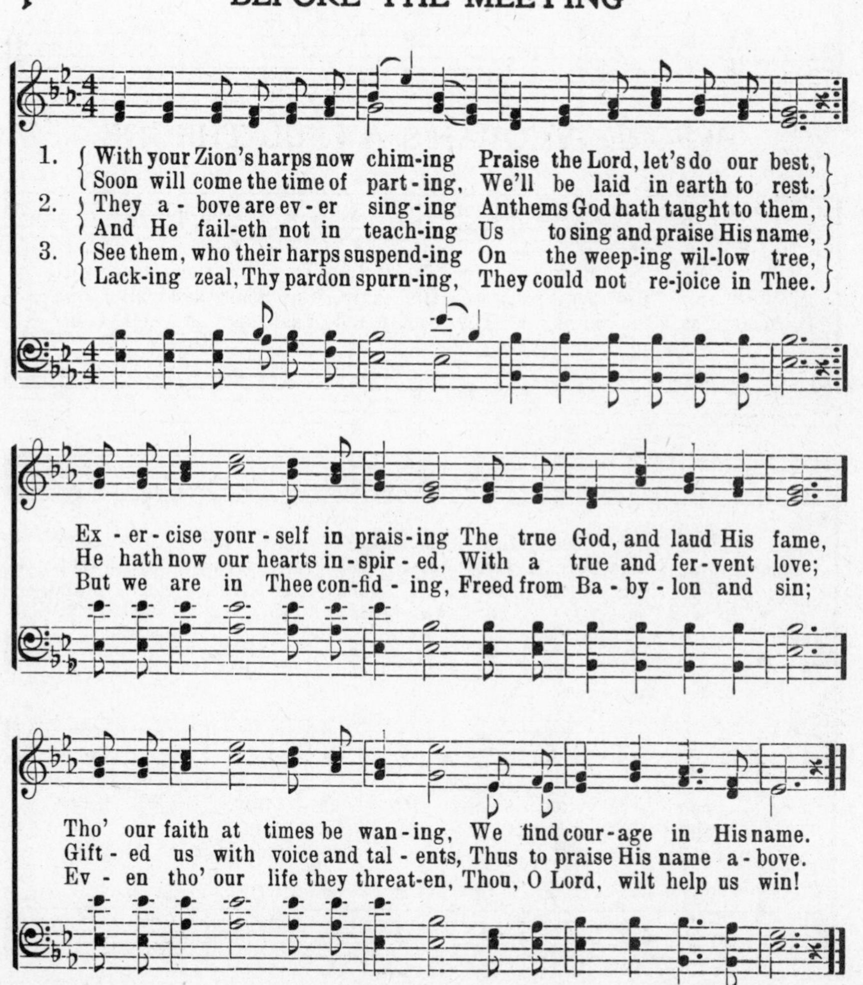

1. With your Zion's harps now chim-ing Praise the Lord, let's do our best,
Soon will come the time of part-ing, We'll be laid in earth to rest.
2. They a-bove are ev-er sing-ing Anthems God hath taught to them,
And He fail-eth not in teach-ing Us to sing and praise His name,
3. See them, who their harps suspend-ing On the weep-ing wil-low tree,
Lack-ing zeal, Thy pardon spurn-ing, They could not re-joice in Thee.
Ex-er-cise your-self in prais-ing The true God, and laud His fame,
He hath now our hearts in-spir-ed, With a true and fer-vent love;
But we are in Thee con-fid-ing, Freed from Ba-by-lon and sin;
Tho' our faith at times be wan-ing, We find cour-age in His name.
Gift-ed us with voice and tal-ents, Thus to praise His name a-bove.
Ev-en tho' our life they threat-en, Thou, O Lord, wilt help us win!

2 OPENING HYMN

Hab. 2: 20

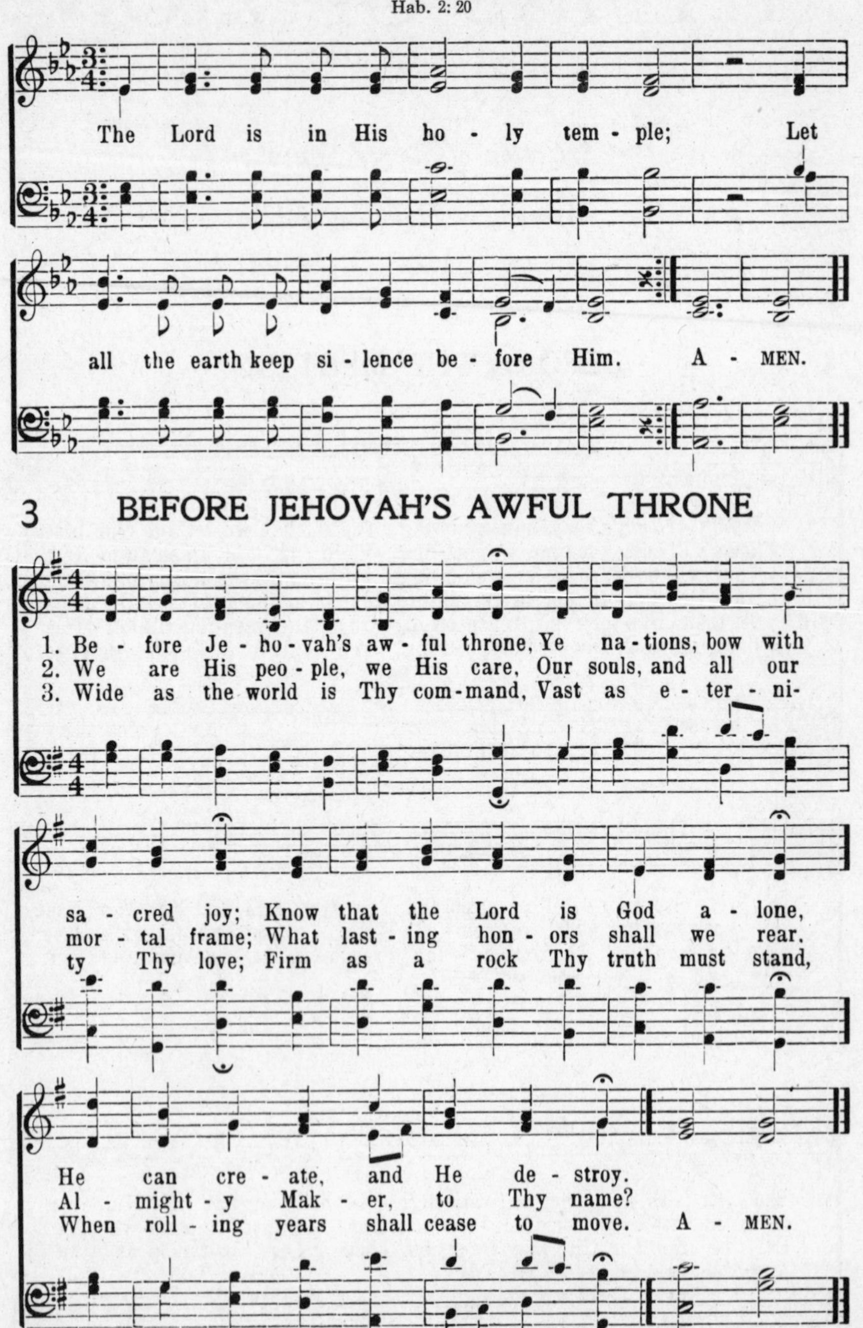
The Lord is in His ho - ly tem - ple; Let
all the earth keep si - lence be - fore Him. A - MEN.
3 BEFORE JEHOVAH'S AWFUL THRONE
1. Be - fore Je - ho - vah's aw - ful throne, Ye na - tions, bow with
2. We are His peo - ple, we His care, Our souls, and all our
3. Wide as the world is Thy com - mand, Vast as e - ter - ni-
sa - cred joy; Know that the Lord is God a - lone,
mor - tal frame; What last - ing hon - ors shall we rear,
ty Thy love; Firm as a rock Thy truth must stand,
He can cre - ate, and He de - stroy.
Al - might - y Mak - er, to Thy name?
When roll - ing years shall cease to move. A - MEN.

GOD IS OUR REFUGE

O. M. S. — O. M. Seamans

1. God is our ref-uge and our strength, A ver - y pres-ent help in-deed;
2. Safe in His ten-der lov-ing care, We have no fear of what shall be,
3. Sure, in the cit - y of our King Se - cure we rest from all a - larm;
4. While heathen rage and kingdoms move, And des - o - la-tions sweep the land;
5. Soon will the day of vic - t'ry come, When wars shall cease in all the earth;
He in the time of trou-ble sends His grace to meet our ev-'ry need.
E'en tho' the earth should be removed, And mountains cast in - to the sea.
For God is in the midst of her, To shield His peo-ple from all harm.
The Lord of hosts is with us still, To save us by His might-y hand.
Soon shall e - ter-nal peace be ours. And new Cre - a - tion have her birth.
CHORUS
God........ is our ref - - - uge, God.................
God is our ref-uge, ref-uge and our strength, God is our ref - uge,
is our ref- - - - uge, With might - y arm re - vealed, He
is our ref-uge and our strength;
is our help and shield, God is our ref - uge and our strength.

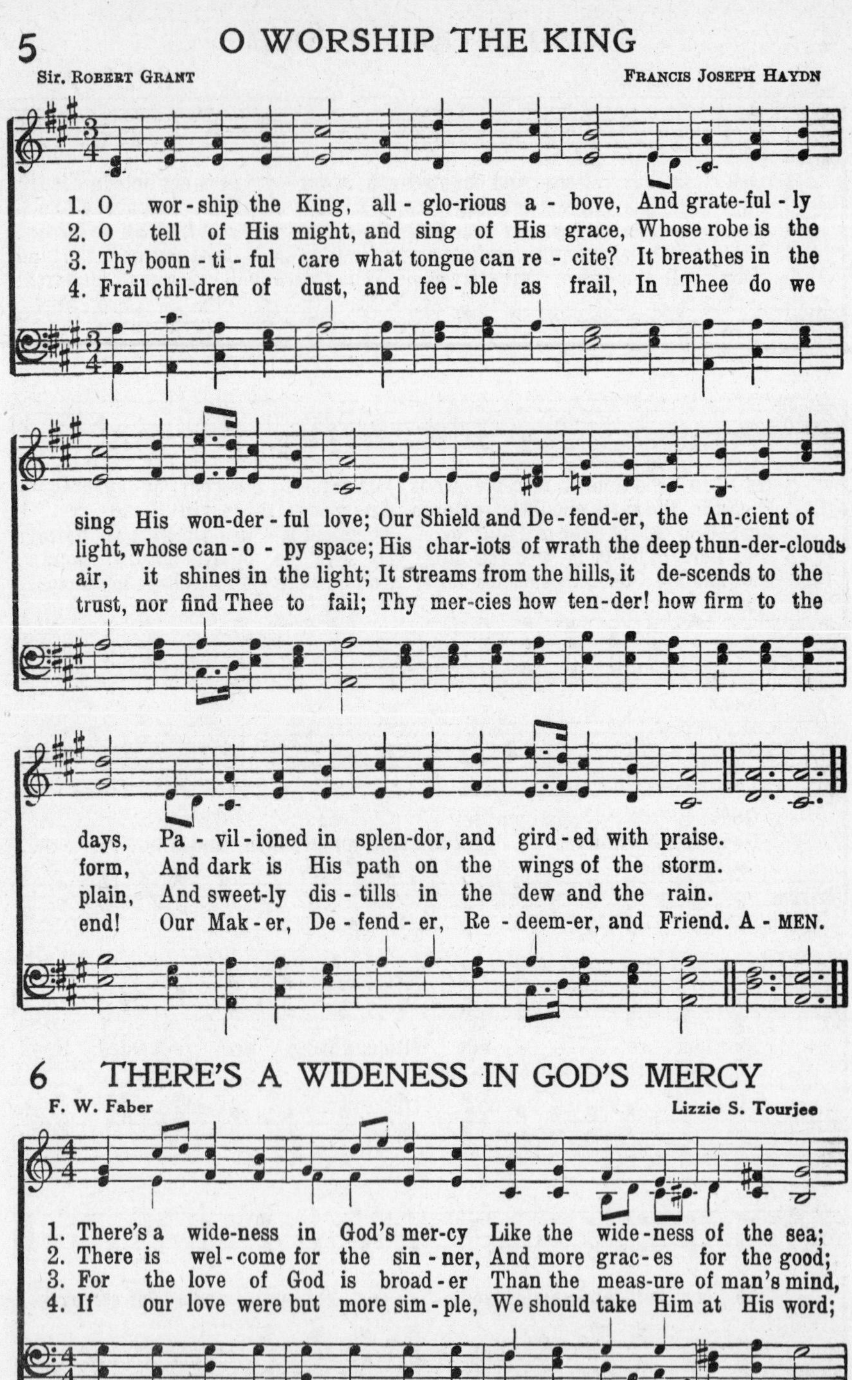
5 O WORSHIP THE KING
Sir. Robert Grant
Francis Joseph Haydn
1. O wor-ship the King, all-glo-rious a-bove, And grate-ful-ly sing His won-der-ful love; Our Shield and De-fend-er, the An-cient of days, Pa-vil-ioned in splen-dor, and gird-ed with praise.
2. O tell of His might, and sing of His grace, Whose robe is the light, whose can-o-py space; His char-iots of wrath the deep thun-der-clouds form, And dark is His path on the wings of the storm.
3. Thy boun-ti-ful care what tongue can re-cite? It breathes in the air, it shines in the light; It streams from the hills, it de-scends to the plain, And sweet-ly dis-tills in the dew and the rain.
4. Frail chil-dren of dust, and fee-ble as frail, In Thee do we trust, nor find Thee to fail; Thy mer-cies how ten-der! how firm to the end! Our Mak-er, De-fend-er, Re-deem-er, and Friend. A-men.
6 THERE'S A WIDENESS IN GOD'S MERCY
F. W. Faber
Lizzie S. Tourjee
1. There's a wide-ness in God's mer-cy Like the wide-ness of the sea;
2. There is wel-come for the sin-ner, And more grac-es for the good;
3. For the love of God is broad-er Than the meas-ure of man's mind,
4. If our love were but more sim-ple, We should take Him at His word;

THERE'S A WIDENESS IN GOD'S MERCY

There's a kind - ness in His jus - tice, Which is more than lib - er - ty.
There is mer - cy with the Sav - iour; There is heal-ing in His blood.
And the heart of the E - ter - nal Is most won - der - ful - ly kind.
And our lives would be all sun-shine In the sweet-ness of our Lord.

7 CHRISTIAN GREETINGS

1. {Greetings be to you, our breth-ren, To our sis - ters in the Lord,
{Here from far and near as - sem - bled, Gathered here in one ac - cord.
2. {Peace and love im - pel the greet-ing, Greetings do our love im - part;
{Christians greetings are a bless-ing, As a pray'r con - sole the heart.
3. {Greetings to our faith-ful breth-ren, Heart and voice we do em - ploy;
{Wish-ing them the Fa-ther's near-ness, Tho' their lot be woe or joy.
4. {Farewell greetings, ho - ly tok - ens, Fill the heart with pain and tears;
{Farewell, farewell, to our breth-ren, When are spent our earth-ly years.

Wel - come, wel-come, All ye loved ones: Greetings in the Saviour's name.
There is com-fort, peace and bless - ing, Of a greet-ing in the Lord.
There's a bless-ing in the greet - ing, Giv - en in the Sav-iour's name.
Res - ur - rec - tion, heav'nly greet-ings, In the pres-ence of our Lord.

8 DAY IS DYING IN THE WEST

Mary A. Lathbury — William F. Sherwin

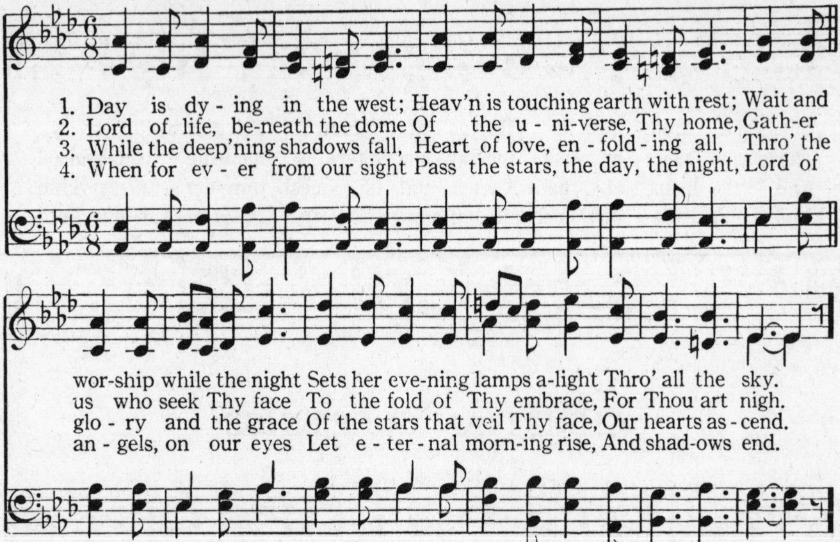

1. Day is dy - ing in the west; Heav'n is touching earth with rest; Wait and wor-ship while the night Sets her eve-ning lamps a-light Thro' all the sky.
2. Lord of life, be-neath the dome Of the u - ni-verse, Thy home, Gath-er us who seek Thy face To the fold of Thy embrace, For Thou art nigh.
3. While the deep'ning shadows fall, Heart of love, en - fold - ing all, Thro' the glo - ry and the grace Of the stars that veil Thy face, Our hearts as - cend.
4. When for ev - er from our sight Pass the stars, the day, the night, Lord of an - gels, on our eyes Let e - ter - nal morn-ing rise, And shad-ows end.

REFRAIN

Ho - ly, Ho - ly, Ho - ly, Lord God of Hosts! Heav'n and earth are full of Thee; Heav'n and earth are praising Thee, O Lord Most High!

9 HOW GENTLE GOD'S COMMANDS

Philip Doddridge — Hans George Naegeli

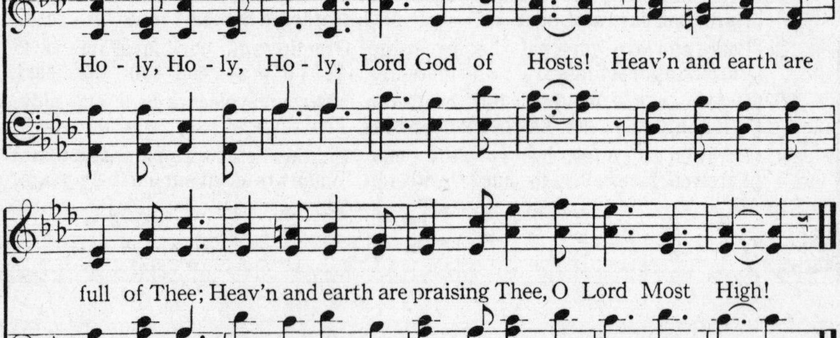

1. How gen - tle God's com-mands! How kind His pre - cepts are!
2. Be - neath His watch-ful eye His saints se - cure - ly dwell;
3. Why should this anx - ious load Press down your wea - ry mind?
4. His good-ness stands ap-proved, Un - changed from day to day:

HOW GENTLE GOD'S COMMANDS

Come, cast your bur-dens on the Lord, And trust His con-stant care.
That hand which bears all na - ture up Shall guard His chil-dren well.
Haste to your heav'nly Fa-ther's throne, And sweet re - fresh-ment find.
I'll drop my bur-den at His feet, And bear a song a - way.
10 BREAK THOU THE BREAD OF LIFE
Mary Ann Lathbury
William L. Sherwin
1. Break Thou the bread of life, Dear Lord, to me, As Thou didst break the loaves Be - side the sea; Be - yond the sa - cred page I seek Thee, Lord; My spir - it pants for Thee, O liv - ing Word!
2. Bless Thou the truth, dear Lord, To me, to me, As Thou didst bless the bread By Gal - i - lee; Then shall all bond - age cease, All fet - ters fall; And I shall find my peace, My All - in - All.
3. Teach me to live, dear Lord, On - ly for Thee, As Thy dis - ci - ples lived In Gal - i - lee; Then, all my strug-gles o'er, Then, vic - t'ry won, I shall be-hold Thee, Lord, The Liv - ing - one.

11 HOW FIRM A FOUNDATION, YE SAINTS

1. How firm a foun-da-tion, ye saints of the Lord, Is laid for your
2. "Fear not, I am with thee, O be not dis-mayed, For I am thy
3. When thru the deep wa-ters I call thee to go, The riv-ers of
4 When thru fier-y tri-als thy path-way shall lie, My grace, all-suf-
5. The soul that on Je-sus hath leaned for re-pose, I will not, I
faith in His ex-cel-lent word! What more can He say than to
God, and will still give thee aid; I'll strength-en thee, help thee, and
sor-row shall not o-ver-flow; For I will be with thee, thy
fi-cient, shall be thy sup-ply; The flame shall not hurt thee; I
will not de-sert to his foes; That soul, though all hell should en-
you He hath said, To you, who for ref-uge to Je-sus have
cause thee to stand, Up-held by My right-eous, om-nip-o-tent
trou-bles to bless, And sanc-ti-fy to thee thy deep-est dis-
on-ly de-sign Thy dross to con-sume, and thy gold to re-
deav-or to shake, I'll nev-er, no nev-er, no nev-er for-
fled, To you who for ref-uge to Je-sus have fled?
hand, Up-held by My right-eous, om-nip-o-tent hand.
t ess. And sanc-ti-fy to thee thy deep-est dis-tress.
fine. Thy dross to con-sume, and thy gold to re-fine.
sake, I'll nev-er, no nev-er, no nev-er for-sake!"

12 HOW PRECIOUS IS THE BOOK DIVINE

John Fawcett — James Walch

1. How pre-cious is the Book di-vine, By in - spi-ra - tion giv'n!
2. Its light de-scend-ing from a-bove, Our gloom-y world to cheer,
3. It shows to man his wand'ring ways, And where his feet have trod;
4. O'er all the strait and nar - row way Its ra - diant beams are cast;
5. It sweet - ly cheers our faint-ing hearts In this dark vale of tears;
6. This lamp thro' all the drear - y night Of life shall guide our way,
Bright as a lamp its doc-trines shine, To guide our souls to heav'n.
Dis - plays a Sav - iour's bound-less love, And brings His glo - ries near.
And brings to view the matchless grace Of a for - giv - ing God.
A light whose nev - er wea - ry ray Grows brightest at the last.
Life, light, and com - fort it im - parts, And calms our anx - ious fears.
Till we be - hold the clear-er light Of an e - ter - nal day.
13 MY SOUL, BE ON THY GUARD
George Heath
Lowell Mason
1. My soul, be on thy guard; Ten thou-sand foes a - rise.
2. O watch, and fight, and pray; The bat - tle ne'er give o'er;
3. Ne'er think the vic - t'ry won, Nor lay thine ar - mor down;
4. Fight on, my soul, till death shall bring thee to thy God;
The hosts of sin are press - ing hard To draw Thee from the skies.
Re - new it bold - ly ev - 'ry day, And help di - vine im - plore.
The work of faith will not be done, Till thou ob - tain the crown.
He'll take thee at thy part - ing breath, To His di - vine a - bode.

14 AS WITH GLADNESS MEN OF OLD

1. As with glad-ness men of old Did the guid-ing star be-hold;
2. As with joy-ful steps they sped To that low-ly man-ger bed,
3. As they of-fered gifts most rare, At that man-ger rude and bare,
4. Ho-ly Je-sus, ev-'ry day, Keep us in the nar-row way,

As with joy they hailed its light, Lead-ing on-ward, beam-ing bright;
There to bend the knee be-fore Him whom heav'n and earth a-dore;
So may we with ho-ly joy, Pure and free from sin's al-loy,
And, when earth-ly things are past, Bring our ran-somed souls at last,

So, most gra-cious Lord, may we Ev-er-more be led to Thee.
So may we with will-ing feet Ev-er seek Thy mer-cy seat.
All our costli-est treas-ures bring, Christ, to Thee, our heav'n-ly King.
Where they need no star to guide, Where no clouds Thy glo-ry hide.

15 QUIET, LORD, MY FROWARD HEART

Isa. 32:18

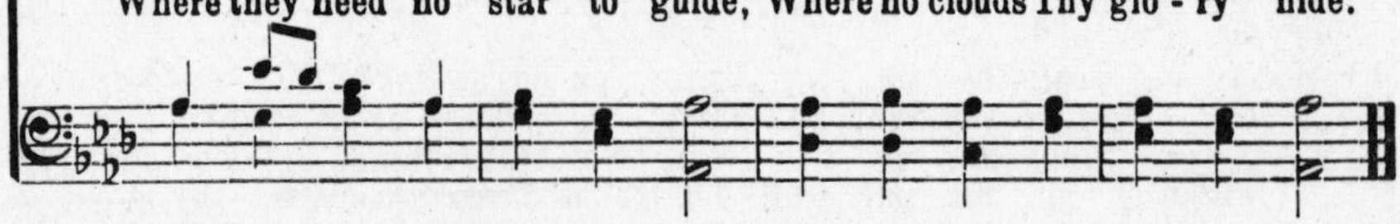

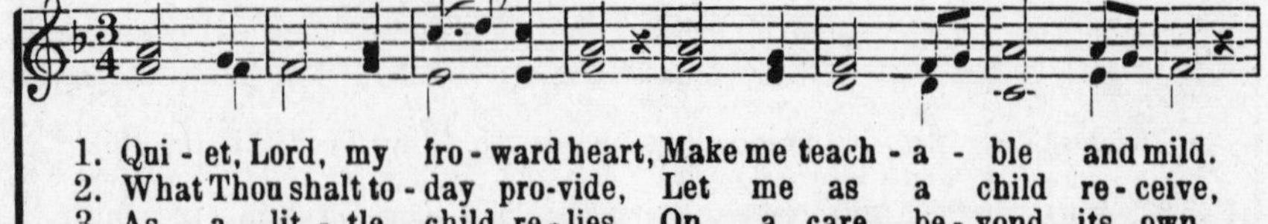
1. Qui-et, Lord, my fro-ward heart, Make me teach-a-ble and mild.
2. What Thou shalt to-day pro-vide, Let me as a child re-ceive,
3. As a lit-tle child re-lies On a care be-yond its own,

QUIET, LORD, MY FROWARD HEART

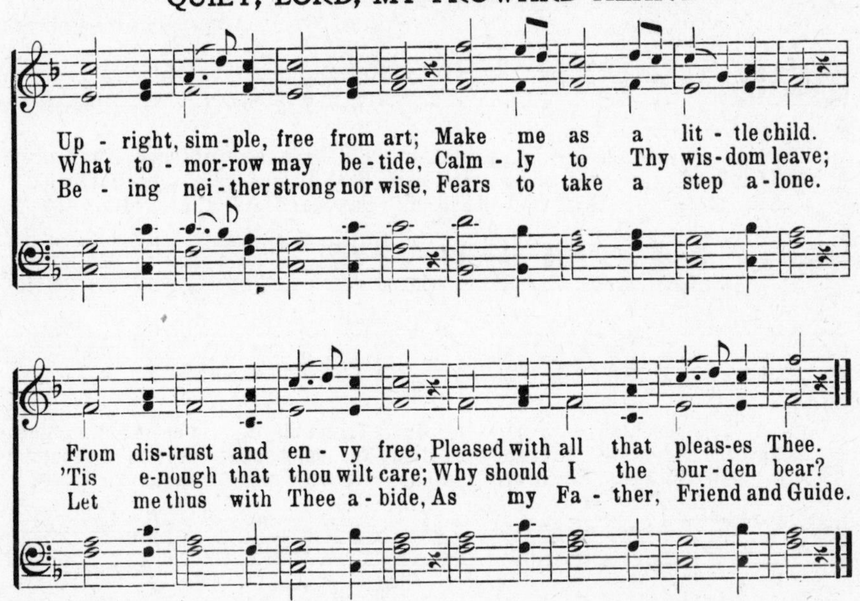
Up - right, sim - ple, free from art; Make me as a lit - tle child.
What to - mor-row may be - tide, Calm - ly to Thy wis - dom leave;
Be - ing nei - ther strong nor wise, Fears to take a step a - lone.
From dis-trust and en - vy free, Pleased with all that pleas-es Thee.
'Tis e-nough that thou wilt care; Why should I the bur - den bear?
Let me thus with Thee a - bide, As my Fa - ther, Friend and Guide.

16 WHAT GLORY GILDS THE SACRED PAGE

William Cowper

William Gardiner

1. What glo - ry gilds the sa - cred page, Ma - jes - tic like the sun!
2. The hand that gave it still sup - plies His gra - cious light and heat;
3. Let ev - er - last - ing thanks be Thine, For such a bright dis - play
4. My soul re - joi - ces to pur - sue The paths of truth and love,

It gives a light to ev - 'ry age; It gives, but bor - rows none.
His truths up - on the na - tions rise; They rise, but nev - er set.
As makes the world of dark - ness shine With beams of heav'n - ly day.
Till glo - ry breaks up - on my view In bright - er worlds a - bove.

17 LORD, DISMISS US
Jos ' Fawcett
Tattersall's Psalmody
1. Lord, dis - miss us with Thy bless-ing, Fill our hearts with joy and peace;
2. Thanks we give, and ad - o - ra - tion, For Thy gos - pel's joy - ful sound;
3. So that when thy love shall call us, Sav-iour, from the world a - way,
Let us each, thy love pos - sess-ing. Tri-umph in re-deem - ing grace:
May the fruits of thy sal - va - tion In our hearts and lives a - bound:
Let no fear of death ap - pal us, Glad thy sum - mons to o - bey:
O re fresh us, O re-fresh us, Trav-'ling thro' this wilder-ness.
Ev - er faith-ful, Ev - er faith-ful, To the truth may we be found.
May we ev - er, May we ev - er Reign with thee in end-less day. A-MEN.
18 THE TRAVELER'S HYMN
Psa. 121: 8
The Lord shall pre - serve thy go - ing out, And thy com - ing in.
From this time forth and for ev - er - more. A - MEN.

19 SAVIOUR, AGAIN TO THY DEAR NAME

JOHN ELLERTON — ELLERS — E. J. HOPKINS

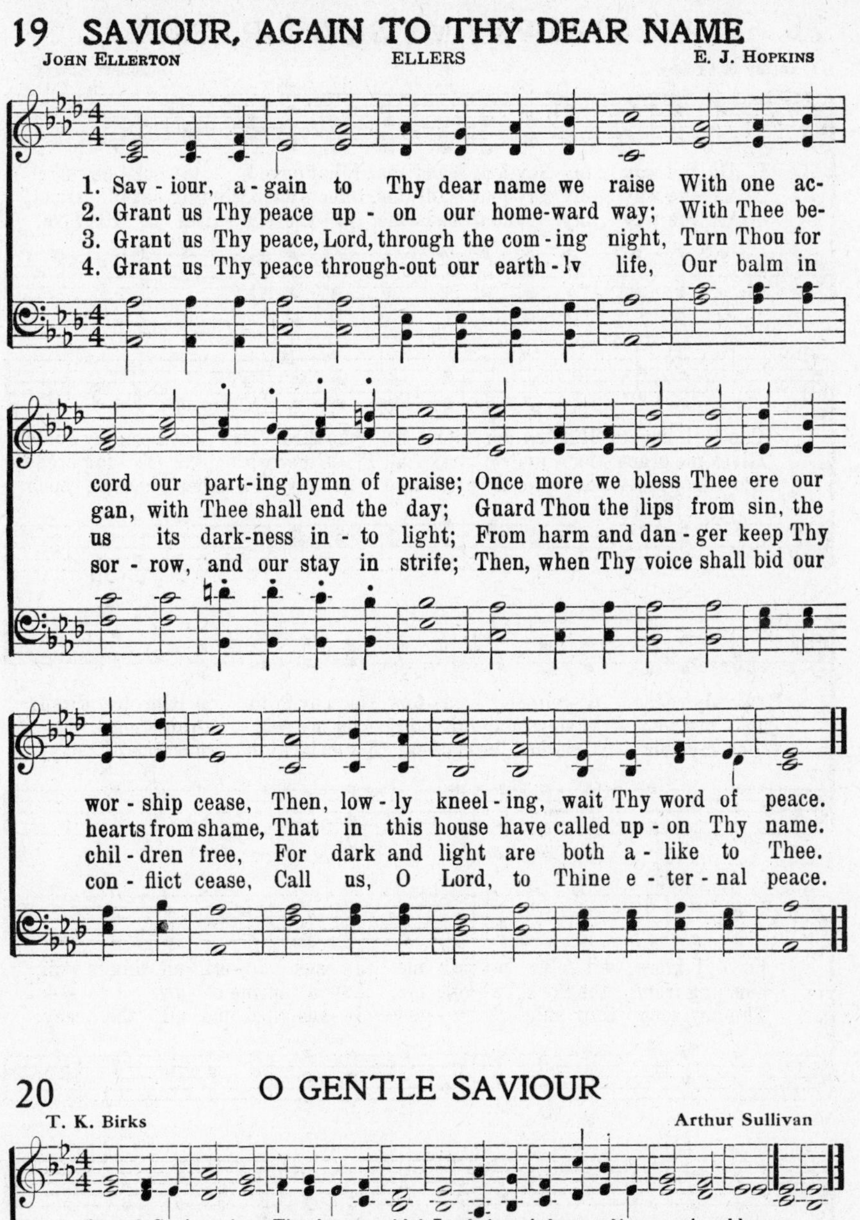
1. Sav - iour, a - gain to Thy dear name we raise With one ac-
2. Grant us Thy peace up - on our home-ward way; With Thee be-
3. Grant us Thy peace, Lord, through the com - ing night, Turn Thou for
4. Grant us Thy peace through-out our earth - ly life, Our balm in
cord our part-ing hymn of praise; Once more we bless Thee ere our
gan, with Thee shall end the day; Guard Thou the lips from sin, the
us its dark-ness in - to light; From harm and dan - ger keep Thy
sor - row, and our stay in strife; Then, when Thy voice shall bid our
wor - ship cease, Then, low - ly kneel - ing, wait Thy word of peace.
hearts from shame, That in this house have called up - on Thy name.
chil - dren free, For dark and light are both a - like to Thee.
con - flict cease, Call us, O Lord, to Thine e - ter - nal peace.

20 O GENTLE SAVIOUR

T. K. Birks — Arthur Sullivan

1. O gentle Saviour, from Thy throne on high Look down in love and hear our humble cry.
2. Go where we go, abide where we abide, In life, in death, our comfort, strength, and guide.
3. O lead us dai-ly with Thine eye of love, And bring us safely to our home a - bove. A-MEN.

21 ALL THE WAY MY SAVIOUR LEADS

Fanny J. Crosby
Robert Lowry
1. All the way my Sav-iour leads me; What have I to ask be-side?
2. All the way my Sav-iour leads me, Cheers each winding path I tread;
3. All the way my Sav-iour leads me; O the ful-ness of His love!
Can I doubt His ten-der mer-cy Who thro' life has been my guide?
Gives me grace for ev-'ry tri-al, Feeds me with the liv-ing bread;
Per-fect rest to me is prom-ised In my Fa-ther's house a-bove;
Heav'nly peace, di-vin-est com-fort, Here by faith in Him to dwell!
Tho' my wea-ry steps may fal-ter, And my soul a-thirst may be,
When my spir-it, clothed, im-mor-tal, Wings its flight to realms of day,
For I know, whate'er be-fall me, Je-sus do-eth all things well;
Gushing from the Rock be-fore me, Lo! a spring of joy I see;
This my song thro' end-less a-ges— Je-sus led me all the way;
For I know, what-e'er be-fall me, Je-sus do-eth all things well.
Gushing from the Rock be-fore me, Lo! a spring of joy I see.
This my song thro' end-less a-ges— Je-sus led me all the way.

22 THE PRODIGAL'S RETURN

John Newton — Arr. by Ira D. Sankey

1. Af- flic-tions, tho' they seem se - vere. In mer - cy oft are sent;
2. "What have I gained by sin," he said, "But hun - ger, shame, and fear?
3. "I'll go and tell him all I've done; Fall down be - fore his face.
4. His fa - ther saw him com - ing back; He saw, he ran, he smiled,
5. "O fa - ther, I have sinned-for-give!" "Enough," the father said.
6. 'Tis thus the Lord His love re - veals, To call poor sin-ners home;
They stopp'd the prod - i - gal's ca - reer, And caused him to re - pent.
My fa - ther's house a-bounds in bread, While I am starv-ing here!"
Un - wor - thy to be called his son, I'll seek a ser-vant's place."
And threw his arms a - round the neck Of his re - bell - ious child!
"Re - joice, my house; my son's a - live For whom I mourned as dead!"
More than a fa - ther's love He feels And wel-comes all that come.
CHORUS
"I'll not die here for bread, I'll not die here for bread," he cries; "Nor
starve in foreign lands; My father's house has large supplies And bounteous are his hands."

23 THE LORD BLESS THEE AND KEEP THEE

Num. 6:24-26

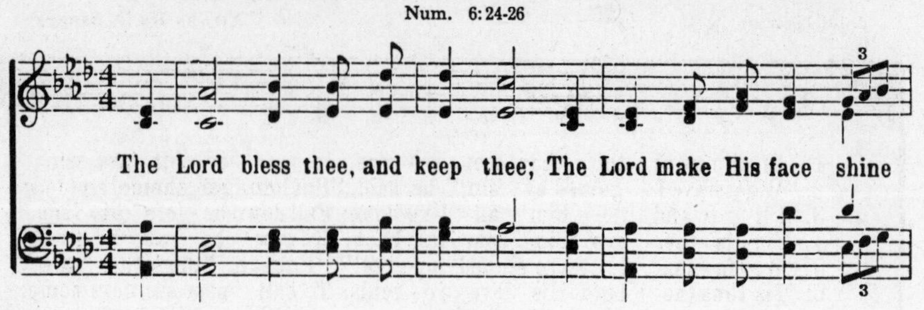
3
The Lord bless thee, and keep thee; The Lord make His face shine
3

up - on thee, And be gra - cious un - to thee, And be

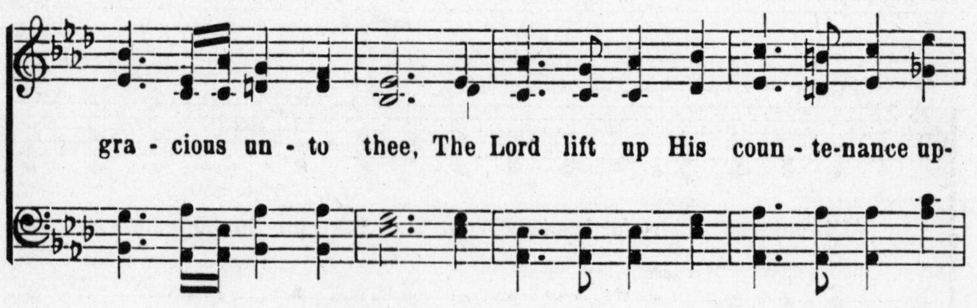
gra - cious un - to thee, The Lord lift up His coun - te-nance up-

on thee, And give thee peace. A - MEN.

24 I KNOW I LOVE THEE BETTER, LORD

Frances R. Havergal

R. E. Hudson

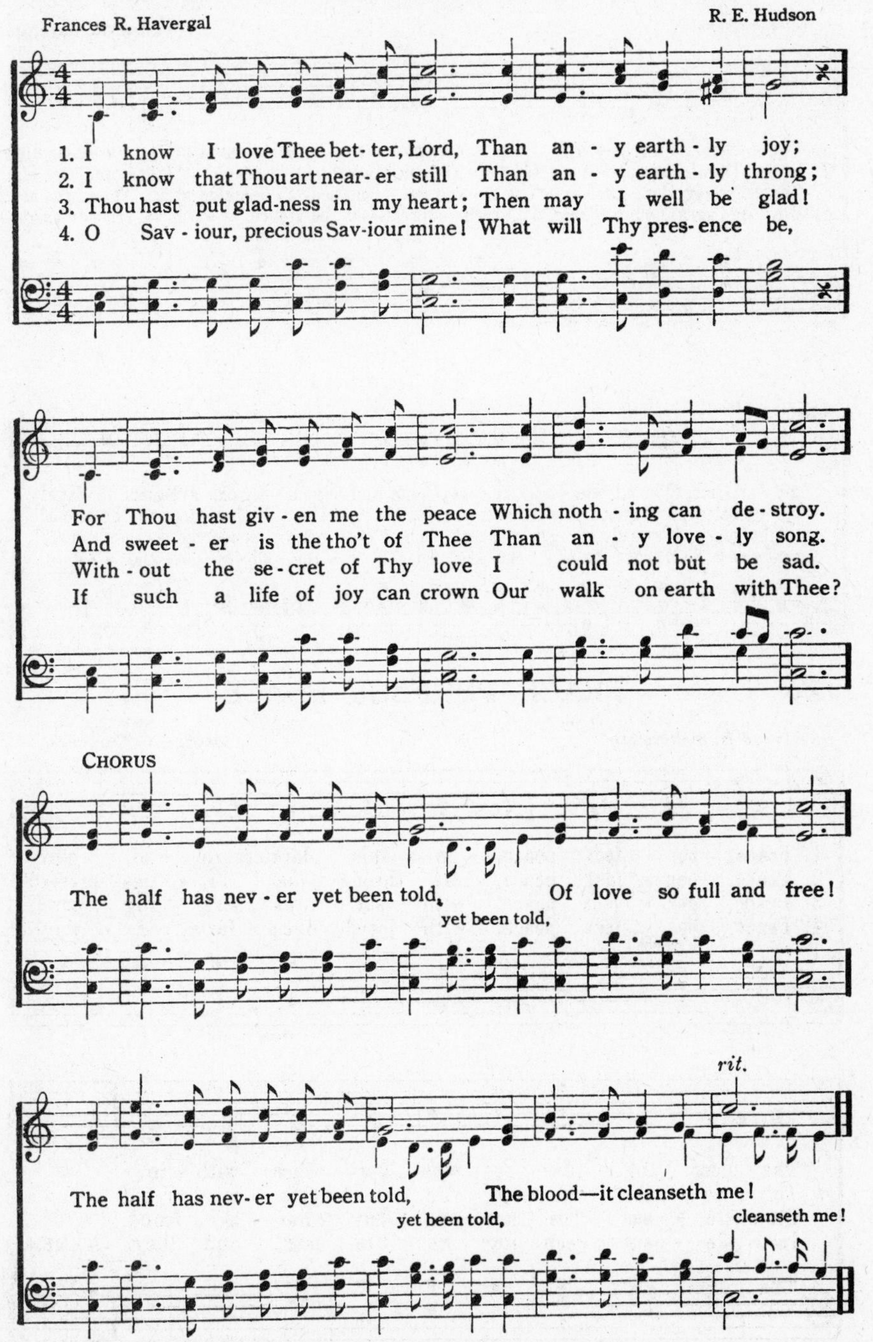
1. I know I love Thee bet- ter, Lord, Than an - y earth - ly joy;
2. I know that Thou art near- er still Than an - y earth - ly throng;
3. Thou hast put glad-ness in my heart; Then may I well be glad!
4. O Sav - iour, precious Sav-iour mine! What will Thy pres- ence be,
For Thou hast giv - en me the peace Which noth - ing can de - stroy.
And sweet - er is the tho't of Thee Than an - y love - ly song.
With - out the se - cret of Thy love I could not but be sad.
If such a life of joy can crown Our walk on earth with Thee?
CHORUS
The half has nev - er yet been told, Of love so full and free!
yet been told,
The half has nev- er yet been told, The blood—it cleanseth me!
yet been told,
cleanseth me!
rit.

25 COME, THOU ALMIGHTY KING

Charles Wesley — Felice De Giardini

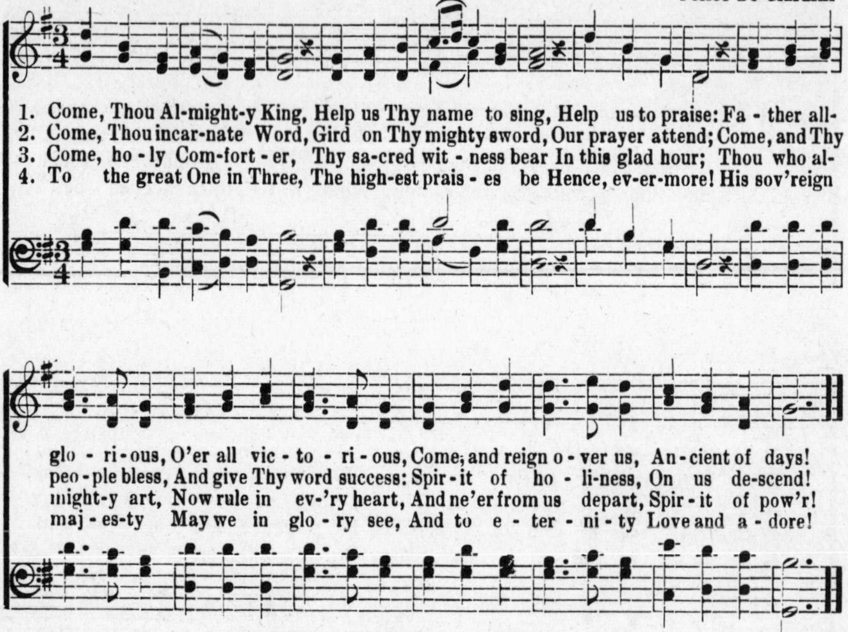

1. Come, Thou Al-might-y King, Help us Thy name to sing, Help us to praise: Fa - ther all-
2. Come, Thou incar-nate Word, Gird on Thy mighty sword, Our prayer attend; Come, and Thy
3. Come, ho - ly Com-fort - er, Thy sa-cred wit - ness bear In this glad hour; Thou who al-
4. To the great One in Three, The high-est prais - es be Hence, ev-er-more! His sov'reign

glo - ri-ous, O'er all vic - to - ri - ous, Come, and reign o - ver us, An-cient of days!
peo - ple bless, And give Thy word success: Spir - it of ho - li-ness, On us de-scend!
might-y art, Now rule in ev-'ry heart, And ne'er from us depart, Spir - it of pow'r!
maj - es-ty May we in glo - ry see, And to e - ter - ni - ty Love and a - dore!

26 PEACE, PERFECT PEACE

Edward H. Bickersteth — George T. Caldbeck

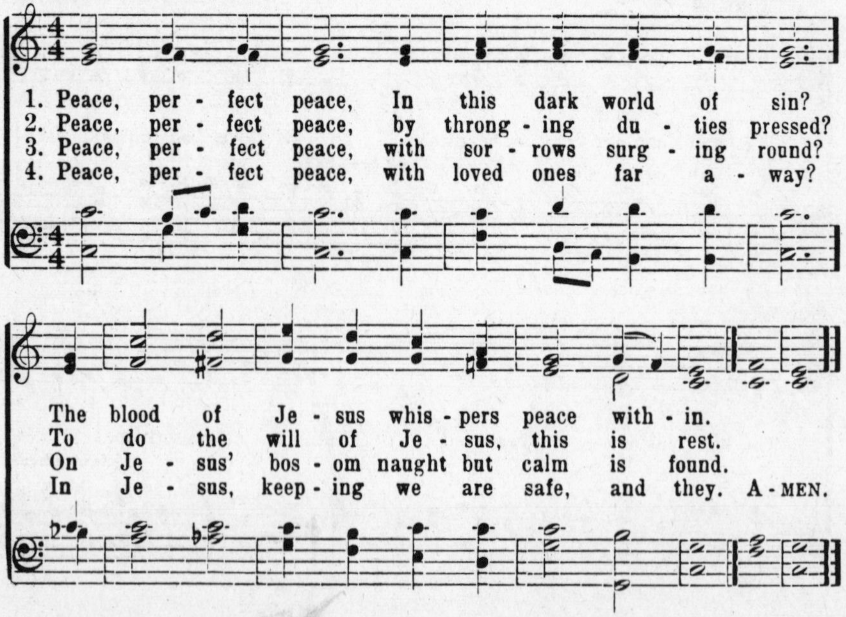

1. Peace, per - fect peace, In this dark world of sin?
2. Peace, per - fect peace, by throng - ing du - ties pressed?
3. Peace, per - fect peace, with sor - rows surg - ing round?
4. Peace, per - fect peace, with loved ones far a - way?

The blood of Je - sus whis - pers peace with - in.
To do the will of Je - sus, this is rest.
On Je - sus' bos - om naught but calm is found.
In Je - sus, keep - ing we are safe, and they. A - MEN.

27 MAJESTIC SWEETNESS SITS ENTHRONED

Samuel Stennett — ORTONVILLE C. M. — Thomas Hastings

1. Majestic sweetness sits enthroned Upon the Saviour's brow; His head with radiant
2. He saw me plunged in deep distress, He flew to my relief; For me He bore the
3. To Him I owe my life and breath, And all the joys I have; He makes me triumph
4. To heav'n, the place of His abode, He brings my weary feet; Shows me the glories
5. Since from His bounty I receive Such proofs of love divine, Had I a thousand

glories crowned, His lips with grace o'erflow, His lips with grace o'erflow.
shameful cross, And carried all my grief, And carried all my grief.
o - ver death, He saves me from the grave, He saves me from the grave.
of my God, And makes my joys complete, And makes my joys complete.
hearts to give, Lord, they should all be Thine, Lord, they should all be Thine. A - men.

28 'TIS MIDNIGHT; AND ON OLIVES' BROW

William B. Tappan — OLIVES' BROW L. M. — William B. Bradbury

1. 'Tis midnight; and on Ol - ives' brow The star is dimmed that lately shone:
2. 'Tis midnight; and from all removed, The Saviour wrestles lone with fears;
3. 'Tis midnight; and for oth - ers' guilt The Man of Sorrows weeps in blood;
4. 'Tis midnight; and from eth - er-plains Is borne the song that an-gels know;

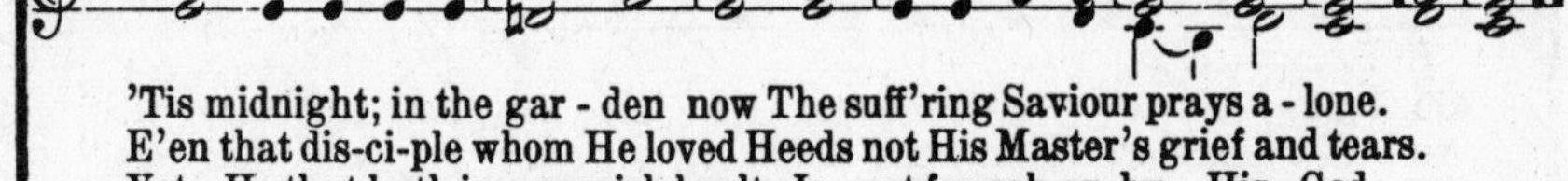

'Tis midnight; in the gar - den now The suff'ring Saviour prays a - lone.
E'en that dis-ci-ple whom He loved Heeds not His Master's grief and tears.
Yet He that hath in an-guish knelt Is not for-sak-en by His God.
Unheard by mortals are the strains That sweetly soothe the Saviour's woe. A-men.

29 JESUS, THE VERY THOUGHT OF THEE

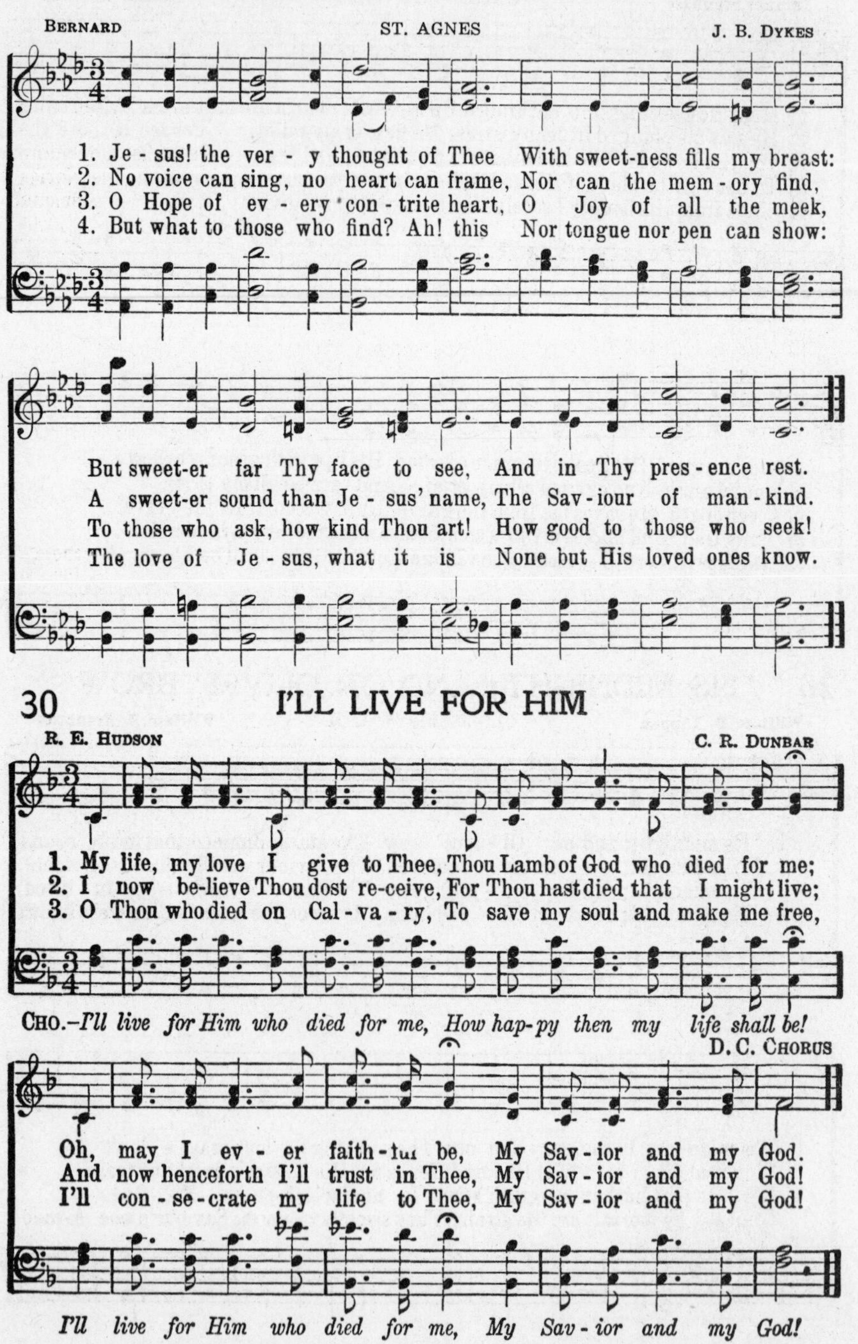
BERNARD
ST. AGNES
J. B. DYKES
1. Je - sus! the ver - y thought of Thee With sweet-ness fills my breast:
2. No voice can sing, no heart can frame, Nor can the mem - ory find,
3. O Hope of ev - ery con - trite heart, O Joy of all the meek,
4. But what to those who find? Ah! this Nor tongue nor pen can show:
But sweet-er far Thy face to see, And in Thy pres - ence rest.
A sweet-er sound than Je - sus' name, The Sav - iour of man - kind.
To those who ask, how kind Thou art! How good to those who seek!
The love of Je - sus, what it is None but His loved ones know.
30 I'LL LIVE FOR HIM
R. E. HUDSON
C. R. DUNBAR
1. My life, my love I give to Thee, Thou Lamb of God who died for me;
2. I now be-lieve Thou dost re-ceive, For Thou hast died that I might live;
3. O Thou who died on Cal - va - ry, To save my soul and make me free,
CHO.–I'll live for Him who died for me, How hap-py then my life shall be!
D. C. CHORUS
Oh, may I ev - er faith - ful be, My Sav - ior and my God.
And now henceforth I'll trust in Thee, My Sav - ior and my God!
I'll con - se - crate my life to Thee, My Sav - ior and my God!
I'll live for Him who died for me, My Sav - ior and my God!

31

I AM PRAYING FOR YOU

S. O'MALEY CLUFF — IRA D. SANKEY

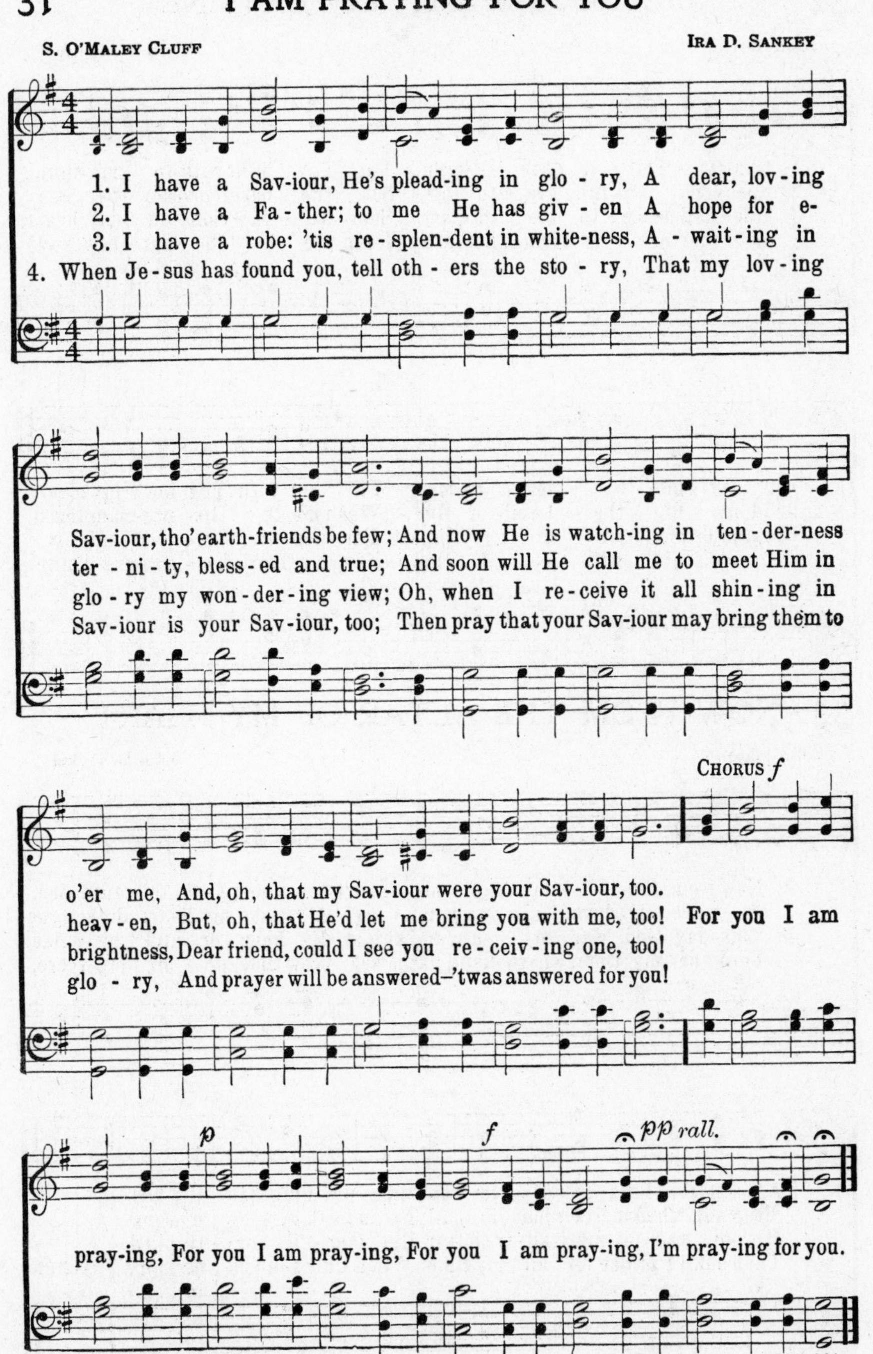
1. I have a Sav-iour, He's plead-ing in glo - ry, A dear, lov-ing
2. I have a Fa-ther; to me He has giv - en A hope for e-
3. I have a robe: 'tis re-splen-dent in white-ness, A - wait-ing in
4. When Je-sus has found you, tell oth - ers the sto - ry, That my lov-ing
Sav-iour, tho' earth-friends be few; And now He is watch-ing in ten-der-ness
ter - ni - ty, bless-ed and true; And soon will He call me to meet Him in
glo - ry my won-der-ing view; Oh, when I re-ceive it all shin-ing in
Sav-iour is your Sav-iour, too; Then pray that your Sav-iour may bring them to
o'er me, And, oh, that my Sav-iour were your Sav-iour, too.
heav - en, But, oh, that He'd let me bring you with me, too!
brightness, Dear friend, could I see you re-ceiv-ing one, too!
glo - ry, And prayer will be answered–'twas answered for you!
CHORUS f
For you I am
pray-ing, For you I am pray-ing, For you I am pray-ing, I'm pray-ing for you.
p
f
pp rall.

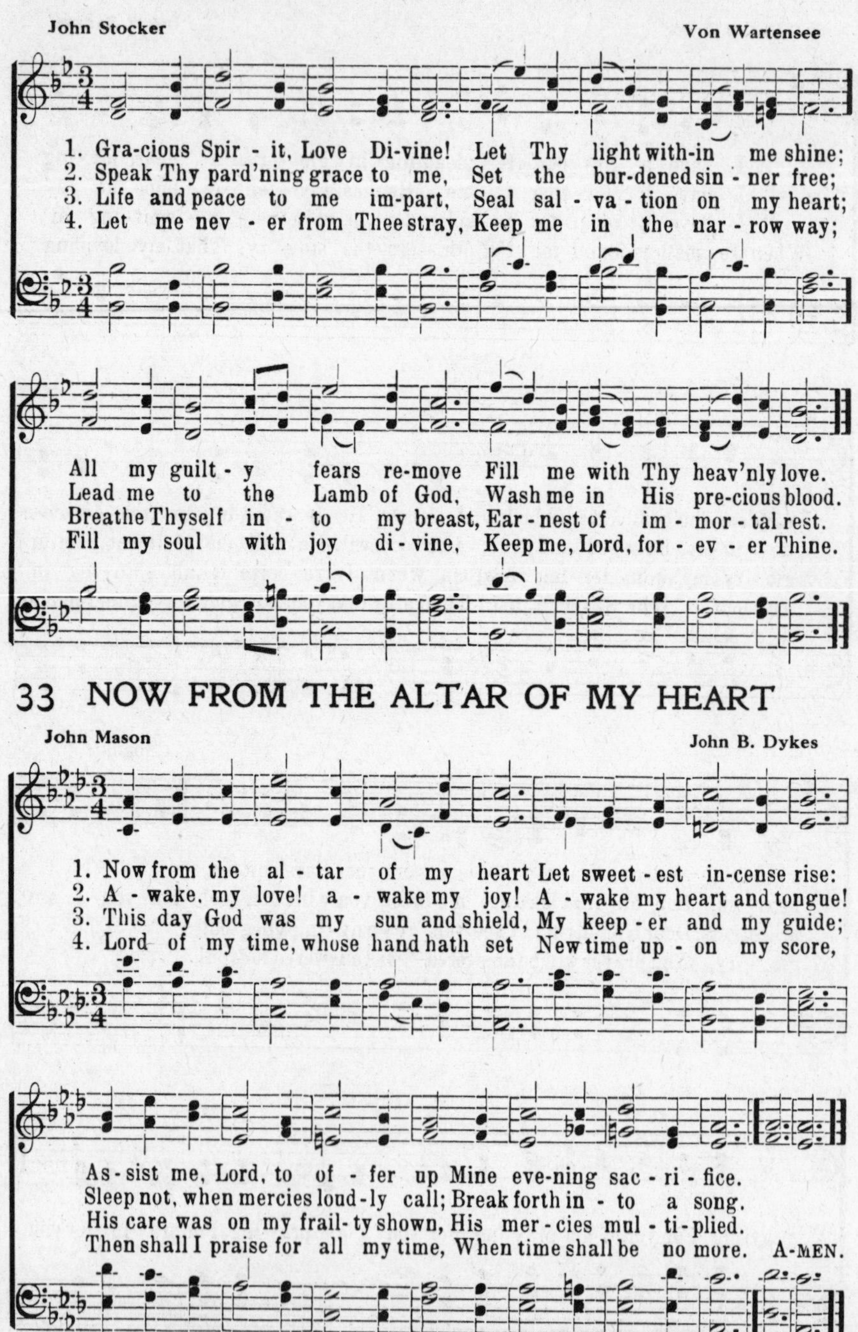
32 GRACIOUS SPIRIT, LOVE DIVINE
John Stocker
Von Wartensee
1. Gra-cious Spir - it, Love Di-vine! Let Thy light with-in me shine;
2. Speak Thy pard'ning grace to me, Set the bur-dened sin - ner free;
3. Life and peace to me im-part, Seal sal - va - tion on my heart;
4. Let me nev - er from Thee stray, Keep me in the nar - row way;
All my guilt - y fears re-move Fill me with Thy heav'nly love.
Lead me to the Lamb of God, Wash me in His pre-cious blood.
Breathe Thyself in - to my breast, Ear - nest of im - mor - tal rest.
Fill my soul with joy di - vine, Keep me, Lord, for - ev - er Thine.
33 NOW FROM THE ALTAR OF MY HEART
John Mason
John B. Dykes
1. Now from the al - tar of my heart Let sweet - est in-cense rise:
2. A - wake, my love! a - wake my joy! A - wake my heart and tongue!
3. This day God was my sun and shield, My keep - er and my guide;
4. Lord of my time, whose hand hath set New time up - on my score,
As-sist me, Lord, to of - fer up Mine eve-ning sac - ri - fice.
Sleep not, when mercies loud-ly call; Break forth in - to a song.
His care was on my frail-ty shown, His mer - cies mul - ti - plied.
Then shall I praise for all my time, When time shall be no more. A-MEN.

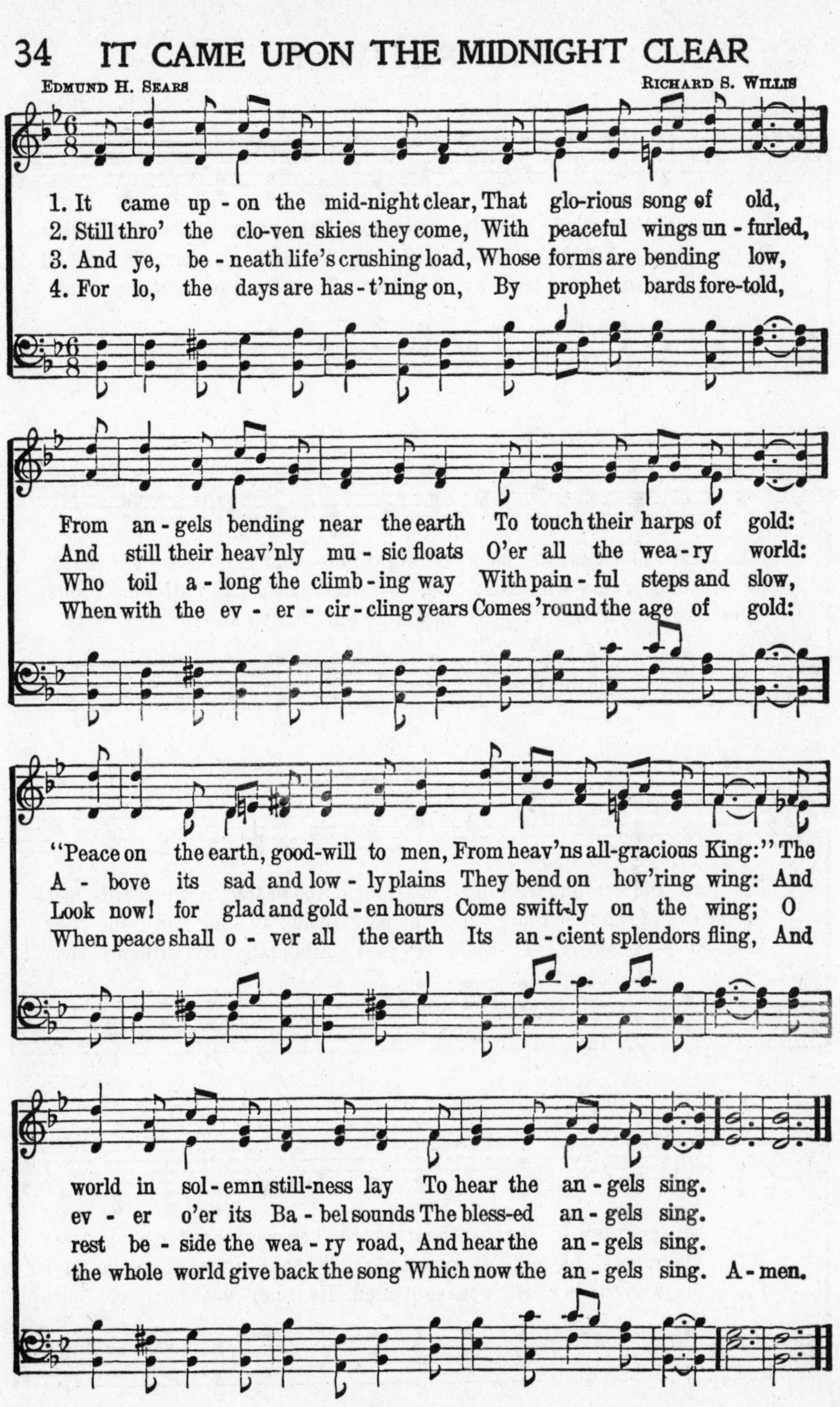
34 IT CAME UPON THE MIDNIGHT CLEAR
Edmund H. Sears
Richard S. Willis
1. It came up - on the mid-night clear, That glo-rious song of old,
2. Still thro' the clo-ven skies they come, With peaceful wings un - furled,
3. And ye, be - neath life's crushing load, Whose forms are bending low,
4. For lo, the days are has - t'ning on, By prophet bards fore-told,
From an - gels bending near the earth To touch their harps of gold:
And still their heav'nly mu - sic floats O'er all the wea - ry world:
Who toil a - long the climb - ing way With pain - ful steps and slow,
When with the ev - er - cir - cling years Comes 'round the age of gold:
"Peace on the earth, good-will to men, From heav'ns all-gracious King:" The
A - bove its sad and low - ly plains They bend on hov'ring wing: And
Look now! for glad and gold - en hours Come swift-ly on the wing; O
When peace shall o - ver all the earth Its an - cient splendors fling, And
world in sol - emn still-ness lay To hear the an - gels sing.
ev - er o'er its Ba - bel sounds The bless-ed an - gels sing.
rest be - side the wea - ry road, And hear the an - gels sing.
the whole world give back the song Which now the an - gels sing. A - men.

35 THE NATIVITY

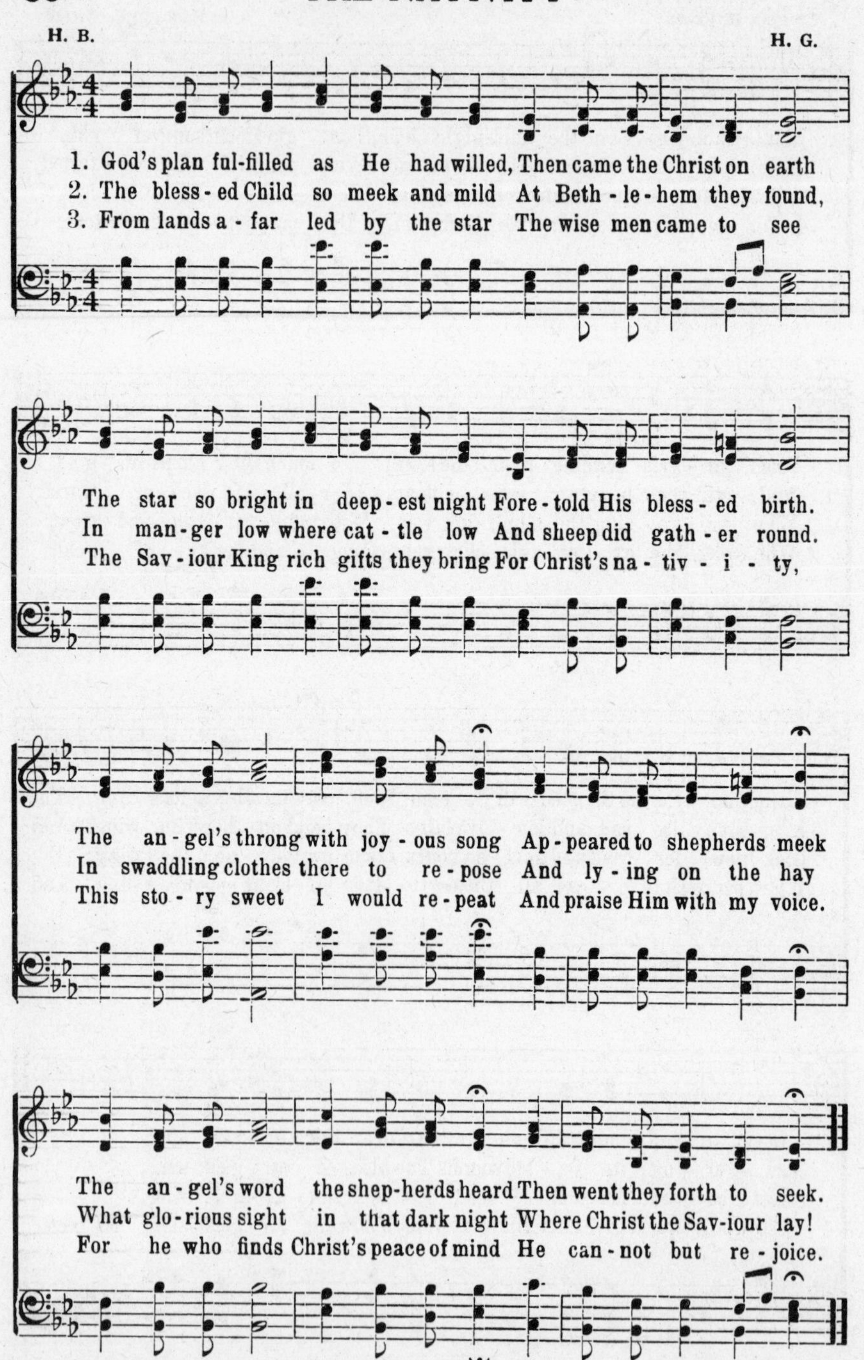
H. B.
H. G.
1. God's plan ful-filled as He had willed, Then came the Christ on earth
2. The bless-ed Child so meek and mild At Beth-le-hem they found,
3. From lands a-far led by the star The wise men came to see
The star so bright in deep-est night Fore-told His bless-ed birth.
In man-ger low where cat-tle low And sheep did gath-er round.
The Sav-iour King rich gifts they bring For Christ's na-tiv-i-ty,
The an-gel's throng with joy-ous song Ap-peared to shepherds meek
In swaddling clothes there to re-pose And ly-ing on the hay
This sto-ry sweet I would re-peat And praise Him with my voice.
The an-gel's word the shep-herds heard Then went they forth to seek.
What glo-rious sight in that dark night Where Christ the Sav-iour lay!
For he who finds Christ's peace of mind He can-not but re-joice.

THE BABE OF BETHLEHEM

H. B.
M. Y. R.
1. The bless - ed sto - ry of the Christ, The babe of Beth - le - hem,
2. Our sav - ing hope is all in vain, If here our love should cease,
3. Be not con - tent this babe to know, Nor stay at Beth - le - hem,
Is wor - thy of our song and praise, And stirs the hearts of men.
For in the man of Gal - i - lee. We find the gift of peace.
But go with Christ to Cal-vary's brow, Be-yond Je - ru - sa - lem.
The full - ness of God's love di - vine, sur-rounds the Christ so mild
'Tis not the babe, but Christ, the man Who walked in Gal - i - lee;
'Tis there men learn to know the Christ, For there He bore man's sin.
A - las how man - y on - ly know The Sav - iour as a child.
'Tis not the man - ger, but the cross, That sets the spir - it free.
Then o - pen wide the door of heart. And let the Sav - iour in.

37 O LITTLE TOWN OF BETHLEHEM

PHILLIPS BROOKS | LEWIS H. REDNER

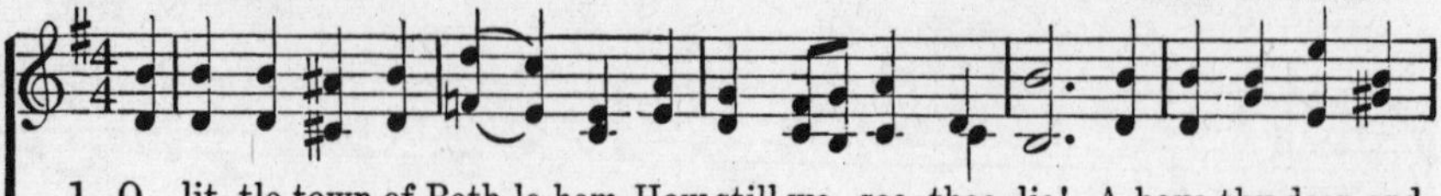

1. O lit-tle town of Beth-le-hem, How still we see thee lie! A-bove thy deep and
2. For Christ is born of Ma - ry; And gath-ered all a-bove, While mortals sleep, the
3. How si-lent-ly, how si-lent-ly The wondrous gift is giv'n! So God im-parts to
4. O ho - ly Child of Beth-le-hem, De-scend to us, we pray; Cast out our sin and

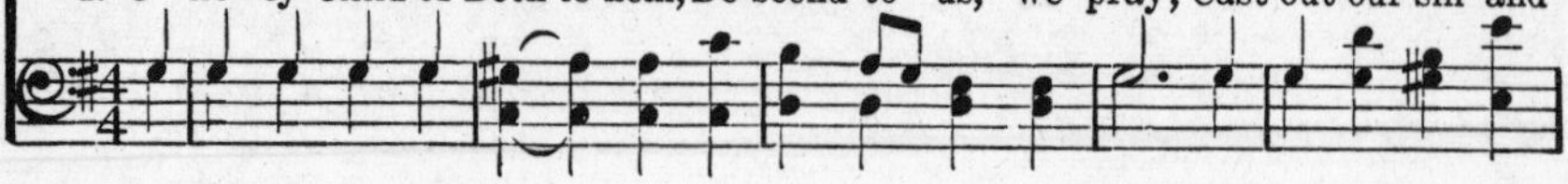

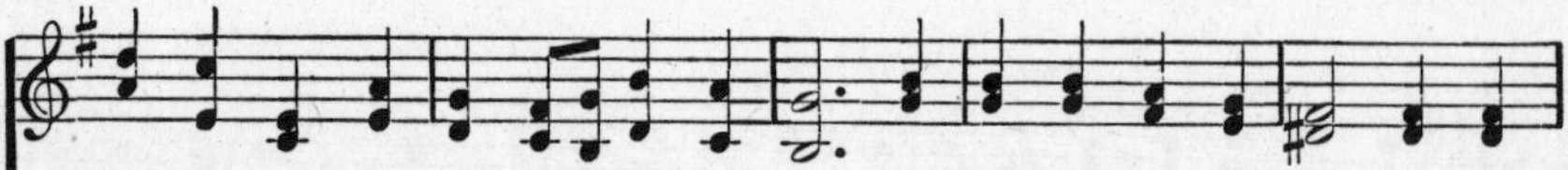

dreamless sleep The si - lent stars go by; Yet in thy dark streets shin-eth The
an - gels keep Their watch of wond'ring love. O morn-ing stars, to - geth - er Pro-
hu-man hearts The bless-ings of His Heav'n. No ear may hear His com - ing; But
en - ter in,—Be born in us to - day. We hear the Christmas an - gels The

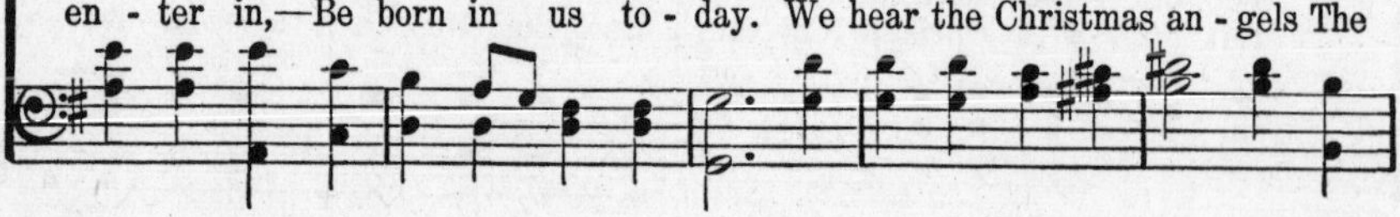

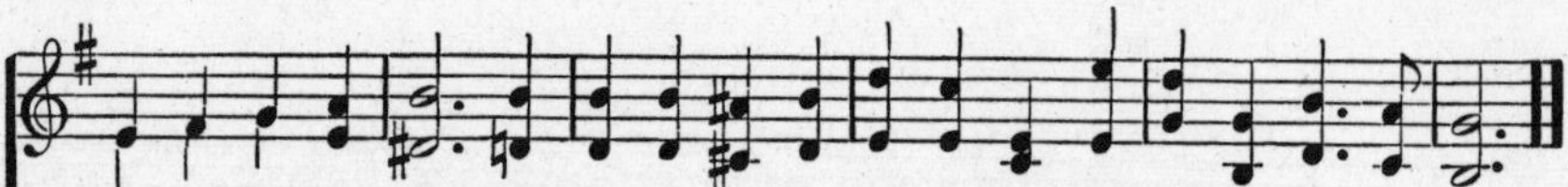

ev - er-last-ing Light; The hopes and fears of all the years Are met in thee to - night.
claim the ho - ly birth, And prais-es sing to God the King, And peace to men on earth.
in this world of sin, Where meek souls will receive Him still, The dear Christ enters in.
great glad tidings tell,—O come to us, a-bide with us, Our Lord Em-man-u - el.

38 AWAY IN A MANGER

M. L. | Martin Luther

1. A - way in a man-ger, No crib for a bed, The lit - tle Lord
2. The cat - tle are low - ing, The Ba - by a - wakes, But lit - tle Lord
3. Be near me, Lord Je - sus, I ask Thee to stay Close by me for-

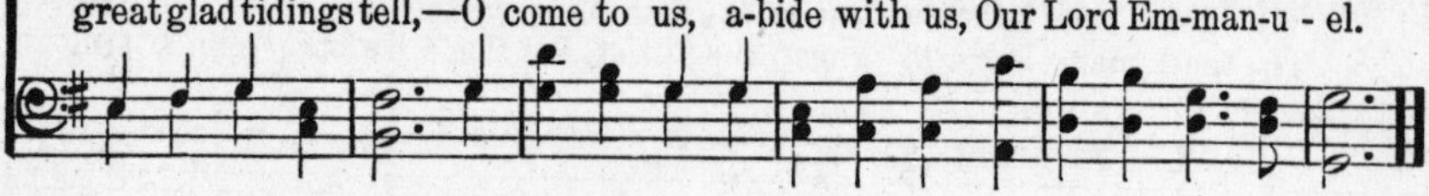

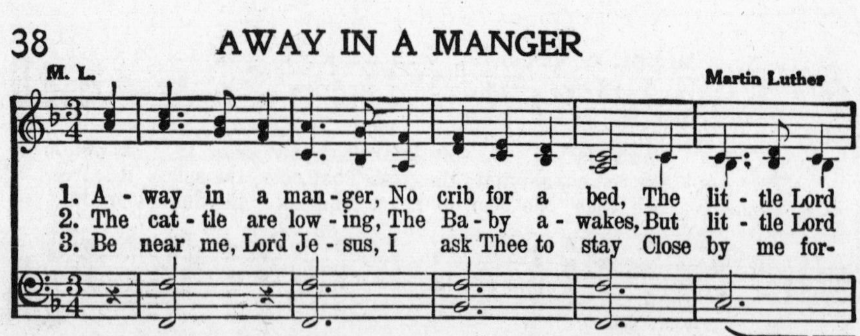

AWAY IN A MANGER

Je - sus Laid down His sweet head; The stars in the sky Looked
Je - sus, No cry - ing He makes; I love Thee, Lord Je - sus! Look
ev - er, And love me, I pray; Bless all the dear chil - dren In

down where He lay,—The lit - tle Lord Je - sus, A - sleep on the hay.
down from the sky, And stay by my cra - dle, Till morn-ing is nigh.
Thy ten - der care, And take us to heav-en, To live with Thee there.

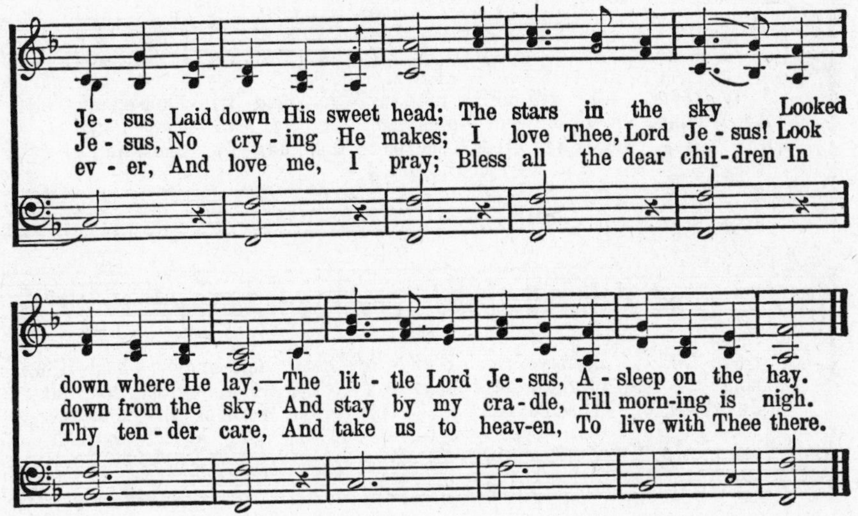

39 WHILE SHEPHERDS WATCHED THEIR FLOCKS

Nahum Tate CHRISTMAS C. M. George F. Handel

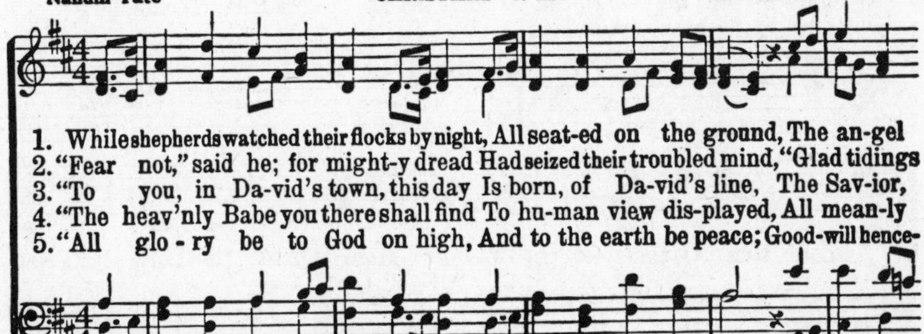

1. While shepherds watched their flocks by night, All seat-ed on the ground, The an-gel
2. "Fear not," said he; for might-y dread Had seized their troubled mind, "Glad tidings
3. "To you, in Da-vid's town, this day Is born, of Da-vid's line, The Sav-ior,
4. "The heav'nly Babe you there shall find To hu-man view dis-played, All mean-ly
5. "All glo - ry be to God on high, And to the earth be peace; Good-will hence-

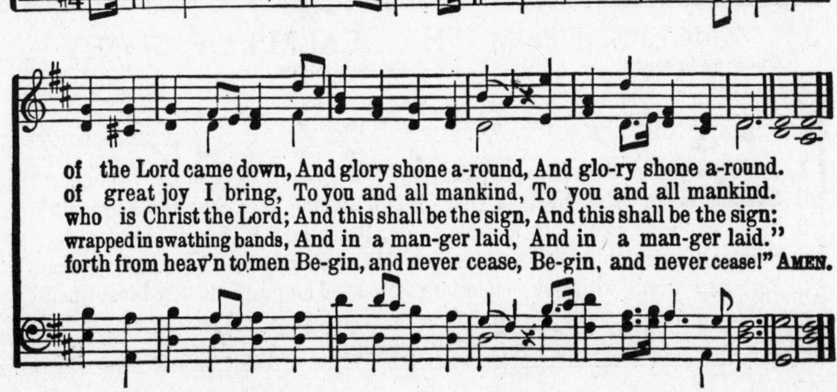

of the Lord came down, And glory shone a-round, And glo-ry shone a-round.
of great joy I bring, To you and all mankind, To you and all mankind.
who is Christ the Lord; And this shall be the sign, And this shall be the sign:
wrapped in swathing bands, And in a man-ger laid, And in a man-ger laid."
forth from heav'n to men Be-gin, and never cease, Be-gin, and never cease!" AMEN.

40 O COME, ALL YE FAITHFUL
Tr. by Frederick Oakeley
Wade's Cantus Diversi
1. O come, all ye faith - ful, joy - ful and tri - um-phant, O
2. Sing, choirs of an - gels, sing in ex - ul - ta - tion, O
3. Yea, Lord, we greet Thee, born this hap - py morn-ing,
come ye, O come ye to Beth - le - hem; Come and be - hold Him,
sing, all ye bright hosts of heav'n a - bove; Glo - ry to God, all
Je - sus, to Thee be all glo - ry giv'n; Word of the Fa - ther,
Refrain
born the King of an - gels.
glo - ry in the high-est. O come, let us a-dore Him, O come, let us a -
now in flesh ap - pear-ing.
dore Him, O come, let us a - dore Him, Christ, the Lord. A - men.
41 ANGELS, FROM THE REALMS OF GLORY
James Montgomery
REGENT SQUARE 8. 7. 6 lines
Henry Smart
1. An - gels, from the realms of glo - ry, Wing your flight o'er all the earth;
2. Shepherds, in the field a - bid - ing, Watching o'er your flocks by night,
3. Sag - es, leave your con - tem-pla - tions, Brighter vis - ions beam a - far;
4. Saints, be - fore the al - tar bend - ing, Watching long in hope and fear,
5. Sin - ners, wrung with true repentance, Doomed for guilt to end-less pains,

ANGELS, FROM THE REALMS OF GLORY

Ye who sang cre - a - tion's sto - ry, Now pro-claim Mes-si - ah's birth:
God with man is now re - sid - ing; Yon - der shines the in-fant light:
Seek the great De - sire of na-tions; Ye have seen His na - tal star:
Sud - den - ly the Lord, de-scend-ing, In His tem - ple shall ap - pear:
Jus - tice now re - vokes the sentence, Mer - cy calls you, break your chains:
Come and wor-ship, come and worship, Worship Christ, the newborn King. A-men.
42
SILENT NIGHT
Joseph Mohr
P. M.
Franz Gruber
1. Si - lent night! ho - ly night! All is calm, all is bright 'Round yon
2. Si - lent night! ho - ly night! Shep - herds quake at the sight! Glo - ries
3. Si - lent night! ho - ly night! Son of God, love's pure light Ra - diant
vir - gin moth - er and Child! Ho - ly In - fant, so ten - der and mild,
stream from heav-en a - far, Heav'n-ly hosts sing Al - le - lu - ia;
beams from Thy ho - ly face, With the dawn of re - deem - ing grace,
Sleep in heav - en - ly peace, Sleep in heav - en - ly peace.
Christ, the Sav-iour, is born, Christ, the Sav-iour, is born.
Je - sus, Lord, at Thy birth, Je - sus, Lord, at Thy birth.
A - MEN.

43 THE FIRST NOEL

Traditional Traditional

1. The first No - el the an - gel did say Was to cer - tain poor
2. And by the light of that same Star, Three wise men
3. This Star drew nigh to the north - west, O'er Beth - le-
4. Then en - tered in, those wise men three, Full rev - 'rent-
shep-herds in fields as they lay; In fields where they lay keep-ing their
came from coun - try far; To seek for a King was their in-
hem it took its rest, And there it did both stop and
ly up - on their knee, And of - fered there in His pres-
REFRAIN
sheep, On a cold win-ter's night that was so deep.
tent, And to fol - low the Star wher - ev - er it went.
stay, Right o - ver the place where Je - sus lay.
ence, Their gold, and myrrh, and frank - in - cense.
No - el, No-
el, No - el, No - el, Born is the King of Is - - ra - el.

ENVY

H. B. H. G.

1. No, I will not en - vy Oth - ers in their lot;
2. Sa - tan us - es en - vy, And, with cun - ning art,
3. Are you prone to cov - et What your friends pos - sess?
Blest are some with rich - es, Blest, who have it not.
Makes the soul to cov - et, Fills with greed the heart.
Cov - et the true rich - es, Je - sus' right - eous - ness.
En - vy is an e - vil; En - vy leads to sin;
En - vy not men's rich - es, Tal - ents, hon - or, fame;
Av - a - rice and en - vy, Cov - et - ing, com - bined,
Guard Thy soul and con - science, Lest it en - ter in.
These can on - ly prof - it, Used in Je - sus' name.
Wea - pons of de - struc - tion, Sa - tan has de - signed.
After the last stanza
Be not en - vi - ous. No, no, no. A - MEN.

45 THE RESSURECTION

1. Why come ye at break of morn - ing, To the Lord's grave
2. Soon from tongue to tongue ex-pound - ing, The res - ur - rec -
3. Songs of praise to Thee are swell - ing, From thou - sand thank-
in such deep mourn - ing; Who'll roll the heav - y stone a-
tion joy is sound - ing; His fol - low - ers a - wait their
ful voic - es tell - ing; Oh, ho - ly He - ro ev - er-
way? 'Tis a - way; oh, do not mur - mur! Ye
Lord. Ev' - ning comes, they tar - ry long - ing. Still
more! Death is now sweet for be - liev - ers; In
faith-ful ones, come now, draw near - er, The stone is gone
trust-ing, hop - ing, tear - ful, doubt - ing, Will He come? Hope!
Je - sus we are heav - en's he - irs; The sting of death

THE RESURRECTION

Oh, look there - in! See an - - gels in the
He's ev - er near. Be - hold from Em - ma-
is now no more. For af - - ter the grave's
1. See an - gels in the
2. Be - hold from Em - ma-
3. For aft - er the grave's
cleft! Bring joy to you be - reft, Ho- -
us. They bring tid - ings joy - ous: Je - sus
rest. Je - sus shall call His blest, Child a-
Bring joy to you be - reft,
san - na, ho - - - san - na, Why seek with tears the Mas - ter
liv - eth, Je - sus liv - eth, Thru pain and scorn to glo - ry's
wak - en! Child a - wak - en! He went be - fore thru heav - en's
f
here? He is not dead, re - joice, He lives!
realm, Thus was His way, our sal - va - tion.
door, And brings us to His Fa - ther's house!

1. Seeds of good-ness we are sow-ing In the hearts of man to-day.
2. Chil-dren come the grain to gath-er, While the morn-ing sun doth shine;
3. Now the field is ripe for har-vest; Let us then all gar-ner in;
4. He who gath-ers not at har-vest, Will a beg-gar be at last.
Bless it, Lord, that it may pros-per, And bear fruit for har-vest day.
And ere long, be-lov-ed breth-ren, It will be your har-vest time.
For if we should stand here i-dle, Who would bring the sheaves of grain?
There-fore rise to-day and la-bor, Gath'ring gold-en sheaves with haste!
CHORUS
Has-ten glad-ly to the la-bor. Con-se-crate to God your heart.
Say this day un-to your Sav-iour, "Lord, I'll glad-ly do my part."

UP YONDER IN HEAVEN

1. Up yon - der in heav - en 'tis well with the soul, If this we con-si - der our cour-age will grow, There Je-sus will bid us that kingdom to share, Which God from begin-ning for us did pre-pare.
2. There we shall be - hold what no eye hath seen here, And feel joys as nev - er our hearts here could cheer, And there we will hear what man nev-er has heard Of good-ness which free-ly is shared by the Lord.
3. The pur - est sweet mus-ic we'll hear in that land, As fond - ly we gaze t'ward the throne of the Lamb, For there that great countless throng sings e'er to praise The One who e'er was, is, and will be al - ways,
4. The Bride and the Spir - it say, "Je - sus come soon" And let all who hear it, say likewise, "Come soon!" And all who are thirs-ty come here and re-ceive The wa - ter of life, which God free - ly doth give.
CHORUS
Praise the Lamb of God; In His love a - bide, For He hath a-chieved our sal-va-tion sweet, He is worth-y of our honor, soon we shall reach our home
Then we'll meet Thee there, In the man - sion fair! Join in end-less song with the holy throng, Praise the Lamb, Oh hallelujah! we'll rest no more to roam

THE SHIP OF FAITH

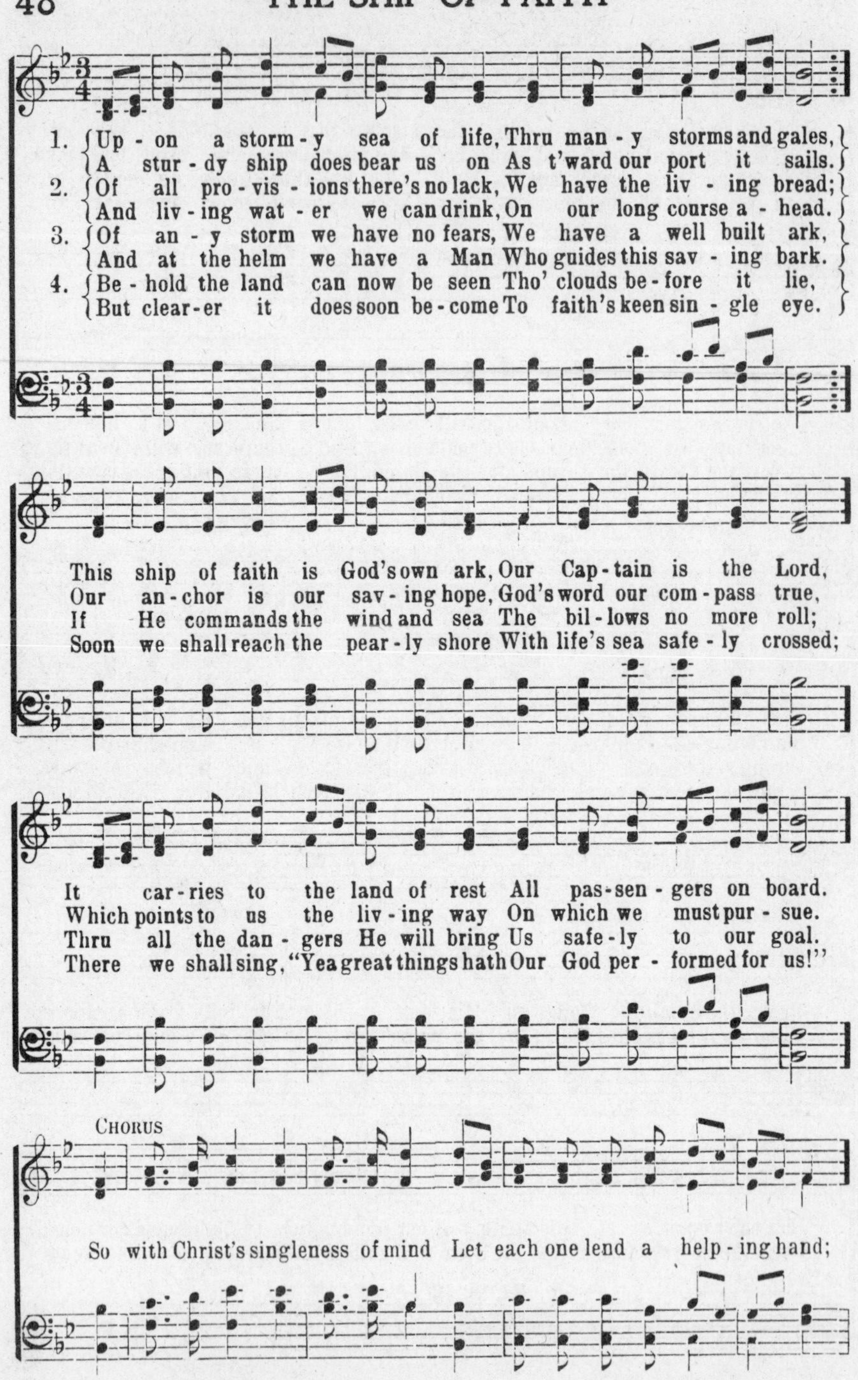
1. Up-on a storm-y sea of life, Thru man-y storms and gales,
A stur-dy ship does bear us on As t'ward our port it sails.
2. Of all pro-vis-ions there's no lack, We have the liv-ing bread;
And liv-ing wat-er we can drink, On our long course a-head.
3. Of an-y storm we have no fears, We have a well built ark,
And at the helm we have a Man Who guides this sav-ing bark.
4. Be-hold the land can now be seen Tho' clouds be-fore it lie,
But clear-er it does soon be-come To faith's keen sin-gle eye.
This ship of faith is God's own ark, Our Cap-tain is the Lord,
Our an-chor is our sav-ing hope, God's word our com-pass true,
If He commands the wind and sea The bil-lows no more roll;
Soon we shall reach the pear-ly shore With life's sea safe-ly crossed;
It car-ries to the land of rest All pas-sen-gers on board.
Which points to us the liv-ing way On which we must pur-sue.
Thru all the dan-gers He will bring Us safe-ly to our goal.
There we shall sing, "Yea great things hath Our God per-formed for us!"
CHORUS
So with Christ's singleness of mind Let each one lend a help-ing hand;

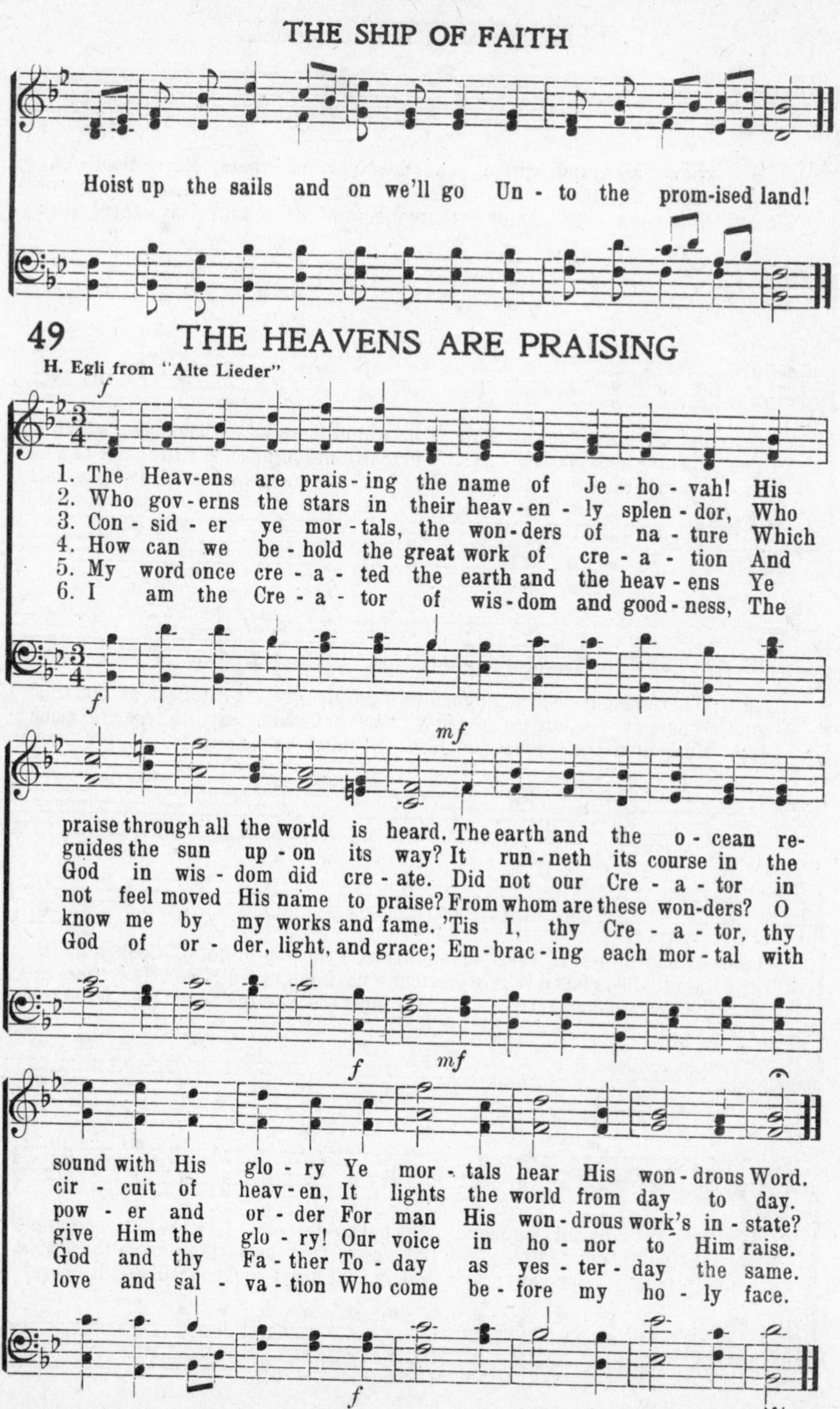
THE SHIP OF FAITH
Hoist up the sails and on we'll go Un - to the prom-ised land!
49 THE HEAVENS ARE PRAISING
H. Egli from "Alte Lieder"
1. The Heav-ens are prais - ing the name of Je - ho - vah! His praise through all the world is heard. The earth and the o - cean re - sound with His glo - ry Ye mor - tals hear His won - drous Word.
2. Who gov - erns the stars in their heav - en - ly splen - dor, Who guides the sun up - on its way? It run - neth its course in the cir - cuit of heav - en, It lights the world from day to day.
3. Con - sid - er ye mor - tals, the won - ders of na - ture Which God in wis - dom did cre - ate. Did not our Cre - a - tor in pow - er and or - der For man His won - drous work's in - state?
4. How can we be - hold the great work of cre - a - tion And not feel moved His name to praise? From whom are these won - ders? O give Him the glo - ry! Our voice in ho - nor to Him raise.
5. My word once cre - a - ted the earth and the heav - ens Ye know me by my works and fame. 'Tis I, thy Cre - a - tor, thy God and thy Fa - ther To - day as yes - ter - day the same.
6. I am the Cre - a - tor of wis - dom and good - ness, The God of or - der, light, and grace; Em - brac - ing each mor - tal with love and sal - va - tion Who come be - fore my ho - ly face.

50
THE BEAUTIFUL LAND
1. I know a land where peace does e'er a - bide, No lead - en
2. I know a land of bless-ed lib - er - ty Where ty - rant
3. Do you wish to know where this land is found? Not thru dark
grey the a - zure blue can hide, Where kind-li-ness a-bounds for which we
rules no slave with tyr - an - ny, Where thy en - light-ened mind can e'er hold
gor - ges and the world a-round, Nor o - ver moun-tains high and gla-ciers
yearn; Where unfeign'd love, sweet love wins in re - turn. Seek'st thou this
sway, Where hy - po - crites thy faith can - not gain - say, Where pre - cious
bleak. Must thou tra - verse this love - ly land to seek. It is so
land (of hap-pi-ness)? Seek'st thou this land (of hap-pi-ness)? Seek not a-
gold (is not called glaze), Where precious gold (is not called glaze), Nay, there the
near (be true and pure). It is so near (be true and pure). Be freed from
far or it can-not be found, Seek not a - far or it can-not be found!
precious gold is ne'er called glaze, But on-ly true de-serts re-ceive the praise.
sin. O bow in fer-vent pray'r Seek in your heart, and you will find it there!

51 I CANNOT TELL HOW PRECIOUS

Charles H. Gabriel
James McGranahan
1. I can-not tell how pre-cious The Sav-iour is to me, Since I have Him ac-
2. I can-not do for Je - sus As much as I should like; But I will e'er en-
3. Whene'er I think of Je - sus, I can-not but re-joice; To me He's ev - er
cept - ed, And He hath made me free; I can-not tell His good - ness, E-
deav- or To work with all my might; For, was not my dear Sav - iour For
precious, For Him I raise my voice: I know He has in glo - ry A
nough to sat - is - fy; And if you'll on - ly take Him, You'll see the reason why.
sin - ners cru - ci - fied? For me, then, sure-ly, Je - sus Hung on the cross and died.
home prepar'd for me, Where I shall live for - ev - er So hap - py, and so free.
CHORUS
I can - not tell how pre - cious The Sav - iour is to me;
I on - ly can en - treat you To come, and taste and see.

52 WAIT, AND MURMUR NOT

W. H. Bellamy
Wm. J. Kirkpatrick
1. O troubled heart, there is a home, Be-yond the reach of toil and care; A
2. Yet when bow'd down beneath the load By heav'n allow'd, thine earthly lot; Look
3. If in thy path some thorns are found, O, think who bore them on His brow; If
4. Toil on, nor deem, tho' sore it be, One sign unheard, one pray'r for-got; The
home where changes nev - er come; Who would not fain be rest-ing there?
up! thoul't reach that blest a - bode, Wait, meek-ly wait, and mur-mur not.
grief thy sorrowing heart has found, It reached a ho - li - er than thou.
day of rest will dawn for thee; Wait, meek-ly wait, and mur-mur not.
CHORUS.
O, wait, meek-ly wait, and mur-mur not, O,
meek-ly wait,
wait, meek-ly wait, and mur-mur not; O, wait,
meek-ly wait, meek-ly wait,
O, wait, O, wait, and mur - mur not.
meek-ly wait, O, mur-mur not.

53 MEETING AND PARTING

1. Meet to - day and part to - mor-row. Smiles of joy and tears of sor-row,
2. Meet to - day in so - cial un - ion. Spend the hour in sweet communion
3. If to - mor-row tears are start-ing, At the ten - der hour of part-ing,
Such is hu - man life, But in gen - tle res - ig - na - tion,
As in sea - sons past, Chris-tian friend-ship is a treas - ure,
Brief will be the pain; Time on ra - pid wings is fly - ing,
And with sweet an - tic - i - pa - tion, Of a high - er, ho - lier sta-tion,
Pure in na - ture, rich in meas - ure, Fill - ing us with heav'nly pleasure,
Christians on their Lord re - ly - ing, Pres-ent, ab - sent, liv-ing, dy - ing,
We en - dure the strife, We en - dure the strife.
While the mo - ments last, While the mo - ments last.
Soon will meet a - gain, Soon will meet a - gain.

THE GOOD SHEPHERD

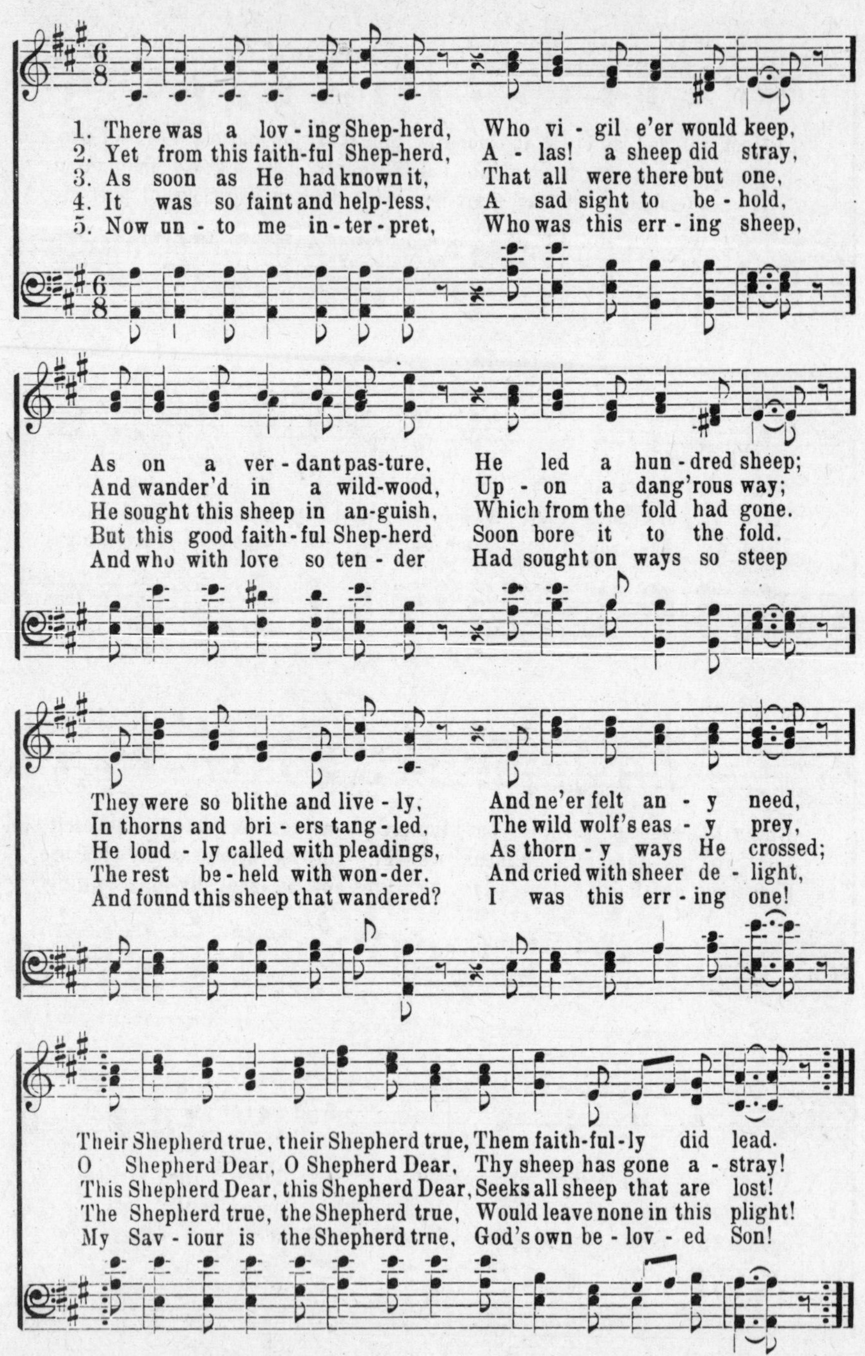
1. There was a lov - ing Shep-herd, Who vi - gil e'er would keep,
2. Yet from this faith-ful Shep-herd, A - las! a sheep did stray,
3. As soon as He had known it, That all were there but one,
4. It was so faint and help-less, A sad sight to be - hold,
5. Now un - to me in - ter - pret, Who was this err - ing sheep,
As on a ver - dant pas-ture, He led a hun - dred sheep;
And wander'd in a wild-wood, Up - on a dang'rous way;
He sought this sheep in an-guish, Which from the fold had gone.
But this good faith - ful Shep-herd Soon bore it to the fold.
And who with love so ten - der Had sought on ways so steep
They were so blithe and live - ly, And ne'er felt an - y need,
In thorns and bri - ers tang - led, The wild wolf's eas - y prey,
He loud - ly called with pleadings, As thorn - y ways He crossed;
The rest be - held with won - der. And cried with sheer de - light,
And found this sheep that wandered? I was this err - ing one!
Their Shepherd true, their Shepherd true, Them faith-ful - ly did lead.
O Shepherd Dear, O Shepherd Dear, Thy sheep has gone a - stray!
This Shepherd Dear, this Shepherd Dear, Seeks all sheep that are lost!
The Shepherd true, the Shepherd true, Would leave none in this plight!
My Sav - iour is the Shepherd true, God's own be - lov - ed Son!

55 IT IS WELL WITH MY SOUL

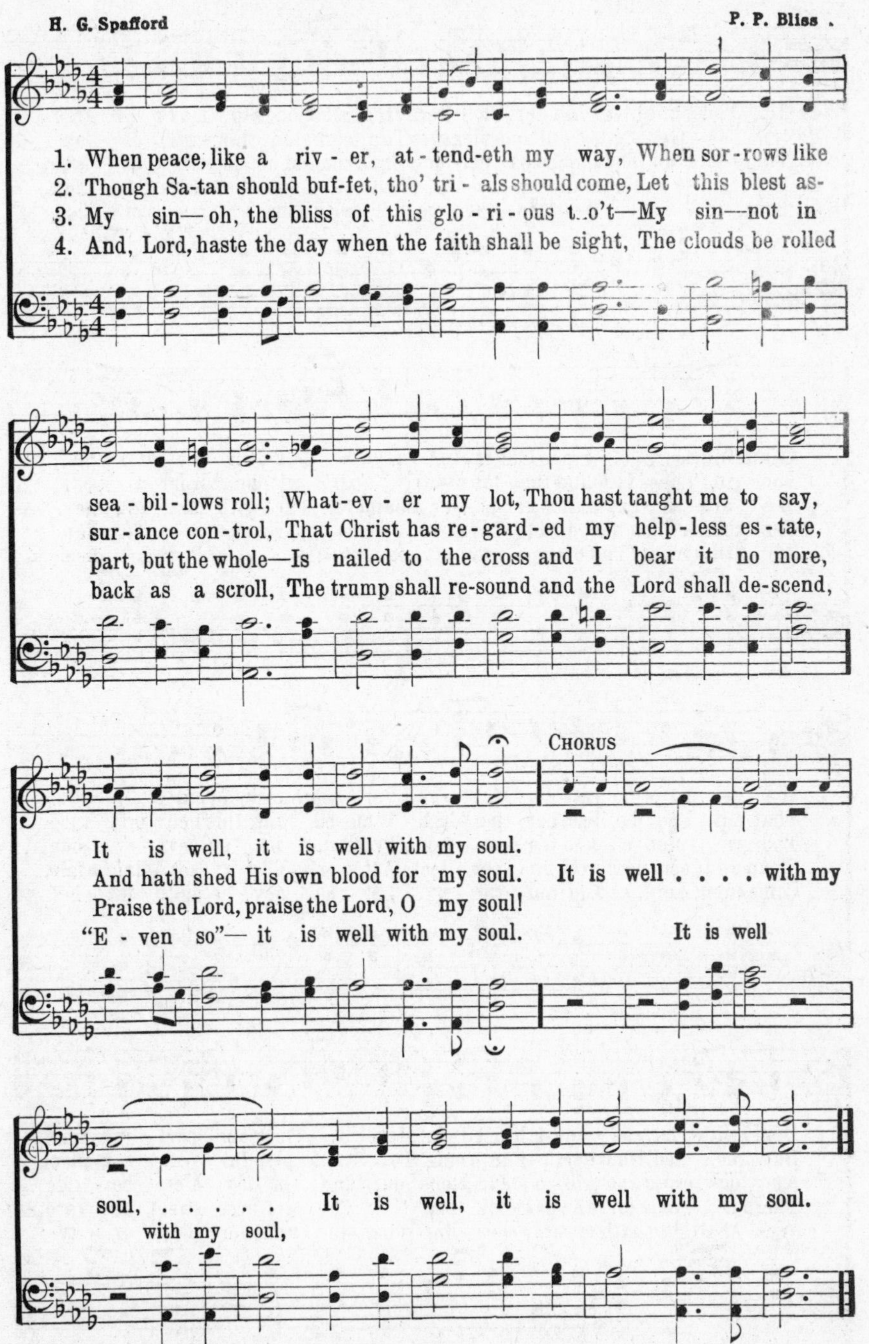
H. G. Spafford
P. P. Bliss
1. When peace, like a riv - er, at - tend-eth my way, When sor - rows like
2. Though Sa-tan should buf-fet, tho' tri - als should come, Let this blest as-
3. My sin— oh, the bliss of this glo - ri - ous thought—My sin—not in
4. And, Lord, haste the day when the faith shall be sight, The clouds be rolled
sea - bil - lows roll; What-ev - er my lot, Thou hast taught me to say,
sur - ance con - trol, That Christ has re - gard - ed my help - less es - tate,
part, but the whole—Is nailed to the cross and I bear it no more,
back as a scroll, The trump shall re-sound and the Lord shall de-scend,
It is well, it is well with my soul.
And hath shed His own blood for my soul.
Praise the Lord, praise the Lord, O my soul!
"E - ven so"— it is well with my soul.
CHORUS
It is well . . . . with my
It is well
soul, ... It is well, it is well with my soul.
with my soul,

1. Je - sus, might-y Lib - er - a - tor, From all bonds to make me free,
2. It is God's good will and pleasure To con-clude this work of love,
3. There-fore do Thou make us per-fect, Thou couldst not do oth - er - wise;
4. Let those who were dearly purchased Not be - come the slaves of man.
5. Lord, in - to Thy death in - clude us, Let with Thee be cru - ci - fied
Changing scorn, dis-grace, dis-fav-or, In - to heav'nly joy for me!
For in Thee is found the ful-ness Of all wis-dom from a - bove;
We are in Thy hands and pow-er Bound to Thee with last - ing ties.
For since Thou hast died to save us, Keep us pure, as in Thy plan.
All that meets Thy dis-ap - prov-al; Lead us in - to Par - a - dise!
We de - mand no rest nor fav - or For our flesh in earth - ly clime;
That not one be lost nor per - ish Who be - gan this heav'n-ly race.
Tho' we stand a - mid temp-ta - tions Press-ing us on ev' - ry side.
Clean and spot-less, true and per - fect, Aft - er Thy re-sem-blance fair,
Come then, Lord, and do not tar - ry, Let us nev - er sloth - ful be!
Deal with us as seem-eth need - ful Here be - fore our part - ing time!
But be led from earth-ly tu - mult To that joy - ful rest - ing place.
And our cross and trib - u - la - tions Soul and bo - dy e'er be - tide.
There is grace for all par - tak - ers Of Thy ful-ness sweet and rare.
We shall sing with great re - joic - ing When we gain our lib - er - ty.

57 WHEN EARTH'S TRIALS ARE OVER

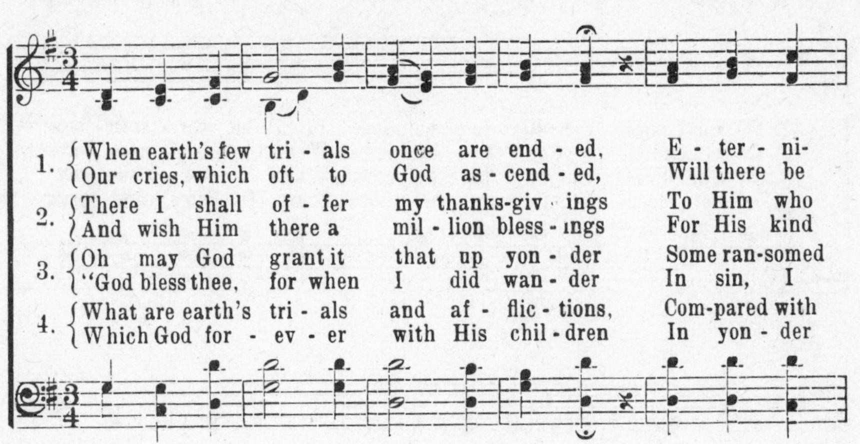
1. When earth's few tri - als once are end - ed, E - ter - ni-
Our cries, which oft to God as - cend - ed, Will there be
2. There I shall of - fer my thanks-giv - ings To Him who
And wish Him there a mil - lion bless - ings For His kind
3. Oh may God grant it that up yon - der Some ran-somed
"God bless thee, for when I did wan - der In sin, I
4. What are earth's tri - als and af - flic - tions, Com-pared with
Which God for - ev - er with His chil - dren In yon - der

REFRAIN
ty a - waits the blest. / changed to peace-ful rest. Here vir - tue doth pur - sue its ways;
bade me choose God's way. / call when I did stray. There I shall meet in heav-en's height,
soul might say to me, / saw God's light in thee." How blest, in - deed, must be the part
heav - en's glo - ries fair? / man - sions once will share? In no wise can with these com - pare

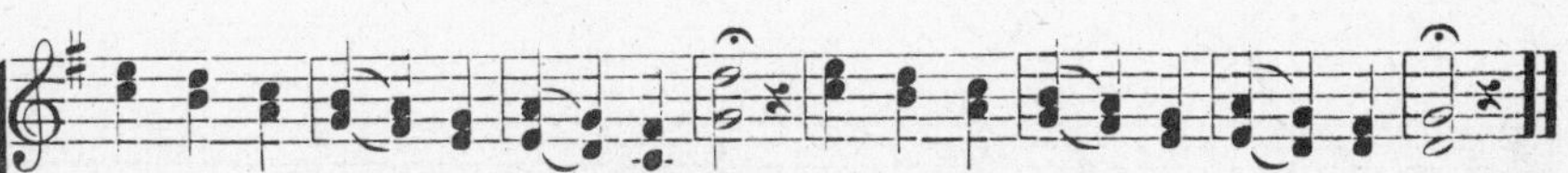

The world to come will sing its praise. The world to come will sing its praise.
The Friend who bro't my soul de-light. The Friend who bro't my soul de-light.
Of Him who saves a sin - ful heart! Of Him who saves a sin - ful heart!
This mo-ment short, of earth-ly care! This moment short, of, earth-ly care!

58 WHAT SHALL I DO TO BE SAVED?

J. W. Holman | Wm. B. Bradbury

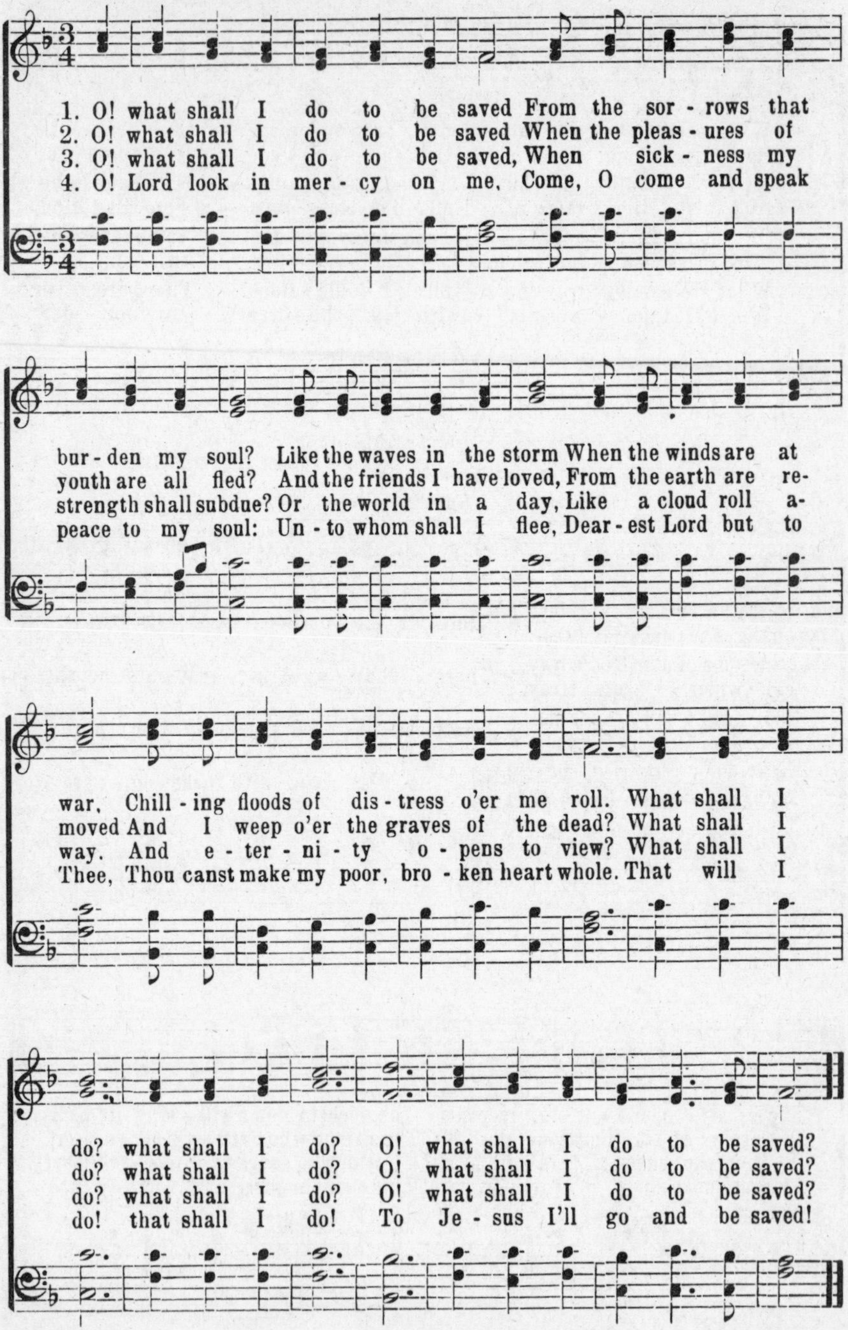

1. O! what shall I do to be saved From the sor - rows that
2. O! what shall I do to be saved When the pleas - ures of
3. O! what shall I do to be saved, When sick - ness my
4. O! Lord look in mer - cy on me, Come, O come and speak

bur - den my soul? Like the waves in the storm When the winds are at
youth are all fled? And the friends I have loved, From the earth are re-
strength shall subdue? Or the world in a day, Like a cloud roll a-
peace to my soul: Un - to whom shall I flee, Dear - est Lord but to

war, Chill - ing floods of dis - tress o'er me roll. What shall I
moved And I weep o'er the graves of the dead? What shall I
way. And e - ter - ni - ty o - pens to view? What shall I
Thee, Thou canst make my poor, bro - ken heart whole. That will I

do? what shall I do? O! what shall I do to be saved?
do? what shall I do? O! what shall I do to be saved?
do? what shall I do? O! what shall I do to be saved?
do! that shall I do! To Je - sus I'll go and be saved!

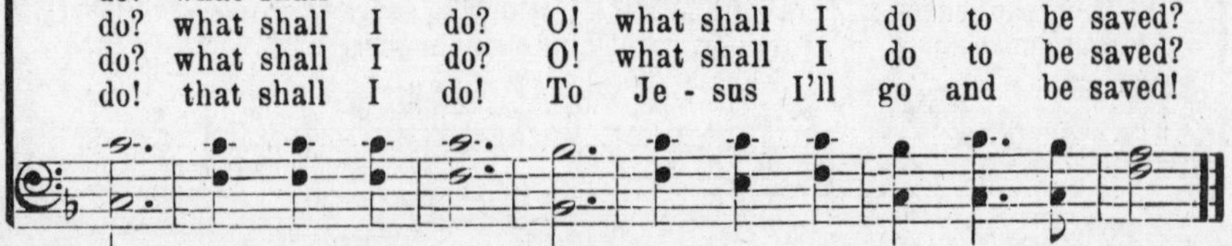

59 A CHRISTIAN'S DESIRE

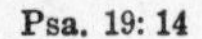
Psa. 19: 14

Let the words of my mouth, and the med-i-ta-tion of my heart, be ac-

cept-a-ble in Thy sight, O Lord, my strength, and my Redeem-er. A-MEN.

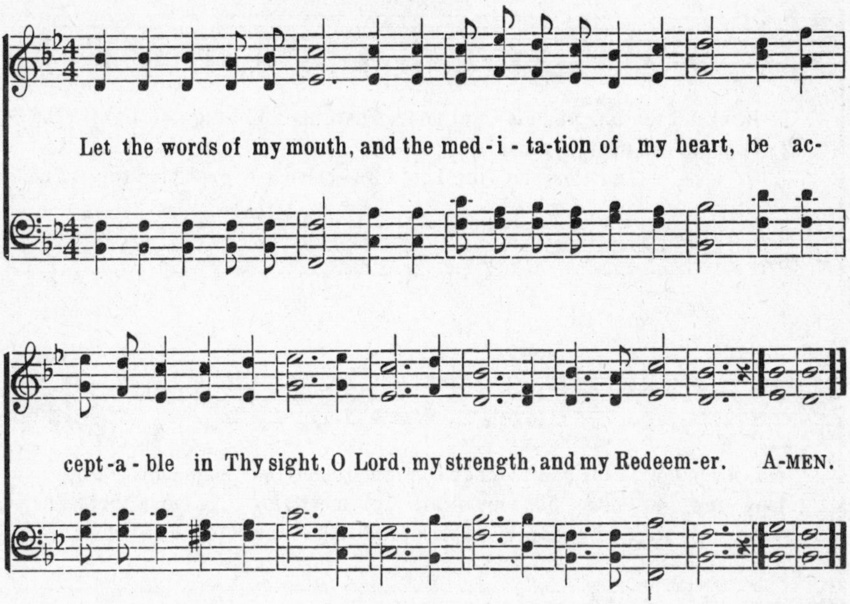

60 ONCE MORE BEFORE WE PART

Joseph Hart

Lowell Mason

1. Once more, be-fore we part, O bless the Sav-iour's name! Let
2. Lord, in Thy grace we came, That bless-ing still im-part; We
3. Still on thy ho-ly word Help us to feed and grow; Still
4. Now, Lord, be-fore we part, Help us to bless Thy name; Let
ev-ery tongue and ev-ery heart A-dore and praise the same.
met in Je-sus' sa-cred name, In Je-sus' name we part.
to go on to know the Lord, And prac-tice what we know.
ev-ery tongue and ev-ery heart A-dore and praise the same. A-MEN.

61 THE DWELLING OF LIGHT

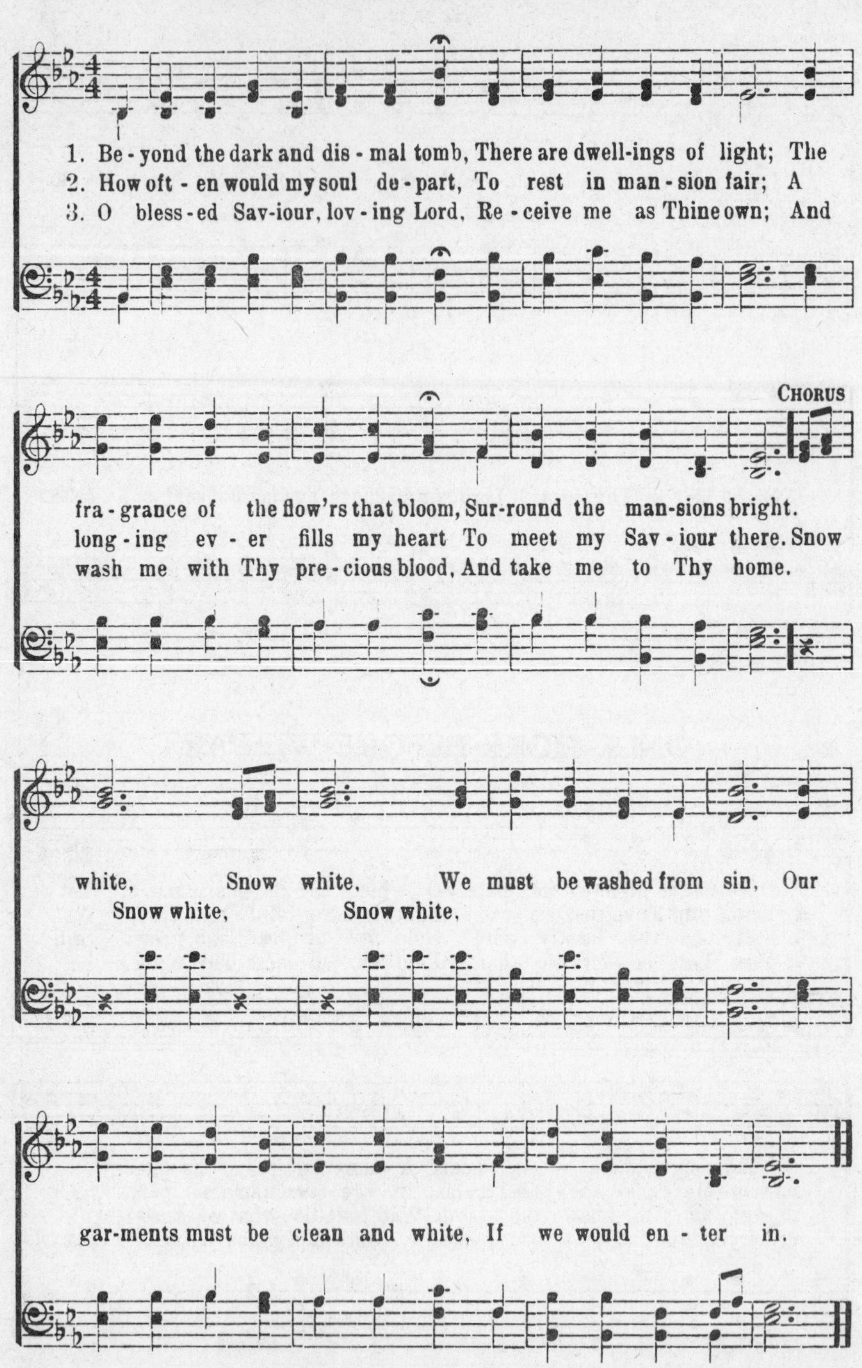
1. Be - yond the dark and dis - mal tomb, There are dwell-ings of light; The
2. How oft - en would my soul de - part, To rest in man - sion fair; A
3. O bless - ed Sav-iour, lov - ing Lord, Re - ceive me as Thine own; And
fra - grance of the flow'rs that bloom, Sur-round the man-sions bright.
long - ing ev - er fills my heart To meet my Sav - iour there.
wash me with Thy pre - cious blood, And take me to Thy home.
CHORUS
Snow white, Snow white, We must be washed from sin, Our
Snow white, Snow white,
gar-ments must be clean and white, If we would en - ter in.

TAKE THE BIBLE IN THE MORNING

1. Take the Bi - ble in the morn - ing, But a
2. 'Tis the gen - tle dew from heav - en, The
3. So in the blush of morn - ing, Take the
mo - ment if no more; It is bet - ter than an ho - ur,
man - na for the day. If you fail to gath - er ear - ly,
of - fered hand of love. And walk in heav - en's path - way,
When the try - ing day is o'er; It is bet - ter than an
A - las, it melts a - way. If you fail to gath - er
And the peace - ful - ness there - of. And walk in heav - en's
ho - ur, When the try - ing day is o'er.
ear - ly, A - las, it melts a - way.
path - way, And the peace - ful - ness there - of. A - MEN.

63 GETHSEMANE

H. B. H. G.

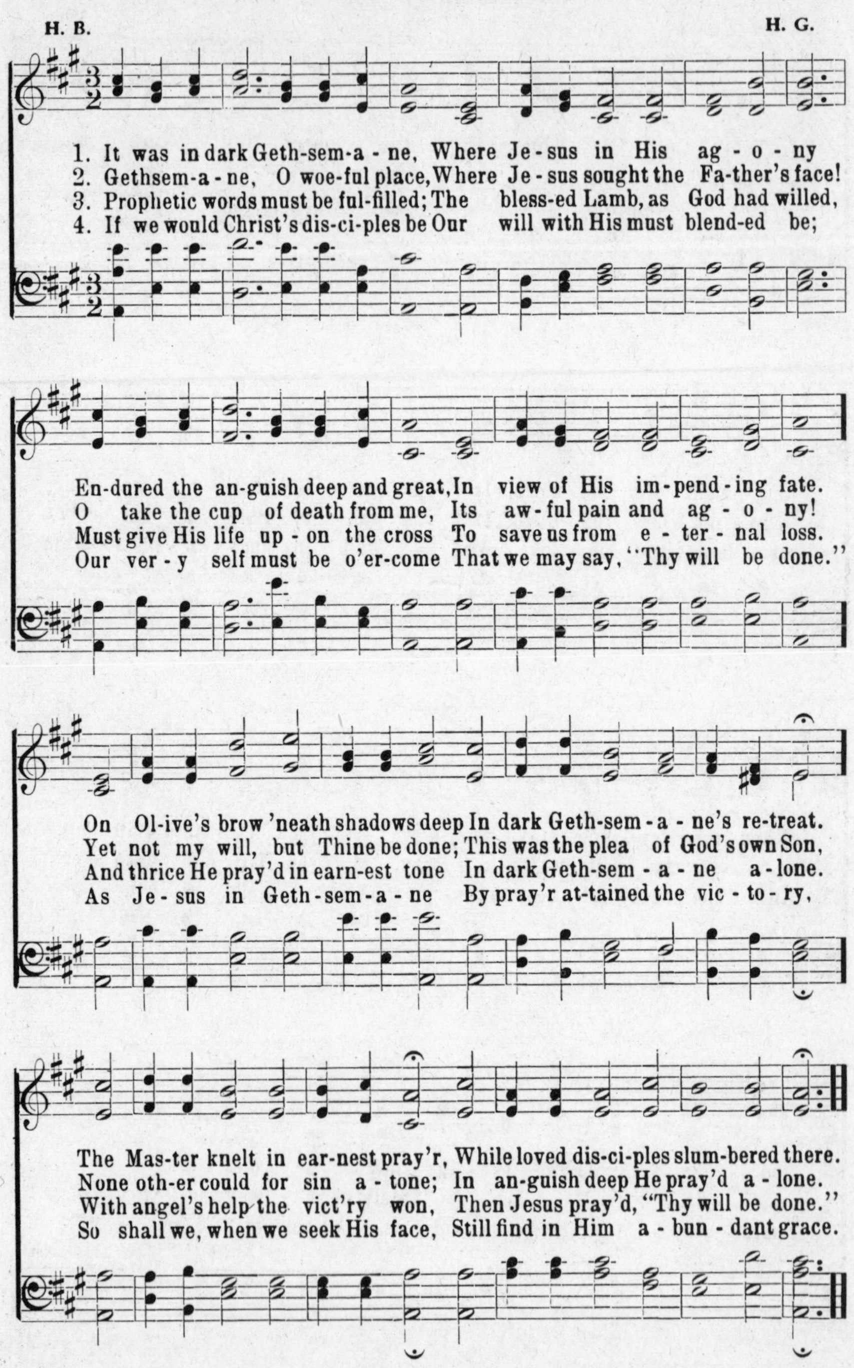
1. It was in dark Geth-sem-a-ne, Where Je-sus in His ag-o-ny
2. Gethsem-a-ne, O woe-ful place, Where Je-sus sought the Fa-ther's face!
3. Prophetic words must be ful-filled; The bless-ed Lamb, as God had willed,
4. If we would Christ's dis-ci-ples be Our will with His must blend-ed be;
En-dured the an-guish deep and great, In view of His im-pend-ing fate.
O take the cup of death from me, Its aw-ful pain and ag-o-ny!
Must give His life up-on the cross To save us from e-ter-nal loss.
Our ver-y self must be o'er-come That we may say, "Thy will be done."
On Ol-ive's brow 'neath shadows deep In dark Geth-sem-a-ne's re-treat.
Yet not my will, but Thine be done; This was the plea of God's own Son,
And thrice He pray'd in earn-est tone In dark Geth-sem-a-ne a-lone.
As Je-sus in Geth-sem-a-ne By pray'r at-tained the vic-to-ry,
The Mas-ter knelt in ear-nest pray'r, While loved dis-ci-ples slum-bered there.
None oth-er could for sin a-tone; In an-guish deep He pray'd a-lone.
With angel's help the vict'ry won, Then Jesus pray'd, "Thy will be done."
So shall we, when we seek His face, Still find in Him a-bun-dant grace.

64 THE CHRISTIAN HOME

J. H. McNaughton
1. There is beau - ty all a - round, When there's love at home;
2. In the cot - tage there is joy, When there's love at home;
3. Kind - ly heav - en smiles a - bove, When there's love at home;
There is joy in ev - 'ry sound, When there's love at home.
Hate and en - vy, ne'er an - noy, When there's love at home.
All the earth is filled with love, When there's love at home.
Peace and plen - ty here a - bide, Smil - ing sweet on ev - 'ry side,
Ro - ses blos - som 'neath our feet, All the earth's a gar - den sweet,
Sweet - er sings the brook - let by, Bright - er beams the az - ure sky;
Time doth soft - ly, sweet - ly glide, When there's love at home.
Mak - ing life a bliss com - plete, When there's love at home.
O there's One who smiles on high, When there's love at home.
Refrain
Love at home. love at home, Time doth soft - ly, sweet - ly glide, When there's love at home.

65 ANGRY WORDS! O LET THEM NEVER

D. K. P.
Horatio R. Palmer
1. An - gry words! O let them nev - er From the tongue un-bri - dled slip;
2. Love is much too pure and ho - ly, Friendship is too sa - cred far,
3. An - gry words are light-ly spok - en, Bit - t'rest tho'ts are rash - ly stirred,
May the heart's best impulse ev - er Check them ere they soil the lip.
For a mo-ment's reckless fol - ly Thus to des - o - late and mar.
Bright-est links of life are brok - en, By a sin - gle an - gry word.
CHORUS
"Love one an - oth - er," thus saith the Sav - iour; Chil-dren, o-
"Love each oth-er, love each oth - er,"
bey the Fa-ther's blest command, "Love one an - oth - er," thus saith the
'Tis the Fa-ther's blest command, "Love each oth-er,
Sav - iour; Chil - dren, O - bey His blest com - mand.
love each oth - er," 'Tis His blest com - mand.

66 BEYOND THE SMILING AND THE WEEPING

Horatius Bonar — George C. Stebbins

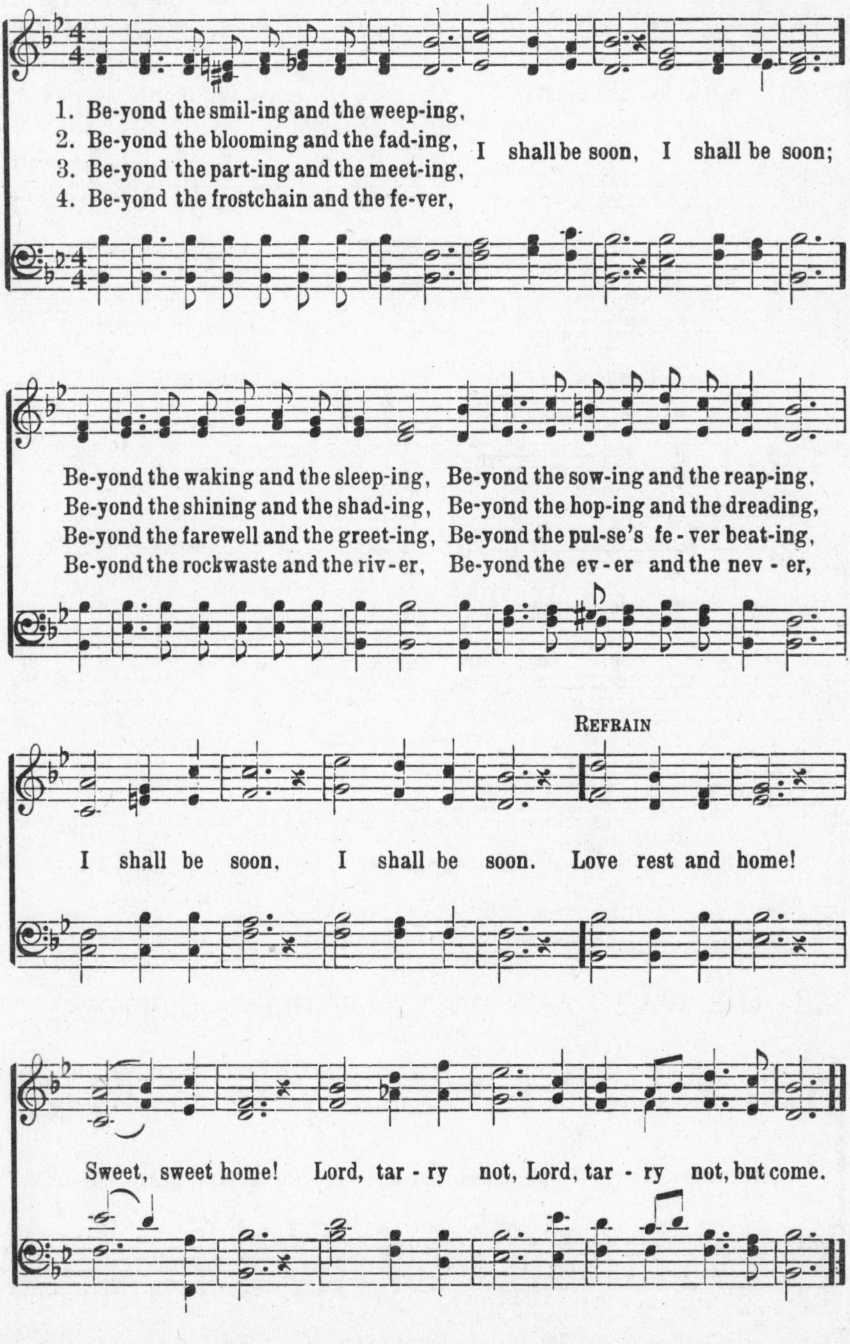

1. Be-yond the smil-ing and the weep-ing,
2. Be-yond the blooming and the fad-ing,
3. Be-yond the part-ing and the meet-ing,
4. Be-yond the frostchain and the fe-ver,

I shall be soon, I shall be soon;

Be-yond the waking and the sleep-ing, Be-yond the sow-ing and the reap-ing,
Be-yond the shining and the shad-ing, Be-yond the hop-ing and the dreading,
Be-yond the farewell and the greet-ing, Be-yond the pul-se's fe-ver beat-ing,
Be-yond the rockwaste and the riv-er, Be-yond the ev-er and the nev-er,

I shall be soon, I shall be soon.

REFRAIN

Love rest and home! Sweet, sweet home! Lord, tar-ry not, Lord, tar-ry not, but come.

67 THE EARTH IS THE LORD'S

68 HIS WAYS ARE WAYS OF PLEASANTNESS

Prov. 3:17

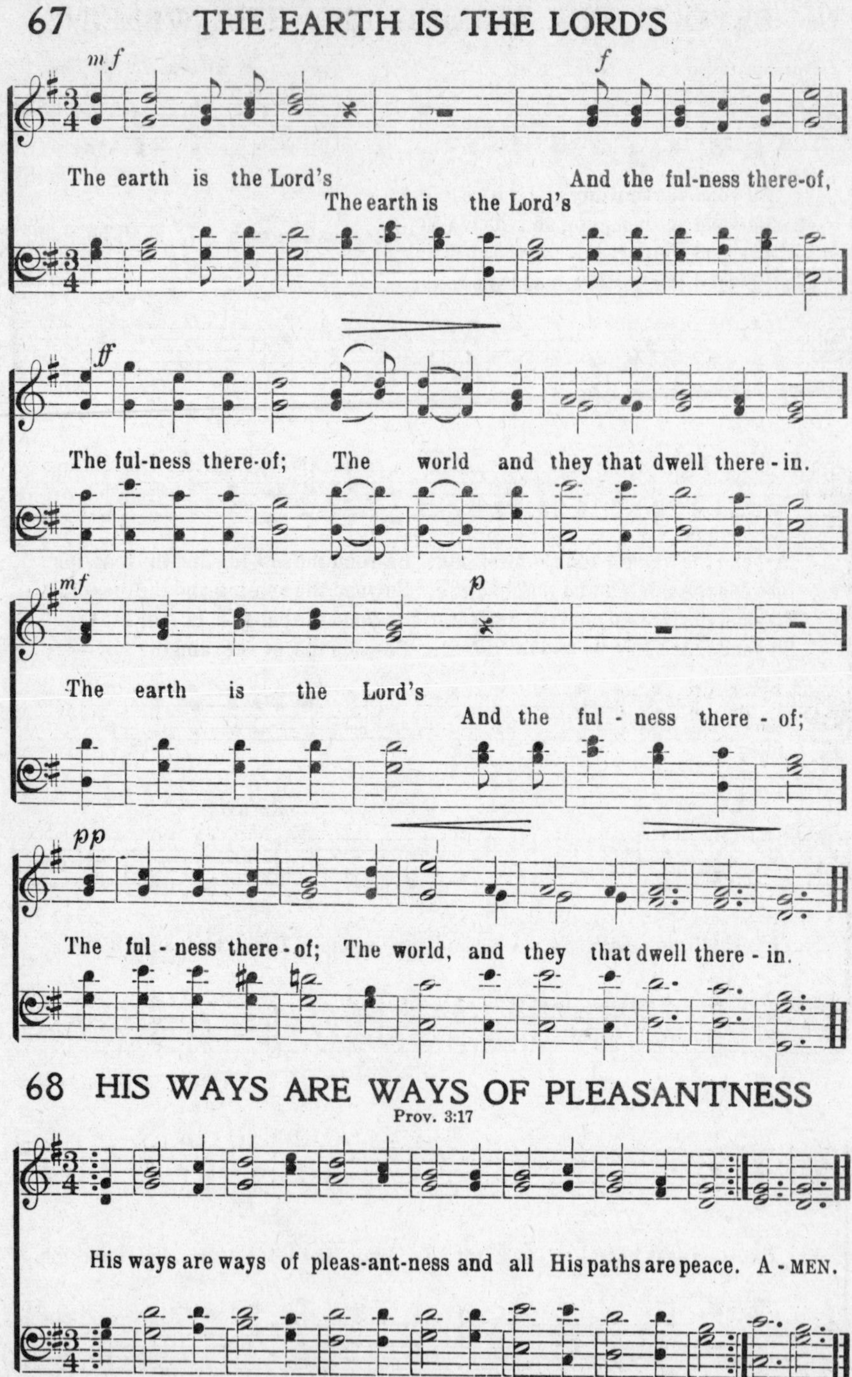
mf
f
The earth is the Lord's
The earth is the Lord's
And the ful-ness there-of,
ff
The ful-ness there-of; The world and they that dwell there-in.
mf
p
The earth is the Lord's
And the ful - ness there - of;
pp
The ful - ness there - of; The world, and they that dwell there - in.
His ways are ways of pleas-ant-ness and all His paths are peace. A - MEN.

69 WAIT UPON THE LORD

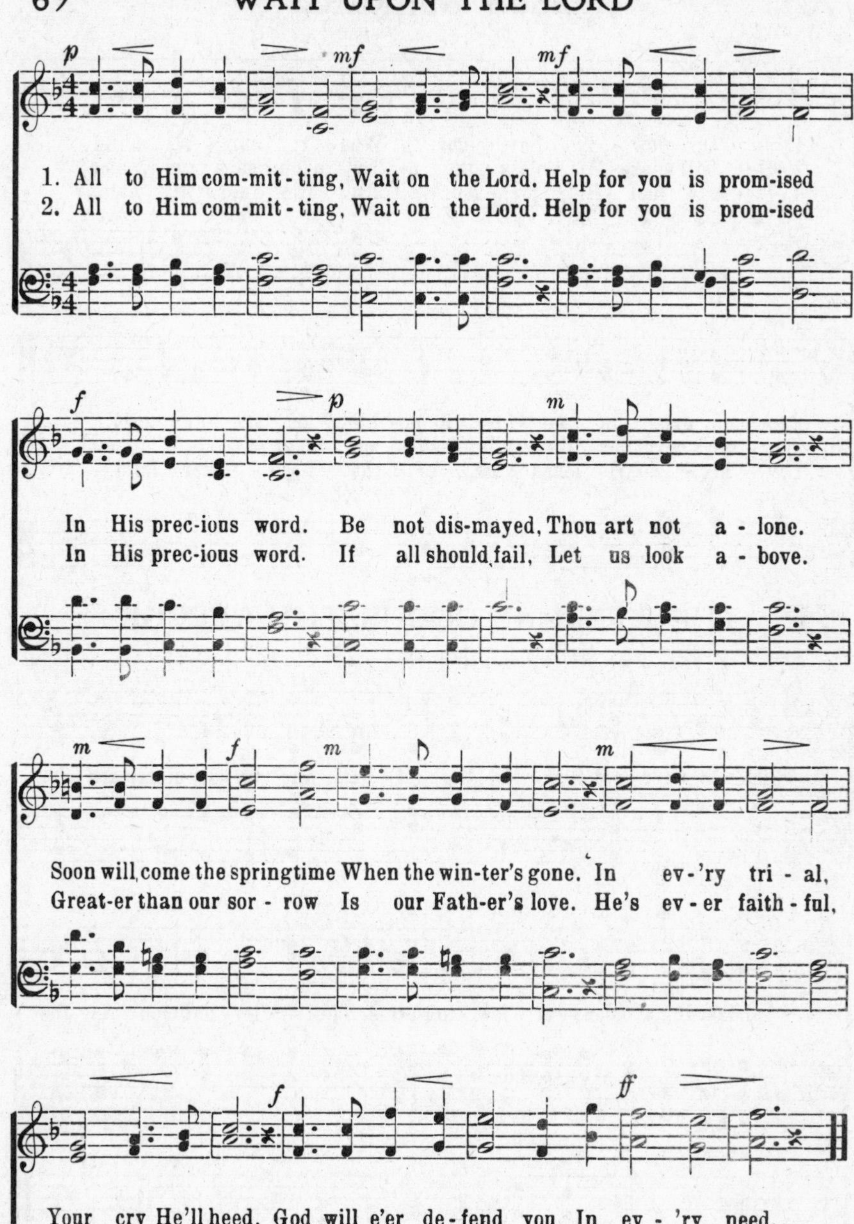
p
mf
mf
1. All to Him com-mit-ting, Wait on the Lord. Help for you is prom-ised
2. All to Him com-mit-ting, Wait on the Lord. Help for you is prom-ised
f
p
m
In His prec-ious word. Be not dis-mayed, Thou art not a-lone.
In His prec-ious word. If all should fail, Let us look a-bove.
m
f
m
m
Soon will come the springtime When the win-ter's gone. In ev-'ry tri-al,
Great-er than our sor-row Is our Fath-er's love. He's ev-er faith-ful,
f
ff
Your cry He'll heed. God will e'er de-fend you In ev-'ry need.
He mak-eth whole. He is our Re-deem-er, Lov-eth our soul.

70 JESUS' NEARNESS

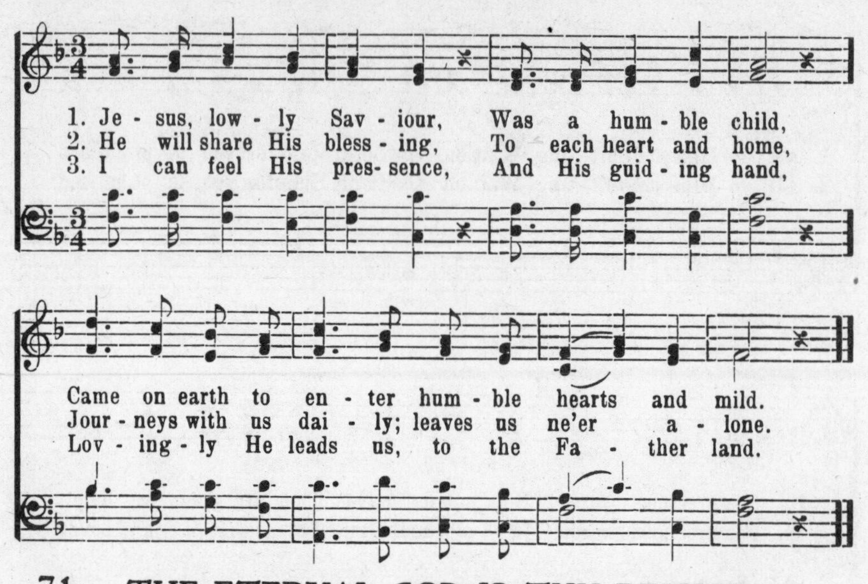

1. Je - sus, low - ly Sav - iour, Was a hum - ble child,
2. He will share His bless - ing, To each heart and home,
3. I can feel His pres- sence, And His guid - ing hand,
Came on earth to en - ter hum - ble hearts and mild.
Jour - neys with us dai - ly; leaves us ne'er a - lone.
Lov - ing - ly He leads us, to the Fa - ther land.

71 THE ETERNAL GOD IS THY REFUGE

Deut. 33:27

The e - ter - nal God is thy ref - uge and un - der-neath are the ev-er-last-ing arms; ev - er - last - ing arms. The e - ter - nal God is thy ref - uge and un - der-neath are the ev - er - last - ing arms. A - MEN.

72 WHEN I SEE THE BLOOD

J. F. G. and E. A. H. J. F. H.

1. Christ our Re-deem-er died on the cross, Died for the sin-ner,
2. Chief-est of sin-ners, Je-sus can save, As He has prom-ised,
3. Judg-ment is com-ing, all will be there, Who have re-ject-ed,
4. Oh, what com-pas-sion, oh, bound-less love! Je-sus hath pow-er,
paid all his due; All who re-ceive Him need nev-er fear,
so will He do; Oh, sin-ner, hear Him, trust in His Word,
who have re-fused? Oh, sin-ner, has-ten, let Je-sus in,
Je-sus is true; All who be-lieve are safe from the storm,
Yes, He will pass, will pass o-ver you.
Then He will pass, will pass o-ver you.
Then God will pass, will pass o-ver you.
Oh, He will pass, will pass o-ver you.
CHORUS
When I see the
When I
blood, When I see the blood, When I see the
see the blood, When I see the blood, When I
rit.
blood, I will pass, I will pass o-ver you.
see the blood, o-ver you.

73 THE SUNDAY SCHOOL

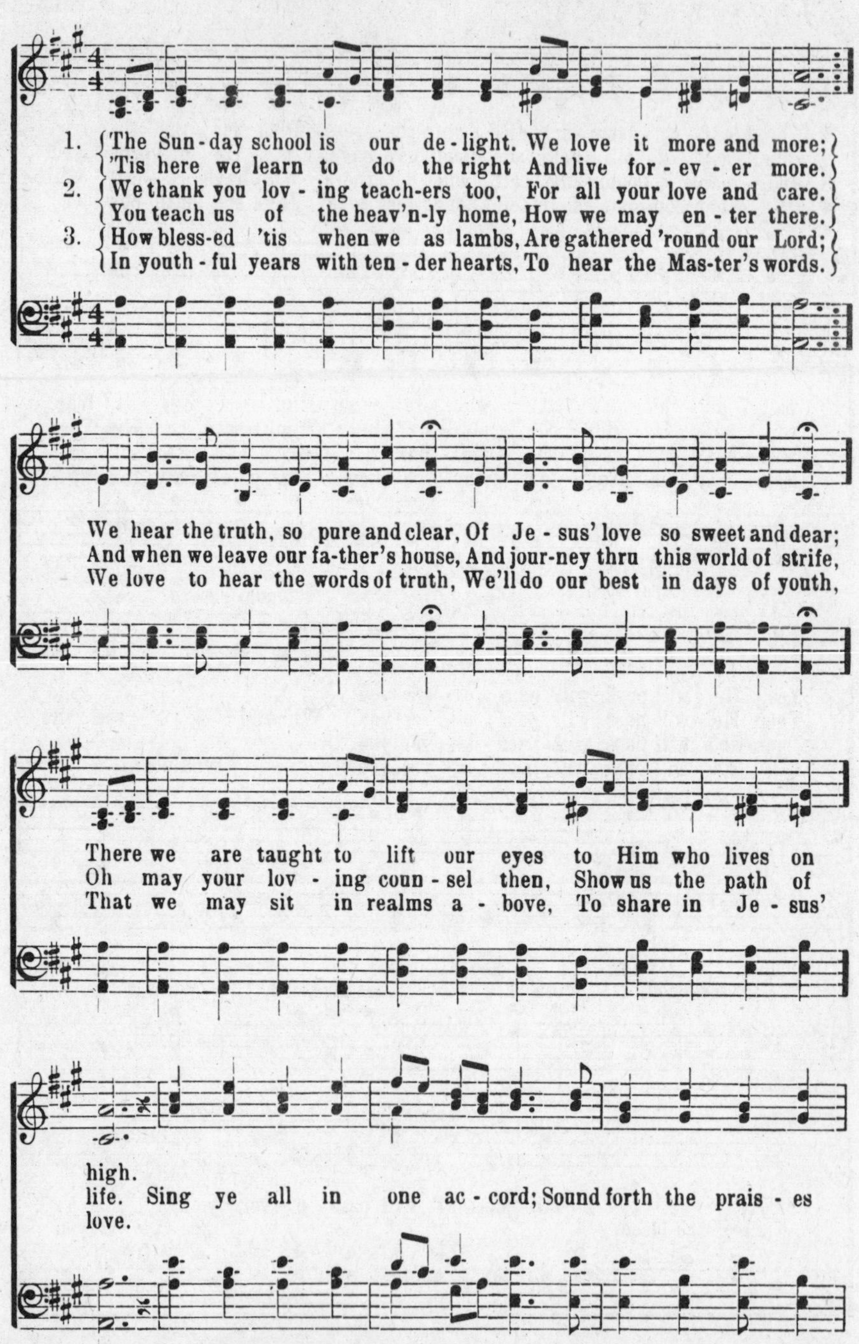
1. The Sun-day school is our de-light. We love it more and more;
'Tis here we learn to do the right And live for-ev-er more.
2. We thank you lov-ing teach-ers too, For all your love and care.
You teach us of the heav'n-ly home, How we may en-ter there.
3. How bless-ed 'tis when we as lambs, Are gathered 'round our Lord;
In youth-ful years with ten-der hearts, To hear the Mas-ter's words.
We hear the truth, so pure and clear, Of Je-sus' love so sweet and dear;
And when we leave our fa-ther's house, And jour-ney thru this world of strife,
We love to hear the words of truth, We'll do our best in days of youth,
There we are taught to lift our eyes to Him who lives on
Oh may your lov-ing coun-sel then, Show us the path of
That we may sit in realms a-bove, To share in Je-sus'
high.
life. Sing ye all in one ac-cord; Sound forth the prais-es
love.

of - the Lord, Ho-san-na, ho - san-na, ho-san-na to the Lamb of God.

74 JESUS KNOWS THY SORROW

1. Je - sus knows thy sor - row, Knows thine ev'ry care; Knows thy deep con-
2. Trust the heart of Je - sus, Thou art pre-cious there; Sure - ly He would
3. Je - sus knows thy con - flict, Hears thy burdened sigh; When thy heart is

tri - tion, Hears thy feeblest pray'rs; Do not fear to trust Him, Tell Him all thy
shield thee From the tempter's snare; Safe-ly He would lead thee By His own sweet
wound-ed, Hears thy plaintive cry; He thy soul will strengthen, O - ver-come thy

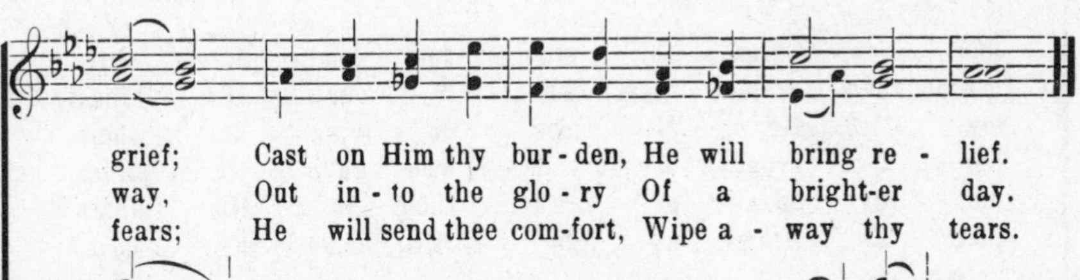
grief; Cast on Him thy bur- den, He will bring re - lief.
way, Out in - to the glo - ry Of a bright-er day.
fears; He will send thee com-fort, Wipe a - way thy tears.

75 READING GOD'S WORD

1. Oft I read the bless - ed Bi - ble, How God sent
2. How He called the lit - tle chil-dren, How each child
3. How His help and ten - der mer - cy, On the sick
4. How He did ac - cept each sin - ner, Who for - sook
5. How He gent - ly led His chil-dren, Light and strength
6. I am nev - er wea - ry read-ing, Hear - ing of
His pre - cious gift; How our Lord in love and
by Him was blest; In His lov - ing arms em-
He did be - stow! To the poor, the meek, and
His err - ing ways, Glad - ly did He lift the
He did im - part; With His love and ten - der
His won - drous love; How His lov - ing, ten - der
mer - cy, Came the sin - ful load to lift.
braced them, Pressed them gent - ly to His breast.
low - ly, He His love di - vine did show.
bur - dens, From the soul who gave Him praise.
mer - cy, Sought to draw them to His heart.
mer - cy, Draws us to His home a - bove.

76 OH, TO BE NOTHING

Georgiana M. Taylor, 1869

R. Geo. Halls
Arr. by P. P. Bliss

Very slow

1. Oh, to be noth-ing, noth - ing, On - ly to lie at His feet,
2. Oh, to be noth-ing, noth - ing, On - ly as led by His hand;
3. Oh, to be noth-ing, noth - ing, Pain-ful the humbling may be,

CHO. *Oh, to be noth - ing, noth - ing, On - ly to lie at His feet,*

FINE

A bro-ken and emp-tied ves - sel, For the Mas - ter's use made meet.
A mes-sen-ger at His gate - way, On - ly waiting for His com - mand,
Yet low in the dust I'd lay me That the world might my Sav - iour see.

A bro-ken aud emp - tied ves - sel, For the Mas - ter's use made meet.

Emp-tied that He might fill me As forth to His ser-vice I go,
On - ly an instrument read - y His prais-es to sound at His will,
Rath-er be noth - ing, noth - ing, To Him let our voic - es be raised,

D. C. CHORUS

Bro - ken, that so un - hin - dered, His life through me might flow.
Willing, should He not re-quire me, In silence to wait on Him still
He is the Fountain of bless-ing, He on - ly is meet to be praised.

77 MY HEAVENLY MANSION

1. My heav'n - ly man - sion, so bright and fair,
2. My glo - r'ous man - sion be - yond the tomb,
3. There in my home - land, in E - den fair,
4. My heav'n - ly man - sion be - yond the sky,
Home of my Sav - iour, Would I were there.
Where Shar - on's ros - es shall ev - er bloom;
Sweet flowers are bloom - ing so pre - cious, rare.
Where they who en - ter shall nev - er die;
The glo - r'ous dwell - ing in yon - der height,
How sweet and peace - ful its tran - quil rest,
'Tis in this home - land my Sav - iour dwells,
There would I jour - ney this ver - y day.
D. S.
How tru - ly love - ly, ar - rayed in light.
There I would en - ter with all the blest.
Of all its glo - ries no tongue can tell.
And with my Je - sus for - ev - er stay.

THE GREATEST JOY

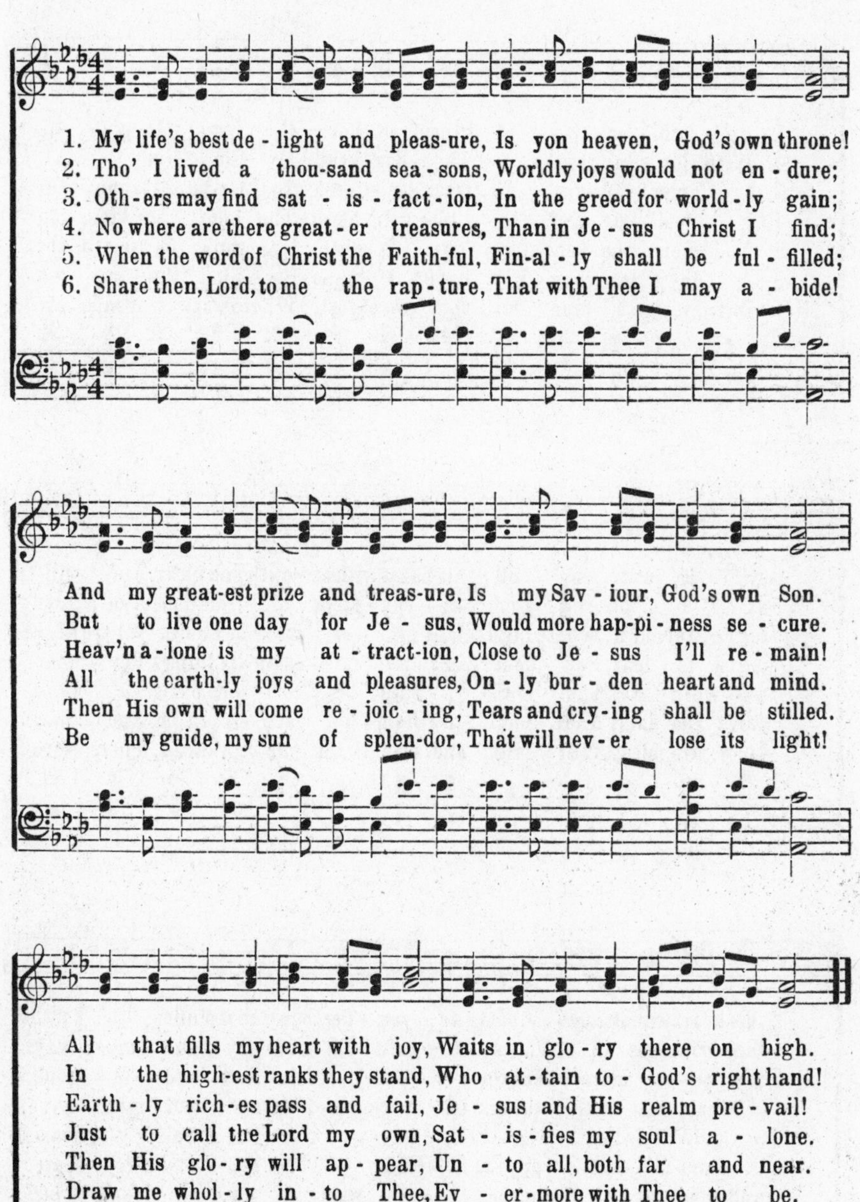
1. My life's best de - light and pleas-ure, Is yon heaven, God's own throne!
2. Tho' I lived a thou-sand sea - sons, Worldly joys would not en - dure;
3. Oth - ers may find sat - is - fact - ion, In the greed for world - ly gain;
4. No where are there great - er treasures, Than in Je - sus Christ I find;
5. When the word of Christ the Faith-ful, Fin - al - ly shall be ful - filled;
6. Share then, Lord, to me the rap - ture, That with Thee I may a - bide!
And my great-est prize and treas-ure, Is my Sav - iour, God's own Son.
But to live one day for Je - sus, Would more hap-pi - ness se - cure.
Heav'n a - lone is my at - tract-ion, Close to Je - sus I'll re - main!
All the earth-ly joys and pleasures, On - ly bur - den heart and mind.
Then His own will come re - joic - ing, Tears and cry-ing shall be stilled.
Be my guide, my sun of splen-dor, That will nev - er lose its light!
All that fills my heart with joy, Waits in glo - ry there on high.
In the high-est ranks they stand, Who at - tain to - God's right hand!
Earth - ly rich - es pass and fail, Je - sus and His realm pre - vail!
Just to call the Lord my own, Sat - is - fies my soul a - lone.
Then His glo - ry will ap - pear, Un - to all, both far and near.
Draw me whol - ly in - to Thee, Ev - er - more with Thee to be.

79 MY DAY'S JOURNEY

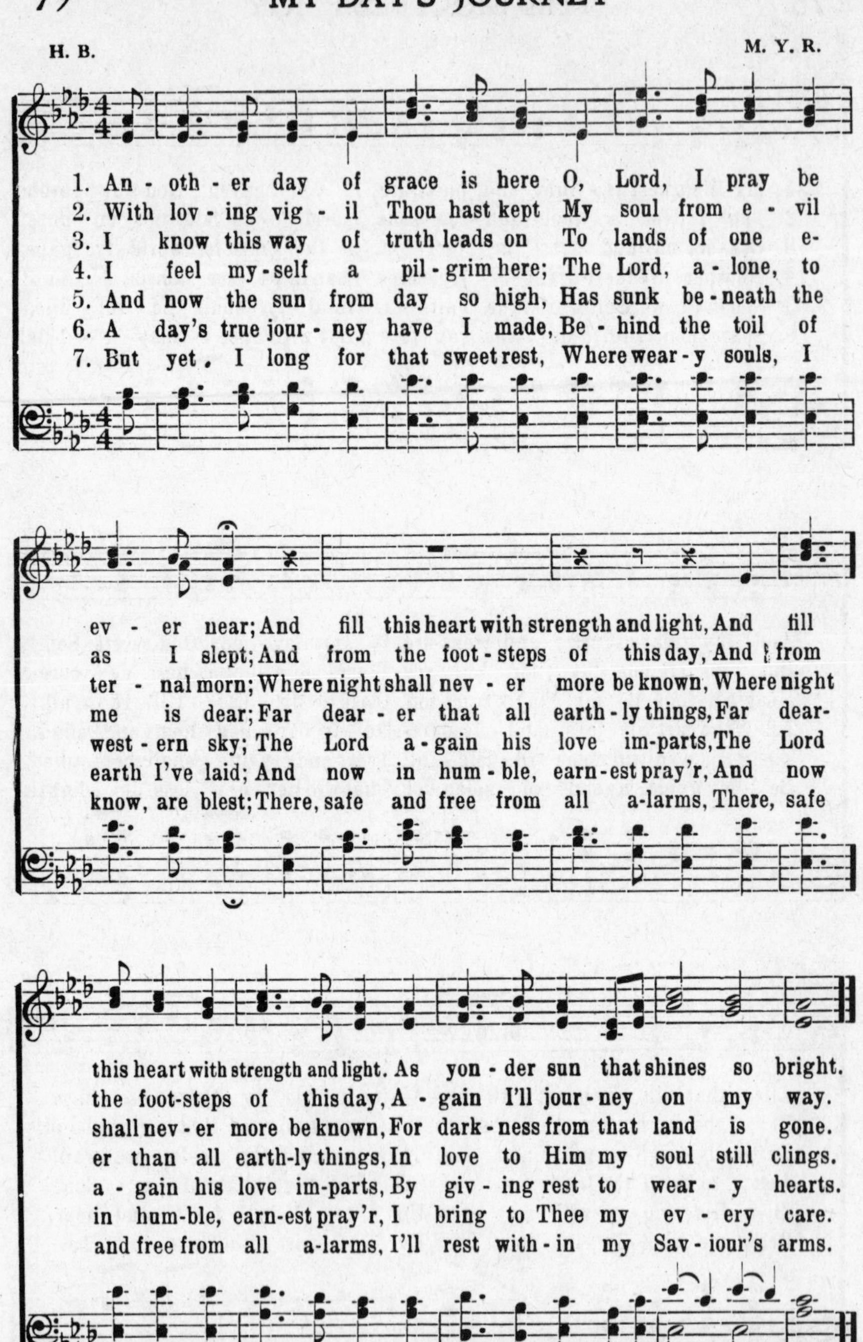

H. B.
M. Y. R.
1. An - oth - er day of grace is here O, Lord, I pray be
2. With lov - ing vig - il Thou hast kept My soul from e - vil
3. I know this way of truth leads on To lands of one e-
4. I feel my-self a pil - grim here; The Lord, a - lone, to
5. And now the sun from day so high, Has sunk be - neath the
6. A day's true jour - ney have I made, Be - hind the toil of
7. But yet, I long for that sweet rest, Where wear - y souls, I
ev - er near; And fill this heart with strength and light, And fill
as I slept; And from the foot - steps of this day, And from
ter - nal morn; Where night shall nev - er more be known, Where night
me is dear; Far dear - er that all earth - ly things, Far dear-
west - ern sky; The Lord a - gain his love im - parts, The Lord
earth I've laid; And now in hum - ble, earn - est pray'r, And now
know, are blest; There, safe and free from all a - larms, There, safe
this heart with strength and light. As yon - der sun that shines so bright.
the foot-steps of this day, A - gain I'll jour - ney on my way.
shall nev - er more be known, For dark - ness from that land is gone.
er than all earth-ly things, In love to Him my soul still clings.
a - gain his love im-parts, By giv - ing rest to wear - y hearts.
in hum-ble, earn-est pray'r, I bring to Thee my ev - ery care.
and free from all a-larms, I'll rest with - in my Sav - iour's arms.

80 ALL HAIL THE POWER OF JESUS' NAME

DIADEM. C. M.

Edward Perronet — James Ellor

1. All hail the power of Je - sus' name! Let an - gels prostrate fall,
2. Ye cho - sen seed of Is - rael's race, Ye ran-somed from the fall,
3. Let ev - 'ry kin - dred, ev - 'ry tribe, On this ter - res - trial ball,
4. O that with yon - der sa - cred throng We at His feet may fall,
Let an - gels pros-trate fall; Bring forth the roy - al di - a - dem,
Ye ran-somed from the fall, Hail Him who saves you by His grace,
On this ter - res - trial ball, To Him all maj - es - ty as - cribe,
We at His feet may fall! We'll join the ev - er - last - ing song,
And crown . . . . Him, Crown Him,
And crown Him, crown Him, crown Him, crown Him, And crown Him Lord of
And crown . . . . Him, Crown Him,
And crown Him, crown Him, crown Him, Crown . . . .
crown Him, crown Him;
all, crown Him; And crown Him Lord of all! A-MEN.
crown . . . . Him;
. . . . Him; And crown Him Lord of all!

81 KNOCKING AT THE DOOR

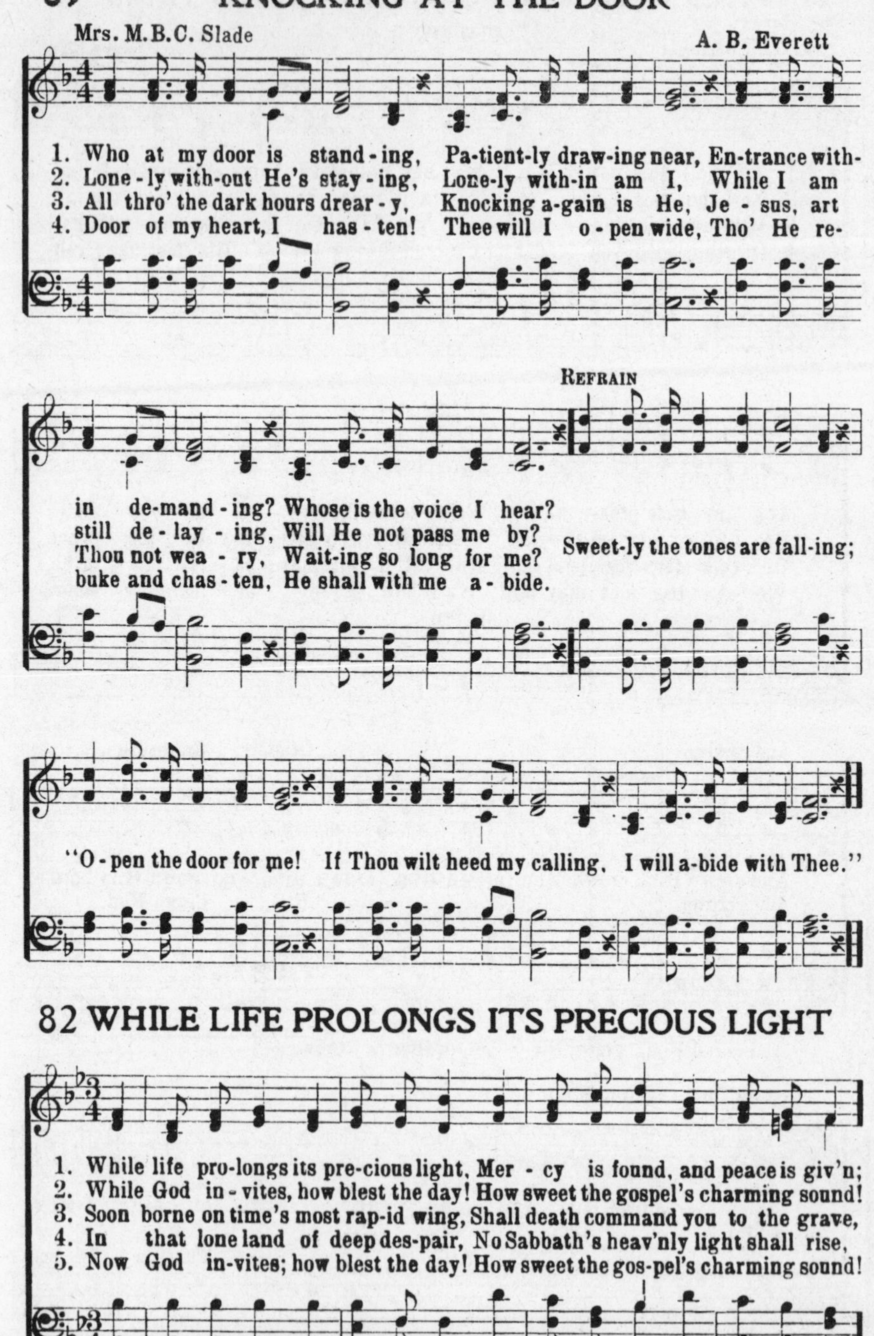
Mrs. M.B.C. Slade
A. B. Everett
1. Who at my door is stand-ing, Pa-tient-ly draw-ing near, En-trance with-in de-mand-ing? Whose is the voice I hear?
2. Lone-ly with-out He's stay-ing, Lone-ly with-in am I, While I am still de-lay-ing, Will He not pass me by?
3. All thro' the dark hours drear-y, Knocking a-gain is He, Je-sus, art Thou not wea-ry, Wait-ing so long for me?
4. Door of my heart, I has-ten! Thee will I o-pen wide, Tho' He re-buke and chas-ten, He shall with me a-bide.
Refrain
Sweet-ly the tones are fall-ing; "O-pen the door for me! If Thou wilt heed my calling, I will a-bide with Thee."
82 WHILE LIFE PROLONGS ITS PRECIOUS LIGHT
1. While life pro-longs its pre-cious light, Mer-cy is found, and peace is giv'n;
2. While God in-vites, how blest the day! How sweet the gospel's charming sound!
3. Soon borne on time's most rap-id wing, Shall death command you to the grave,
4. In that lone land of deep des-pair, No Sabbath's heav'nly light shall rise,
5. Now God in-vites; how blest the day! How sweet the gos-pel's charming sound!

WHILE LIFE PROLONGS ITS PRECIOUS LIGHT

But soon, ah, soon, approaching night Shall blot out ev - 'ry hope of heav'n.
Come, sinners, haste, O haste a-way, While yet a pard'ning God is found.
Be - fore His bar your spir - it bring, And none be found to hear or save.
No God re-gard your bit-ter pray'r, No Sav-iour call you to the skies.
Come, sinners, haste, O haste a - way, While yet a pard'n-ing God is found.
83
THE HEAVENS DECLARE
Psa. 19: 1
The heav-en's de - clare the glo - ry of God; And the fir - ma-ment
shew-eth His hand - y - work, The heav-en's de - clare the glo - ry of
FINE.
God; And the fir - ma - ment shew - eth His hand - y - work. A - MEN.

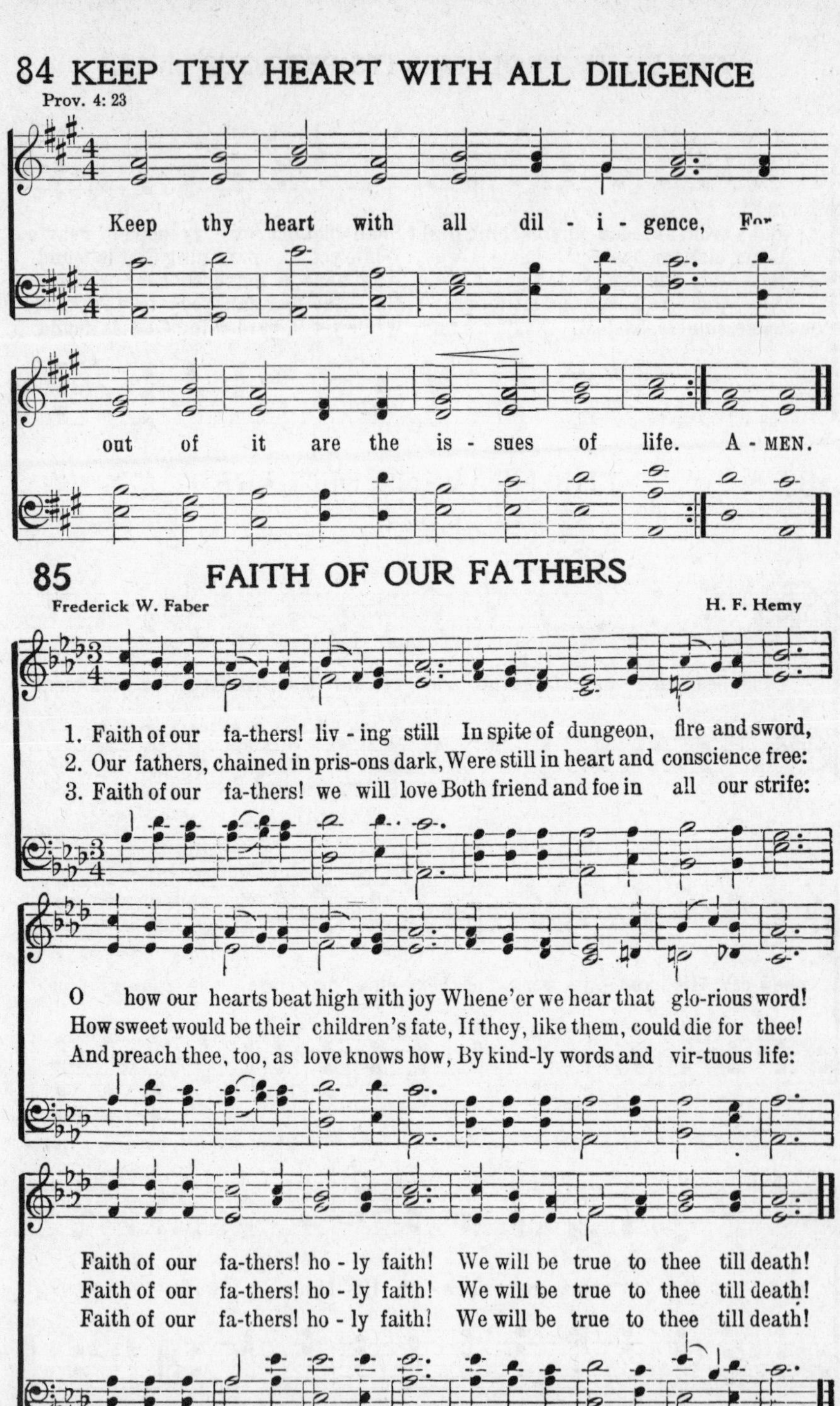
84 KEEP THY HEART WITH ALL DILIGENCE
Prov. 4: 23
Keep thy heart with all dil - i - gence, For
out of it are the is - sues of life. A - MEN.
85 FAITH OF OUR FATHERS
Frederick W. Faber
H. F. Hemy
1. Faith of our fa-thers! liv - ing still In spite of dungeon, fire and sword,
2. Our fathers, chained in pris-ons dark, Were still in heart and conscience free:
3. Faith of our fa-thers! we will love Both friend and foe in all our strife:
O how our hearts beat high with joy Whene'er we hear that glo-rious word!
How sweet would be their children's fate, If they, like them, could die for thee!
And preach thee, too, as love knows how, By kind-ly words and vir-tuous life:
Faith of our fa-thers! ho - ly faith! We will be true to thee till death!
Faith of our fa-thers! ho - ly faith! We will be true to thee till death!
Faith of our fa-thers! ho - ly faith! We will be true to thee till death!

SHALL YOU? SHALL I?

G. M. J.
James McGranahan
f
pp
1. Some one will en - ter the pearl - y gate By and by, by and by,
2. Some one will glad - ly his cross lay down By and by, by and by,
3. Some one will knock when the door is shut By and by, by and by,
4. Some one will sing the tri - umph - ant song By and by, by and by,
f
Repeat pp
Taste of the glo - ries that there a - wait, Shall you? shall I?
Faith - ful, ap - proved, shall re - ceive a crown, Shall you? shall I?
Hear a voice say - ing, "I know you not," Shall you? shall I?
Join in the praise with the blood - bought throng, Shall you? shall I?
Some one will trav - el the streets of gold, Beau - ti - ful vi - sions will
Some one the glo - ri - ous King will see, Ev - er from sor - row of
Some one will call and shall not be heard, Vain - ly will strive when the
Some one will greet on the gold - en shore Loved ones of earth who have
f
Repeat pp
there be - hold; Feast on the pleas - ures so long fore - told; Shall you? shall I?
earth be free, Hap - py with Him thro' e - ter - ni - ty; Shall you? shall I?
door is barr'd Some one will fail of the saint's re - ward: Shall you? shall I?
gone be - fore, Safe in the glo - ry for - ev - er - more: Shall you? shall I?

87 O I LOVE TO TALK WITH JESUS

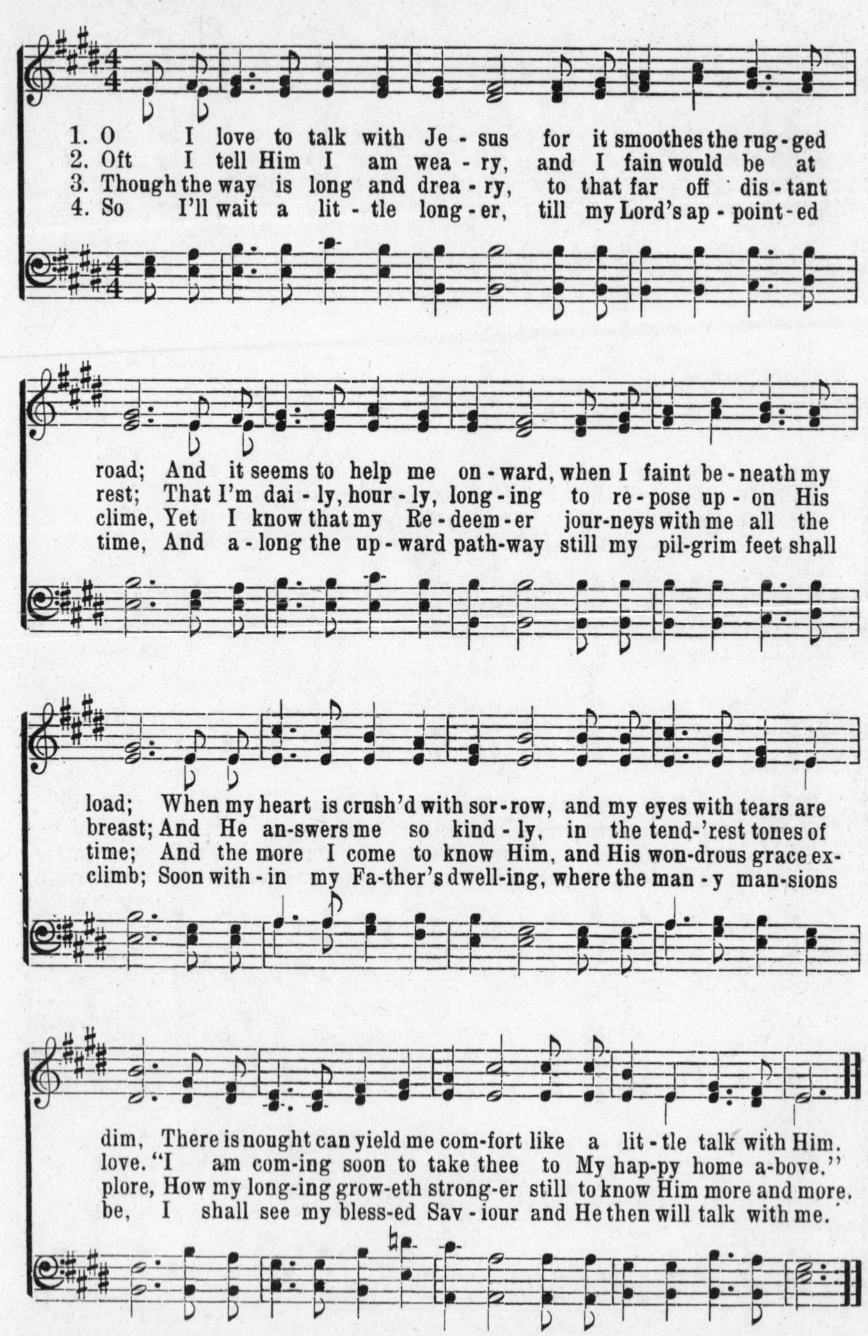

1. O I love to talk with Je - sus for it smoothes the rug - ged
2. Oft I tell Him I am wea - ry, and I fain would be at
3. Though the way is long and drea - ry, to that far off dis - tant
4. So I'll wait a lit - tle long - er, till my Lord's ap - point - ed
road; And it seems to help me on - ward, when I faint be - neath my
rest; That I'm dai - ly, hour - ly, long - ing to re - pose up - on His
clime, Yet I know that my Re - deem - er jour-neys with me all the
time, And a - long the up - ward path-way still my pil-grim feet shall
load; When my heart is crush'd with sor - row, and my eyes with tears are
breast; And He an-swers me so kind - ly, in the tend-'rest tones of
time; And the more I come to know Him, and His won-drous grace ex-
climb; Soon with - in my Fa-ther's dwell-ing, where the man - y man-sions
dim, There is nought can yield me com-fort like a lit - tle talk with Him.
love. "I am com-ing soon to take thee to My hap-py home a-bove."
plore, How my long-ing grow-eth strong-er still to know Him more and more.
be, I shall see my bless-ed Sav - iour and He then will talk with me.

FOREVER WITH THE LORD

1. For - ev - er with the Lord, My bless - ed lot shall be. His word is like a
2. I oft - en look a - bove, Un - to my home so fair. For oft - en in life's
3. Dark clouds will oft ob - scure, My view to heav'n a - bove. I take my flight to
4. When once my sens - es fail, And death shall set me free, From death to ev - er-

shin - ing star And gen - tly lead - eth me, I jour - ney thru this world, I
jour - ney here I wish that I were there, A long - ing fills my heart To
Christ, the Ark, Like un - to No - ah's dove. The clouds will pass a - way, When
last - ing life. I'll rise tri - umph - ant - ly. I'll see the glo - ries there Fore-

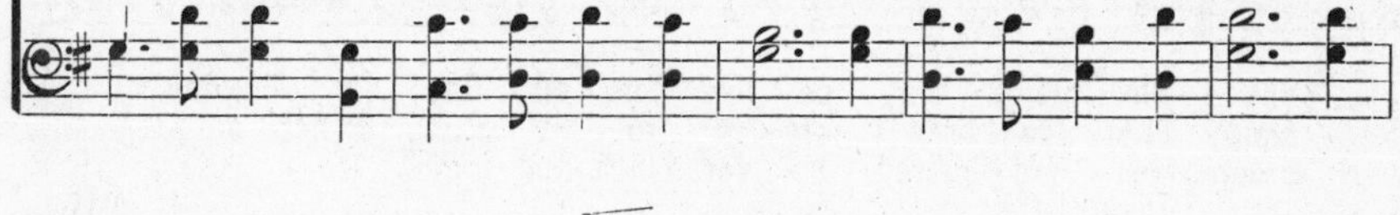

am a strang - er here. I shall pur - sue my pil - grim's course, Un - to my
see the cit - y's light, The gol - den new Je - ru - sa - lem, A - dorned with
storms and pain de - part; The rain - bow of His prom - ise true, Will cheer my
told in Thy good word, Then shall I be, O won - drous tho't! For - ev - er

Sav - iour dear. Near to Thee; Near to Thee, I'm draw - ing near to Thee.
jew - els bright, O how fair, O how fair, I wish to en - ter there.
long - ing heart. Peace - ful light, Peace - ful light, Con - sol - ing to my heart.
with the Lord. Won - der - ful! Won - der - ful! For - ev - er with the Lord.

EASTER

H. B. M. Y. R.

1. Oh who a - mong the sons of men, By word
2. The bless - ed Pas - chal feast of old, With mys-
3. Christ is the world's dear Pas - chal Lamb He is
1. By word
or song or deed or pen, Can ev - er fit - ting - ly con-
tic mean - ing does un - fold, For there the Pas - chal Lamb was
the great "I was, I Am" Through Cal-v'ry's pain and dis - mal
vey The mean - ing of this bless - ed day. It gilds
slain, The He - brew's safe - ty to at - tain. When an-
gloom, He con - quered o - ver death and tomb. He rose
It gilds
the ho - ly sa - cred page, It brings
gels saw the blood ap - plied, Up - on
His own to jus - ti - fy, And draws
It brings
to ev - 'ry clime and age, To ev - 'ry peo - ple
the lin - tel, door - post wide Then they pass'd o - ver
all men up to the sky. If you have found the

EASTER
rit.
tribe and race The sto - ry of re - deem - ing grace.
ev - ery home In mer - cy, where the blood was shown.
Christ, His way, Then you can keep this Eas - ter day.
90 ALL THAT THRILLS MY SOUL
COPYRIGHT © 1931, BY THORO HARRIS IN "REVIVAL ECHOES"
ASSIGNED TO NAZARENE PUBLISHING COMPANY
ALL RIGHTS RESERVED. USED BY PERMISSION
T. H.
Thoro Harris
1. Who can cheer the heart like Je - sus, By His pres-ence all di - vine?
2. Love of Christ so free - ly giv - en, Grace of God be-yond de - gree,
3. What a won-der - ful re-demp-tion! Nev - er can a mor-tal know
4. Ev - 'ry need His hand sup-ply - ing, Ev - 'ry good in Him I see;
5. By the crys-tal flow - ing riv - er With the ran-somed I will sing,
True and ten-der, pure and pre - cious, O how blest to call Him mine!
Mer - cy high-er than the heav - en, Deep - er than the deep-est sea.
How my sin, tho' red like crim - son, Can be whit - er than the snow.
On His strength di-vine re - ly - ing, He is all in all to me.
And for - ev - er and for - ev - er Praise and glo - ri - fy the King.
All that thrills my soul is Je - sus; He is more than life to me; (to me;)
And the fair - est of ten-thou-sand, In my bless-ed Lord I see.

91 CHRISTIAN FRIENDSHIP

H. B. H. G.

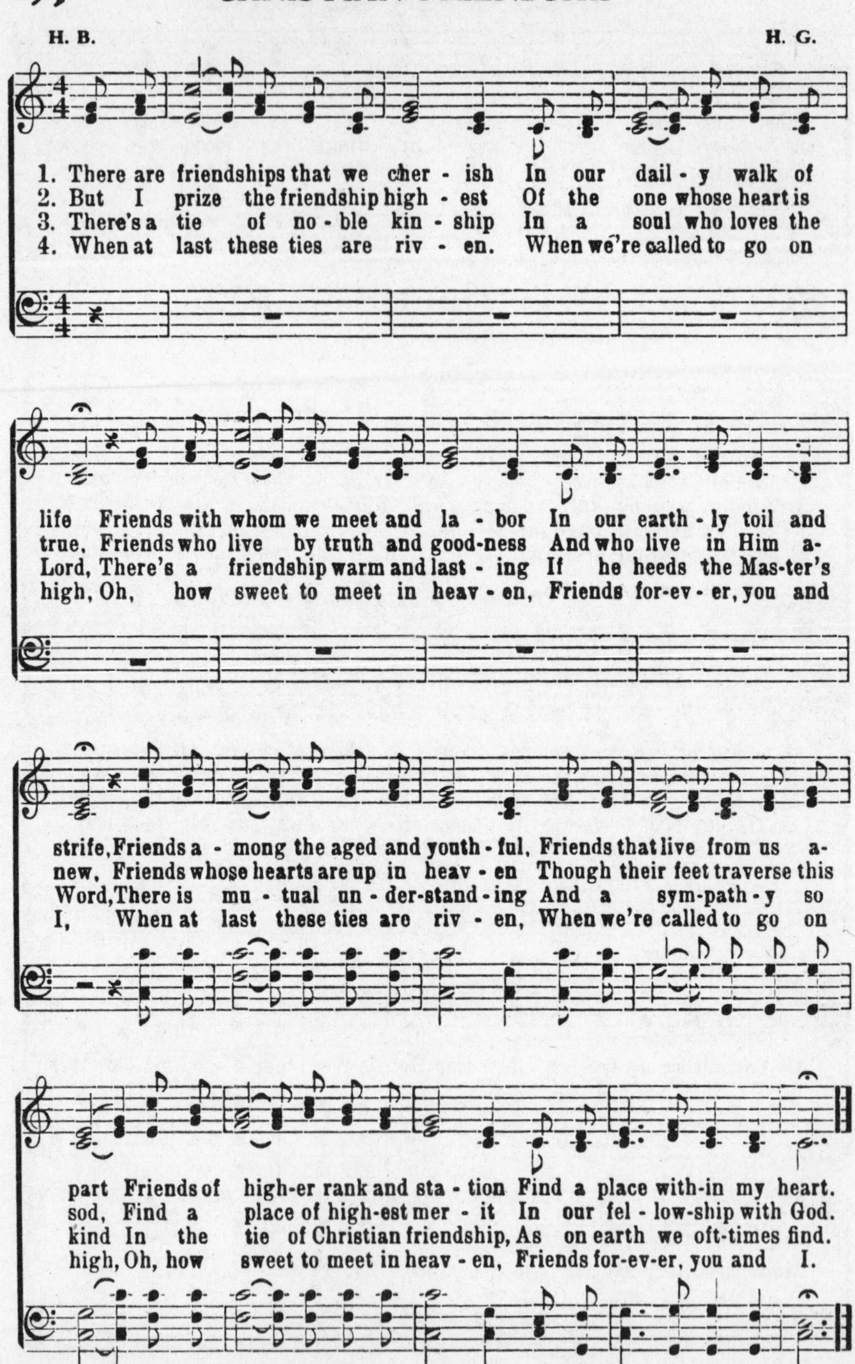

1. There are friendships that we cher - ish In our dail - y walk of
2. But I prize the friendship high - est Of the one whose heart is
3. There's a tie of no - ble kin - ship In a soul who loves the
4. When at last these ties are riv - en. When we're called to go on
life Friends with whom we meet and la - bor In our earth - ly toil and
true, Friends who live by truth and good-ness And who live in Him a-
Lord, There's a friendship warm and last - ing If he heeds the Mas-ter's
high, Oh, how sweet to meet in heav - en, Friends for-ev - er, you and
strife, Friends a - mong the aged and youth - ful, Friends that live from us a-
new, Friends whose hearts are up in heav - en Though their feet traverse this
Word, There is mu - tual un - der-stand - ing And a sym-path - y so
I, When at last these ties are riv - en, When we're called to go on
part Friends of high-er rank and sta - tion Find a place with-in my heart.
sod, Find a place of high-est mer - it In our fel - low-ship with God.
kind In the tie of Christian friendship, As on earth we oft-times find.
high, Oh, how sweet to meet in heav - en, Friends for-ev-er, you and I.

92 NEARER MY GOD TO THEE

Swiss Melody

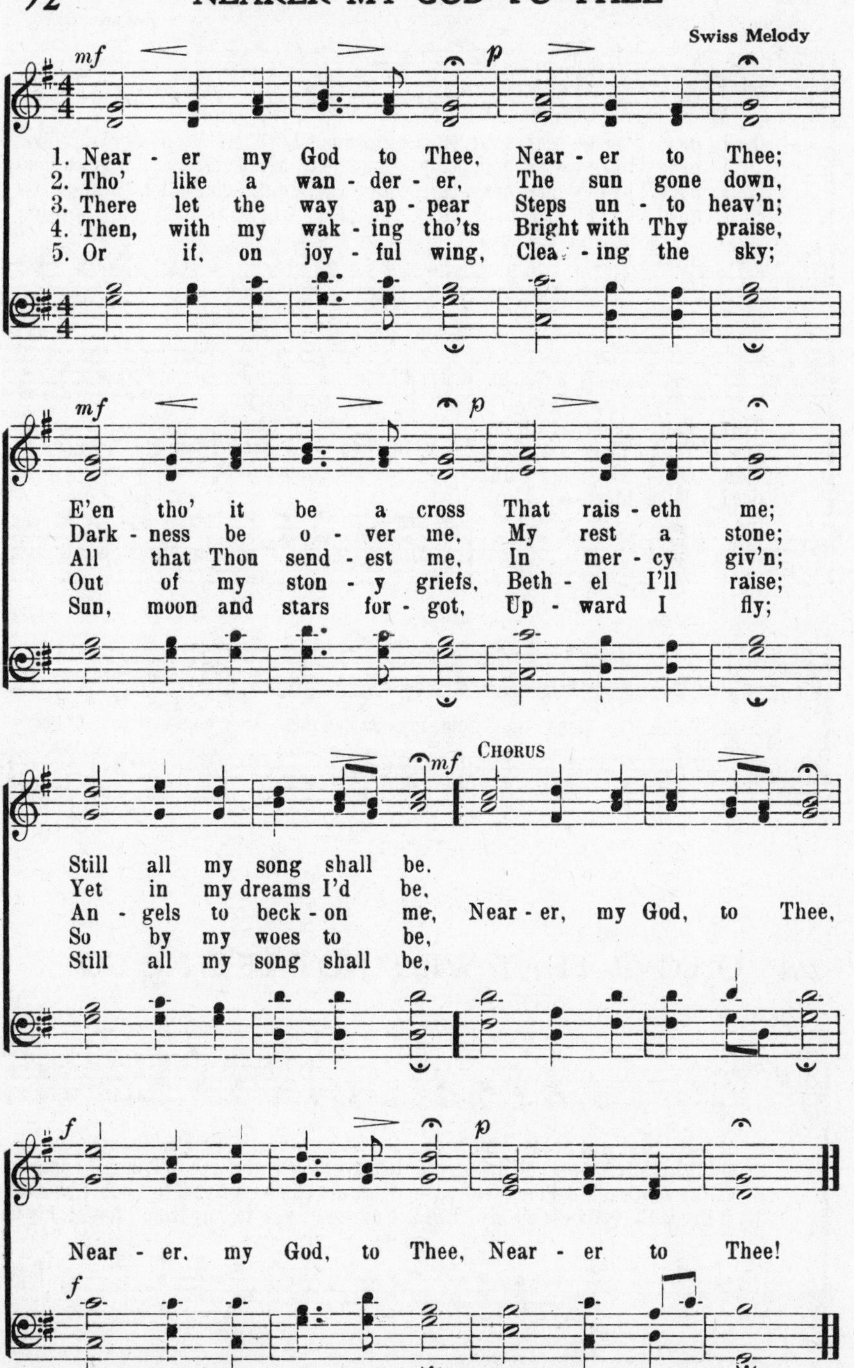
mf
p
1. Near - er my God to Thee, Near - er to Thee;
2. Tho' like a wan - der - er, The sun gone down,
3. There let the way ap - pear Steps un - to heav'n;
4. Then, with my wak - ing tho'ts Bright with Thy praise,
5. Or if, on joy - ful wing, Clea - ing the sky;
E'en tho' it be a cross That rais - eth me;
Dark - ness be o - ver me, My rest a stone;
All that Thou send - est me, In mer - cy giv'n;
Out of my ston - y griefs, Beth - el I'll raise;
Sun, moon and stars for - got, Up - ward I fly;
Chorus
Still all my song shall be.
Yet in my dreams I'd be,
An - gels to beck - on me, Near - er, my God, to Thee,
So by my woes to be,
Still all my song shall be,
f
Near - er, my God, to Thee, Near - er to Thee!

93 I NEED THEE EVERY HOUR

Annie S. Hawks — Robert Lowry

1. I need Thee ev-'ry hour, Most gra-cious Lord, No ten-der voice like Thine Can peace af-ford.
2. I need Thee ev-'ry hour, Stay Thou near by; Temp-ta-tions lose their pow'r When Thou art nigh.
3. I need Thee ev-'ry hour, In joy or pain; Come quick-ly and a-bide, Or life is vain.
4. I need Thee ev-'ry hour, Most Ho-ly One; Oh! make me Thine in-deed, Thou bless-ed Son!

CHORUS

I need Thee, O I need Thee; Ev-'ry hour I need Thee; O bless me now, my Sav-iour, I come to Thee!

94 O LOVE THAT WILT NOT LET ME GO

George Matheson — A. L. Peace

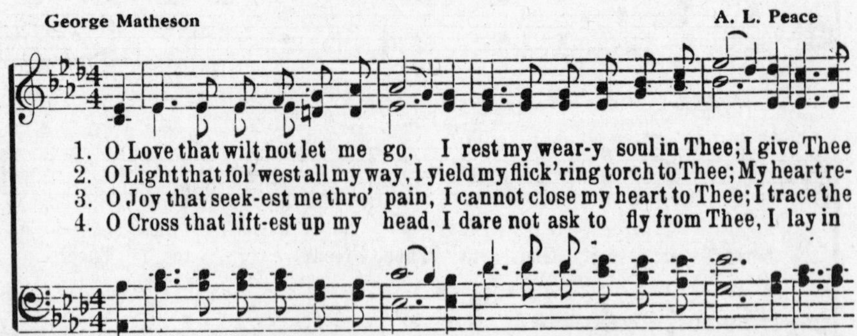

1. O Love that wilt not let me go, I rest my wear-y soul in Thee; I give Thee
2. O Light that fol'west all my way, I yield my flick'ring torch to Thee; My heart re-
3. O Joy that seek-est me thro' pain, I cannot close my heart to Thee; I trace the
4. O Cross that lift-est up my head, I dare not ask to fly from Thee, I lay in

O LOVE THAT WILT NOT LET ME GO

back the life I owe, That in Thine ocean depths its flow May richer, full-er be.
stores its borrow'd ray, That in Thy sunshine's glow its day May brighter, fairer be.
rainbow thro' the rain, And feel the promise is not vain That morn shall tearless be.
dust life's glory dead, And from the ground there blossoms red Life that shall endless be.

95 PRAISE GOD, FROM WHOM ALL BLESSINGS

Thomas Ken — OLD HUNDREDTH. L. M. — Louis Bourgeois

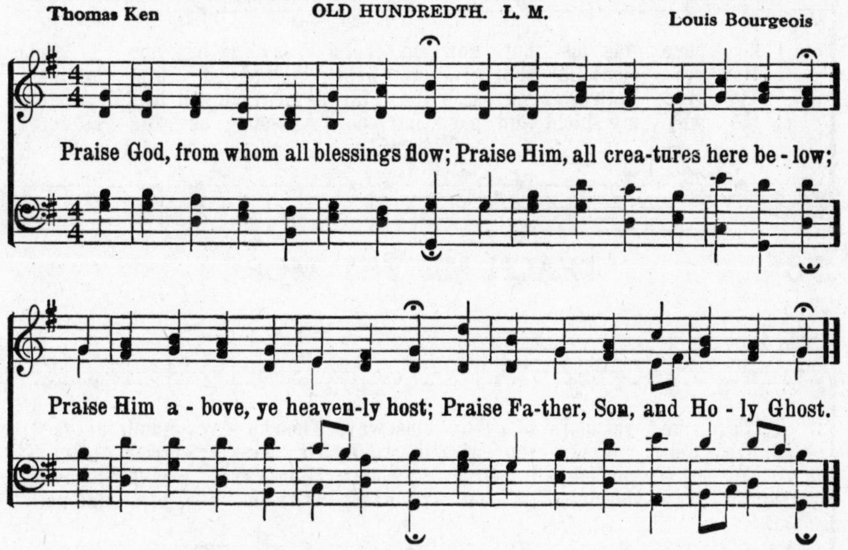
Praise God, from whom all blessings flow; Praise Him, all crea-tures here be - low;
Praise Him a - bove, ye heaven-ly host; Praise Fa-ther, Son, and Ho - ly Ghost.

96 HEAR OUR PRAYER, O LORD

George Whelpton

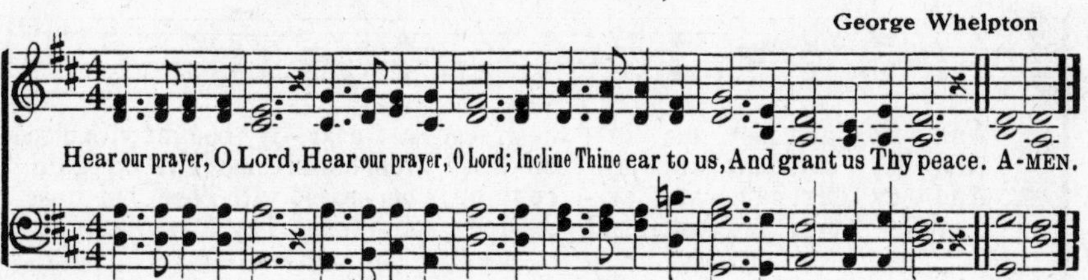
Hear our prayer, O Lord, Hear our prayer, O Lord; Incline Thine ear to us, And grant us Thy peace. A-MEN.

97 AMAZING GRACE

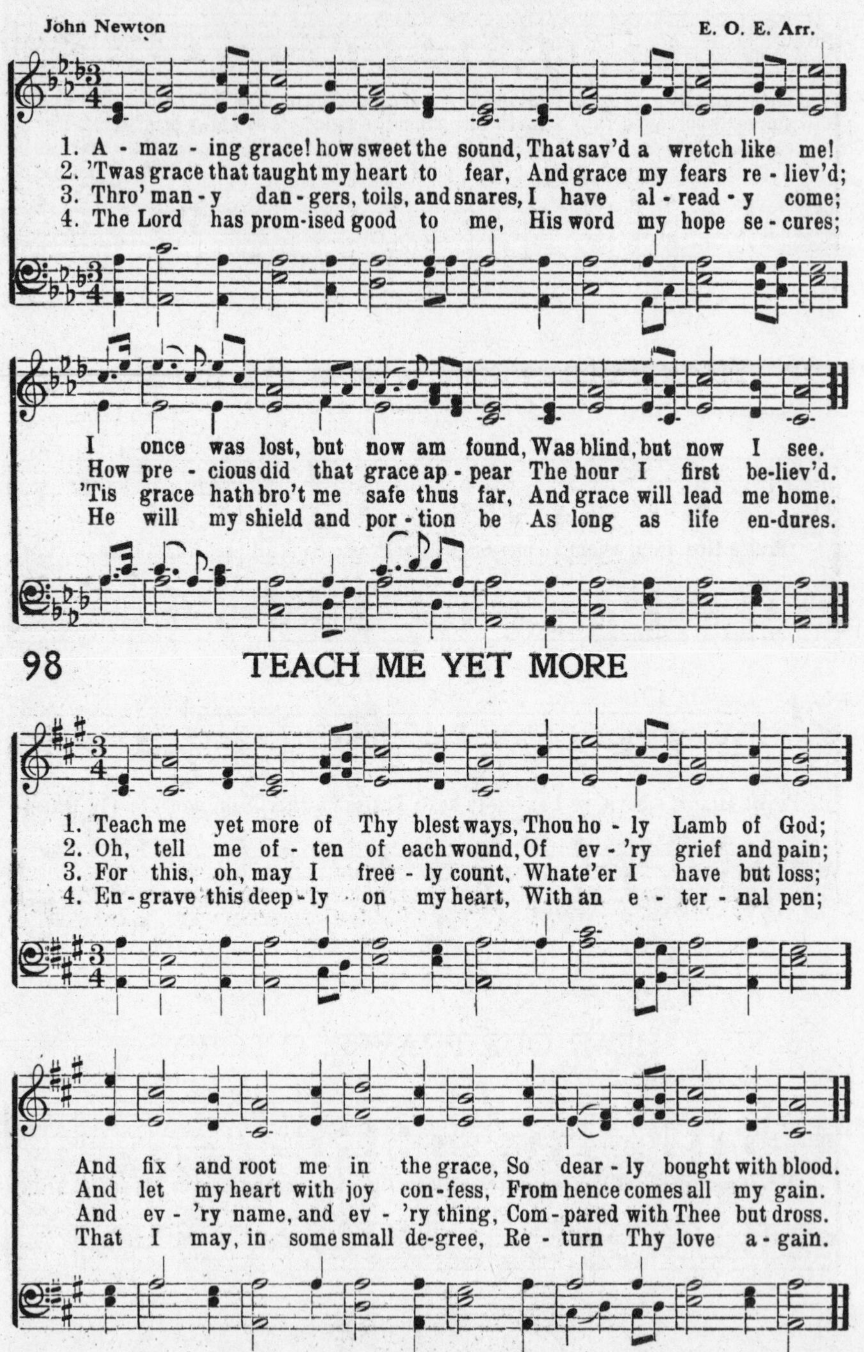
John Newton
E. O. E. Arr.
1. A - maz - ing grace! how sweet the sound, That sav'd a wretch like me!
2. 'Twas grace that taught my heart to fear, And grace my fears re - liev'd;
3. Thro' man - y dan - gers, toils, and snares, I have al - read - y come;
4. The Lord has prom-ised good to me, His word my hope se - cures;
I once was lost, but now am found, Was blind, but now I see.
How pre - cious did that grace ap - pear The hour I first be-liev'd.
'Tis grace hath bro't me safe thus far, And grace will lead me home.
He will my shield and por - tion be As long as life en-dures.
98 TEACH ME YET MORE
1. Teach me yet more of Thy blest ways, Thou ho - ly Lamb of God;
2. Oh, tell me of - ten of each wound, Of ev - 'ry grief and pain;
3. For this, oh, may I free - ly count, Whate'er I have but loss;
4. En - grave this deep - ly on my heart, With an e - ter - nal pen;
And fix and root me in the grace, So dear - ly bought with blood.
And let my heart with joy con - fess, From hence comes all my gain.
And ev - 'ry name, and ev - 'ry thing, Com - pared with Thee but dross.
That I may, in some small de - gree, Re - turn Thy love a - gain.

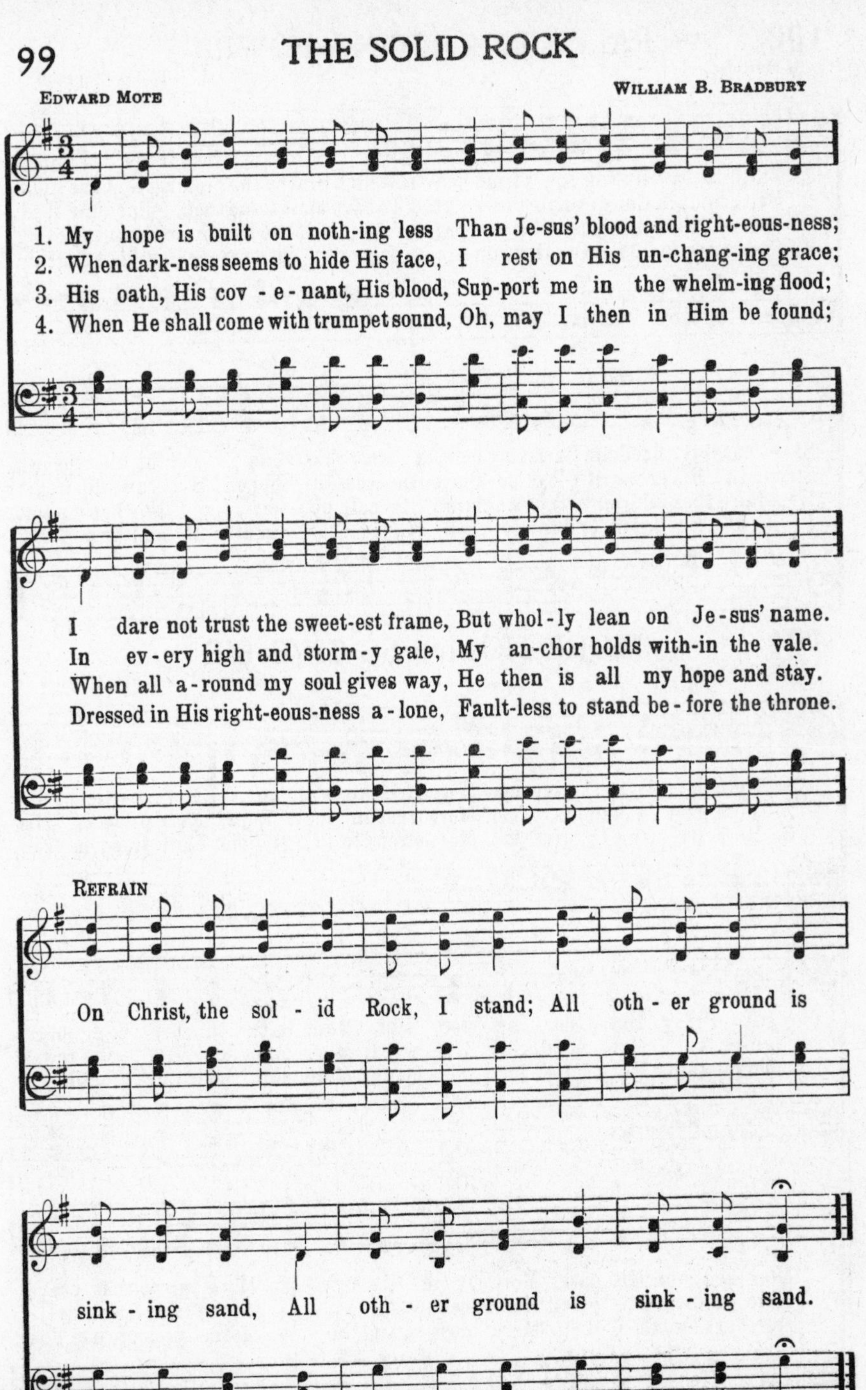
99
THE SOLID ROCK
Edward Mote
William B. Bradbury
1. My hope is built on noth-ing less Than Je-sus' blood and right-eous-ness;
2. When dark-ness seems to hide His face, I rest on His un-chang-ing grace;
3. His oath, His cov - e - nant, His blood, Sup-port me in the whelm-ing flood;
4. When He shall come with trumpet sound, Oh, may I then in Him be found;
I dare not trust the sweet-est frame, But whol-ly lean on Je-sus' name.
In ev-ery high and storm-y gale, My an-chor holds with-in the vale.
When all a-round my soul gives way, He then is all my hope and stay.
Dressed in His right-eous-ness a-lone, Fault-less to stand be-fore the throne.
Refrain
On Christ, the sol - id Rock, I stand; All oth - er ground is
sink - ing sand, All oth - er ground is sink - ing sand.

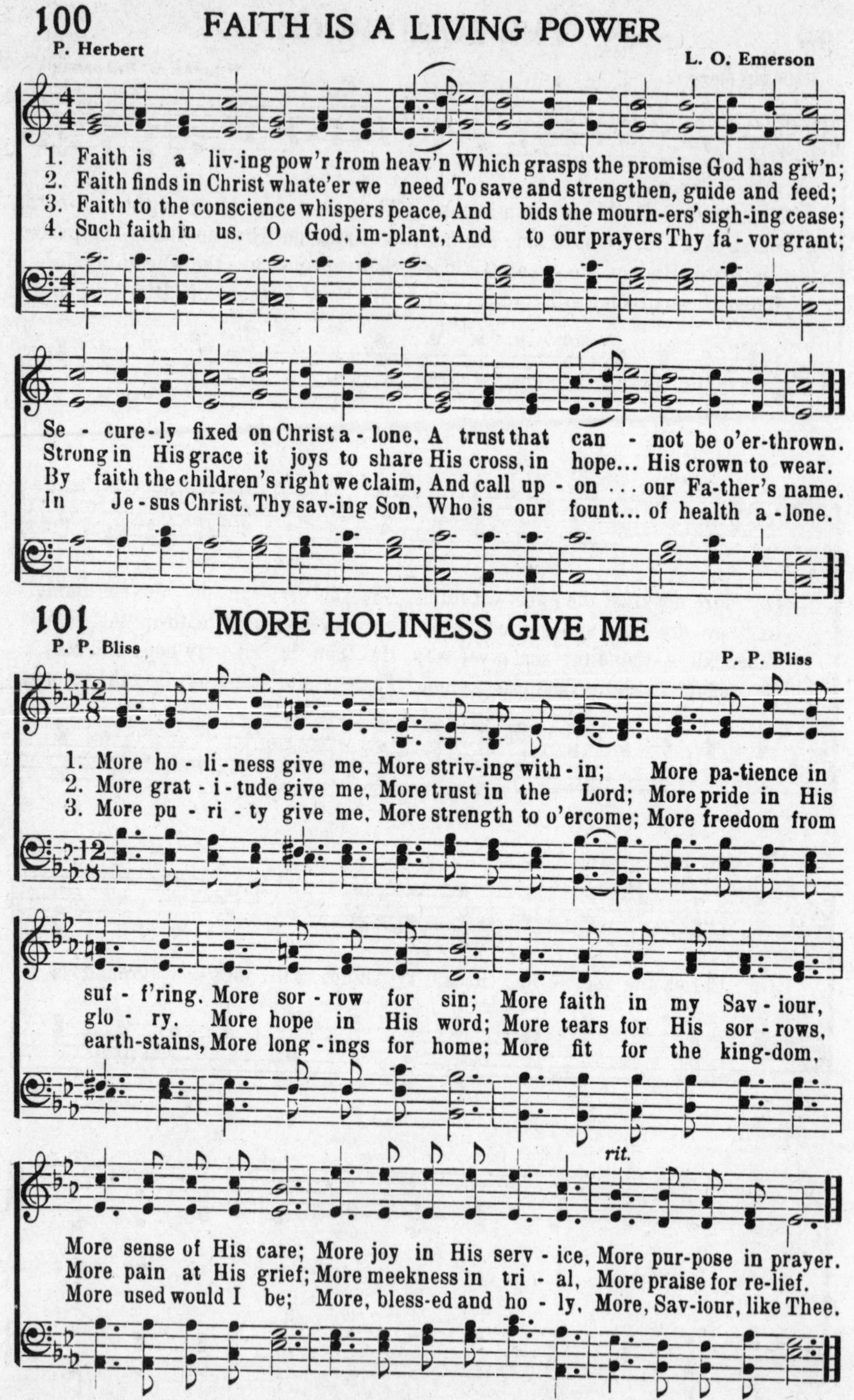
100 FAITH IS A LIVING POWER
P. Herbert
L. O. Emerson
1. Faith is a liv-ing pow'r from heav'n Which grasps the promise God has giv'n;
2. Faith finds in Christ whate'er we need To save and strengthen, guide and feed;
3. Faith to the conscience whispers peace, And bids the mourn-ers' sigh-ing cease;
4. Such faith in us. O God, im-plant, And to our prayers Thy fa - vor grant;
Se - cure-ly fixed on Christ a-lone, A trust that can - not be o'er-thrown.
Strong in His grace it joys to share His cross, in hope... His crown to wear.
By faith the children's right we claim, And call up - on ... our Fa-ther's name.
In Je-sus Christ, Thy sav-ing Son, Who is our fount... of health a-lone.
101 MORE HOLINESS GIVE ME
P. P. Bliss
P. P. Bliss
1. More ho - li - ness give me, More striv-ing with - in; More pa-tience in
2. More grat - i - tude give me, More trust in the Lord; More pride in His
3. More pu - ri - ty give me, More strength to o'ercome; More freedom from
suf - f'ring, More sor - row for sin; More faith in my Sav - iour,
glo - ry, More hope in His word; More tears for His sor - rows,
earth-stains, More long - ings for home; More fit for the king-dom,
rit.
More sense of His care; More joy in His serv - ice, More pur-pose in prayer.
More pain at His grief; More meekness in tri - al, More praise for re-lief.
More used would I be; More, bless-ed and ho - ly, More, Sav-iour, like Thee.

102 CHRIST, THE LORD, IS RISEN TODAY

Charles Wesley (WORGAN) From "Lyra Davidica"

1. Christ the Lord is ris'n to - day, Al - - - le - lu - ia!
2. Lives a - gain our glo-rious King: Al - - - le - lu - ia!
3. Love's re - deem-ing work is done, Al - - - le - lu - ia!
4. Soar we now, where Christ has led, Al - - - le - lu - ia!
Sons of men and an - gels say: Al - - - le - lu - ia!
Where, O death, is now thy sting? Al - - - le - lu - ia!
Fought the fight, the bat - tle won; Al - - - le - lu - ia!
Fol - l'wing our ex - alt - ed Head; Al - - - le - lu - ia!
Raise your joys and tri-umphs high, Al - - - le - lu - ia!
Dy - ing once, He all doth save: Al - - - le - lu - ia!
Death in vain for - bids Him rise; Al - - - le - lu - ia!
Made like Him, like Him we rise; Al - - - le - lu - ia!
Sing, ye heav'ns, and earth re - ply, Al - - - le - lu - ia!
Where thy vic - to - ry, O grave? Al - - - le - lu - ia!
Christ has o - pened Par - a - dise. Al - - - le - lu - ia!
Ours the cross, the grave, the skies. Al - - - le - lu - ia!

103 COME, SINNER, COME!

W. E. WITTER H. R. PALMER

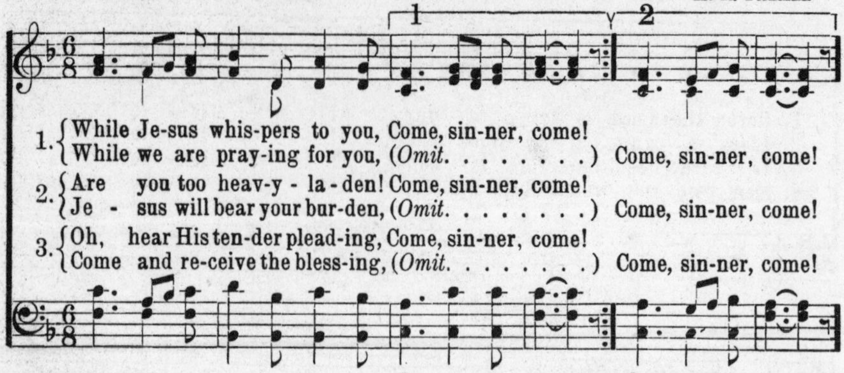

1
2
1. While Je-sus whis-pers to you, Come, sin-ner, come!
While we are pray-ing for you, (Omit. . . . .) Come, sin-ner, come!
2. Are you too heav-y - la - den! Come, sin-ner, come!
Je - sus will bear your bur-den, (Omit. . . . .) Come, sin-ner, come!
3. Oh, hear His ten-der plead-ing, Come, sin-ner, come!
Come and re-ceive the bless-ing, (Omit. . . . .) Come, sin-ner, come!

1
2
Now is the time to own Him, Come, sin-ner, come!
Now is the time to know Him, (Omit. . . . . . .) Come, sin-ner, come!
Je - sus will not de-ceive you, Come, sin-ner, come!
Je - sus can now re-deem you, (Omit. . . . . . .) Come, sin-ner, come!
While Je-sus whis-pers to you, Come, sin-ner, come!
While we are pray-ing for you, (Omit. . . . . . .) Come, sin-ner, come!

104 THE LORD WATCH

Gen. 31: 49

The Lord watch be - tween me and thee, When we are

ab - sent one from an - oth - er. A - MEN.

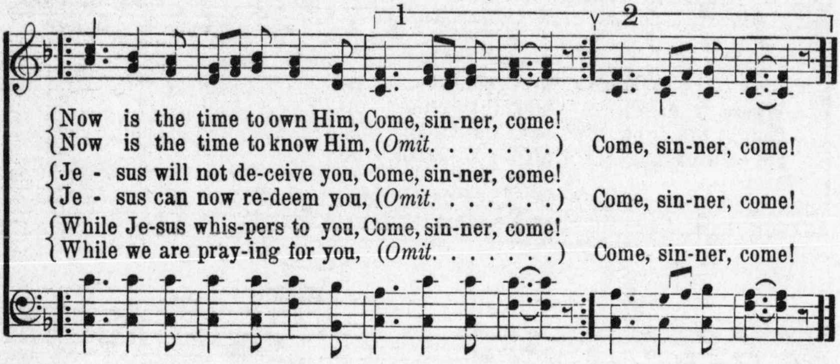

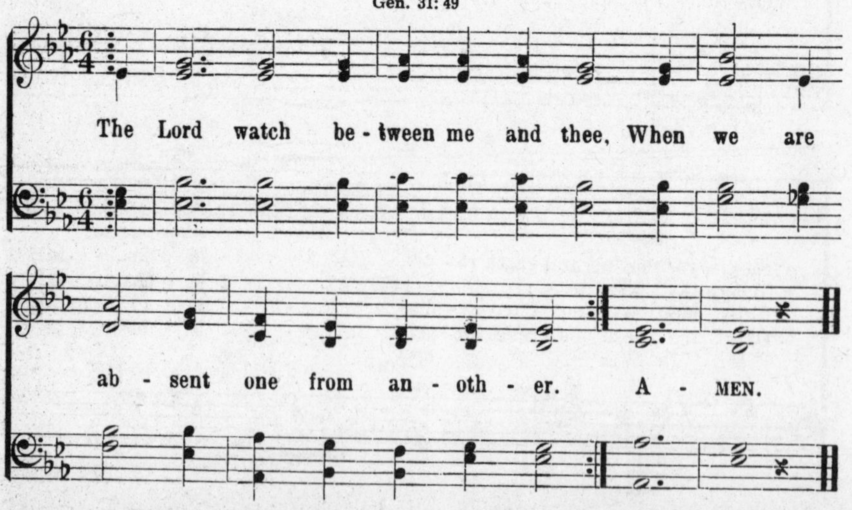

105 JUST AS I AM

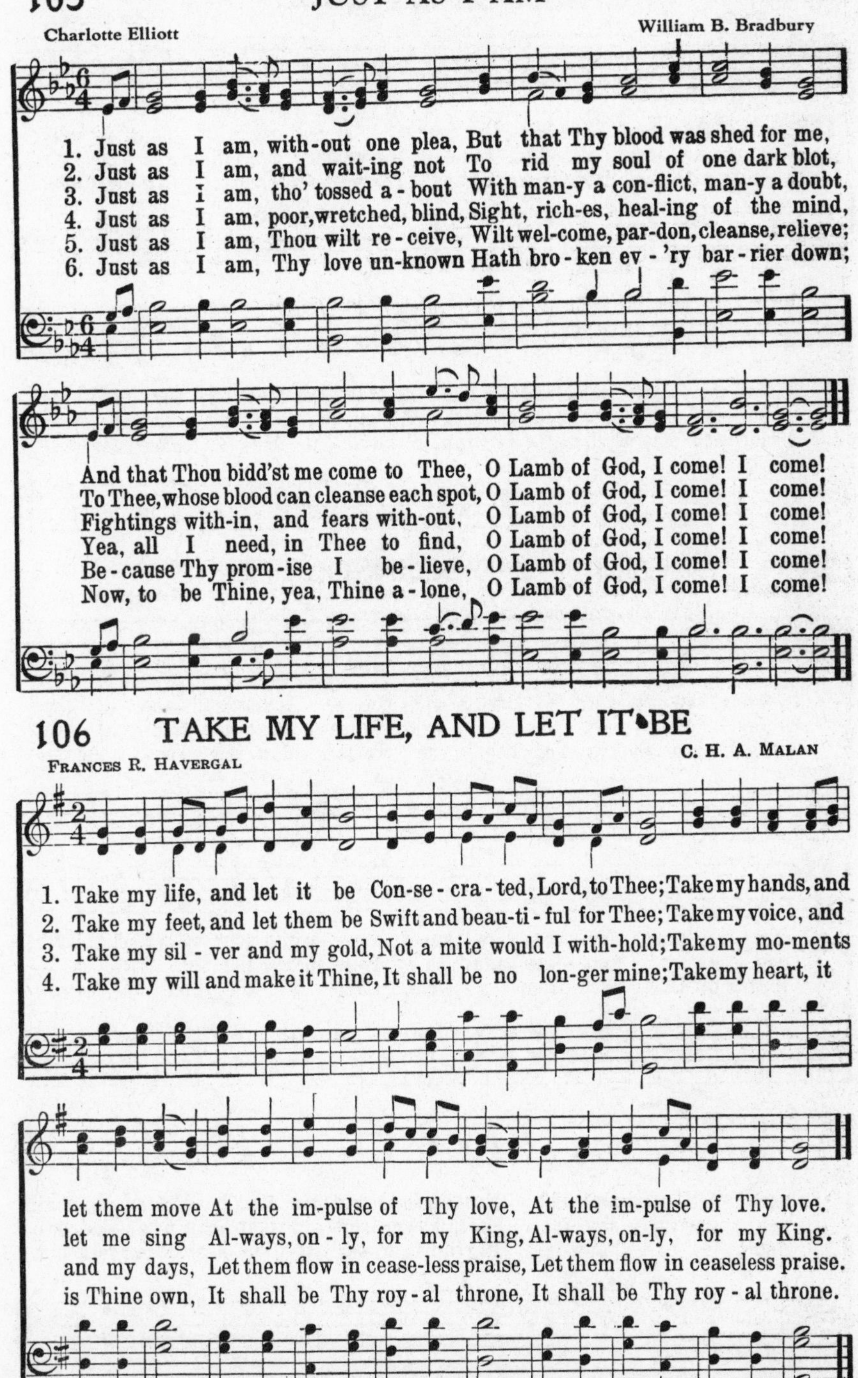
Charlotte Elliott
William B. Bradbury
1. Just as I am, with-out one plea, But that Thy blood was shed for me,
2. Just as I am, and wait-ing not To rid my soul of one dark blot,
3. Just as I am, tho' tossed a-bout With man-y a con-flict, man-y a doubt,
4. Just as I am, poor, wretched, blind, Sight, rich-es, heal-ing of the mind,
5. Just as I am, Thou wilt re-ceive, Wilt wel-come, par-don, cleanse, relieve;
6. Just as I am, Thy love un-known Hath bro-ken ev-'ry bar-rier down;
And that Thou bidd'st me come to Thee, O Lamb of God, I come! I come!
To Thee, whose blood can cleanse each spot, O Lamb of God, I come! I come!
Fightings with-in, and fears with-out, O Lamb of God, I come! I come!
Yea, all I need, in Thee to find, O Lamb of God, I come! I come!
Be-cause Thy prom-ise I be-lieve, O Lamb of God, I come! I come!
Now, to be Thine, yea, Thine a-lone, O Lamb of God, I come! I come!
106 TAKE MY LIFE, AND LET IT BE
C. H. A. MALAN
FRANCES R. HAVERGAL
1. Take my life, and let it be Con-se-cra-ted, Lord, to Thee; Take my hands, and
2. Take my feet, and let them be Swift and beau-ti-ful for Thee; Take my voice, and
3. Take my sil-ver and my gold, Not a mite would I with-hold; Take my mo-ments
4. Take my will and make it Thine, It shall be no lon-ger mine; Take my heart, it
let them move At the im-pulse of Thy love, At the im-pulse of Thy love.
let me sing Al-ways, on-ly, for my King, Al-ways, on-ly, for my King.
and my days, Let them flow in cease-less praise, Let them flow in ceaseless praise.
is Thine own, It shall be Thy roy-al throne, It shall be Thy roy-al throne.

107
SUN OF MY SOUL
John Keble
Peter Ritter
1. Sun of my soul, Thou Sav - iour dear, It is not night if Thou be near:
2. When the soft dews of kind - ly sleep My wearied eye - lids gen - tly steep,
3. A - bide with me from morn till eve, For with out Thee I can - not live;
O may no earth-born cloud a - rise To hide Thee from Thy serv-ant's eyes.
Be my last tho't, how sweet to rest For-ev - er on my Sav-ior's breast.
A-bide with me when night is nigh, For with-out Thee I dare not die.
108
COME YE DISCONSOLATE
T. Moore
Samuel Webbe
1. Come. ye dis-con - so-late, wher-e'er ye lan-guish. Come to the
2. Joy of the des - o-late, light of the stray-ing, Hope of the
3. Here see the bread of life; see wa-ters flow-ing—Forth from the
mer - cy-seat, fer - vent - ly kneel; Here bring your wound-ed hearts,
pen - i - tent, fade - less and pure; Here speaks the Com - fort - er,
throne of God, pure from a - bove, Come to the feast of love;
here tell your an-guish; Earth has no sor - row that heav'n can-not heal.
ten - der-ly say - ing, "Earth has no sor - row that heav'n can-not cure."
come, ev - er know-ing, Earth has no sor - row but heav'n can re-move.

109 I KNOW WHOM I HAVE BELIEVED

Maj. D. W. Whittle (El Nathan)
James McGranahan
Moderato
1. I know not why God's won-drous grace To me He hath made known,
2. I know not how this sav-ing faith To me He did im-part,
3. I know not how the Spir-it moves, Con-vinc-ing men of sin,
4. I know not what of good or ill May be re-served for me,
5. I know not when my Lord may come, At night or noon-day fair,
Nor why un-wor-thy—Christ in love Re-deemed me for His own.
Nor how be-liev-ing in His Word Wrought peace with-in my heart.
Re-veal-ing Je-sus thro' the Word, Cre-at-ing faith in Him.
Of wea-ry ways or gold-en days, Be-fore His face I see.
Nor if I'll walk the vale with Him, Or "meet Him in the air."
CHORUS
But "I know whom I have be-liev-ed, and am per-suad-ed that He is
a-ble To keep that which I've com-mit-ted Un-to Him a-gainst that day."

110 ABIDE WITH ME

H. F. Lyte

Wm. H. Monk

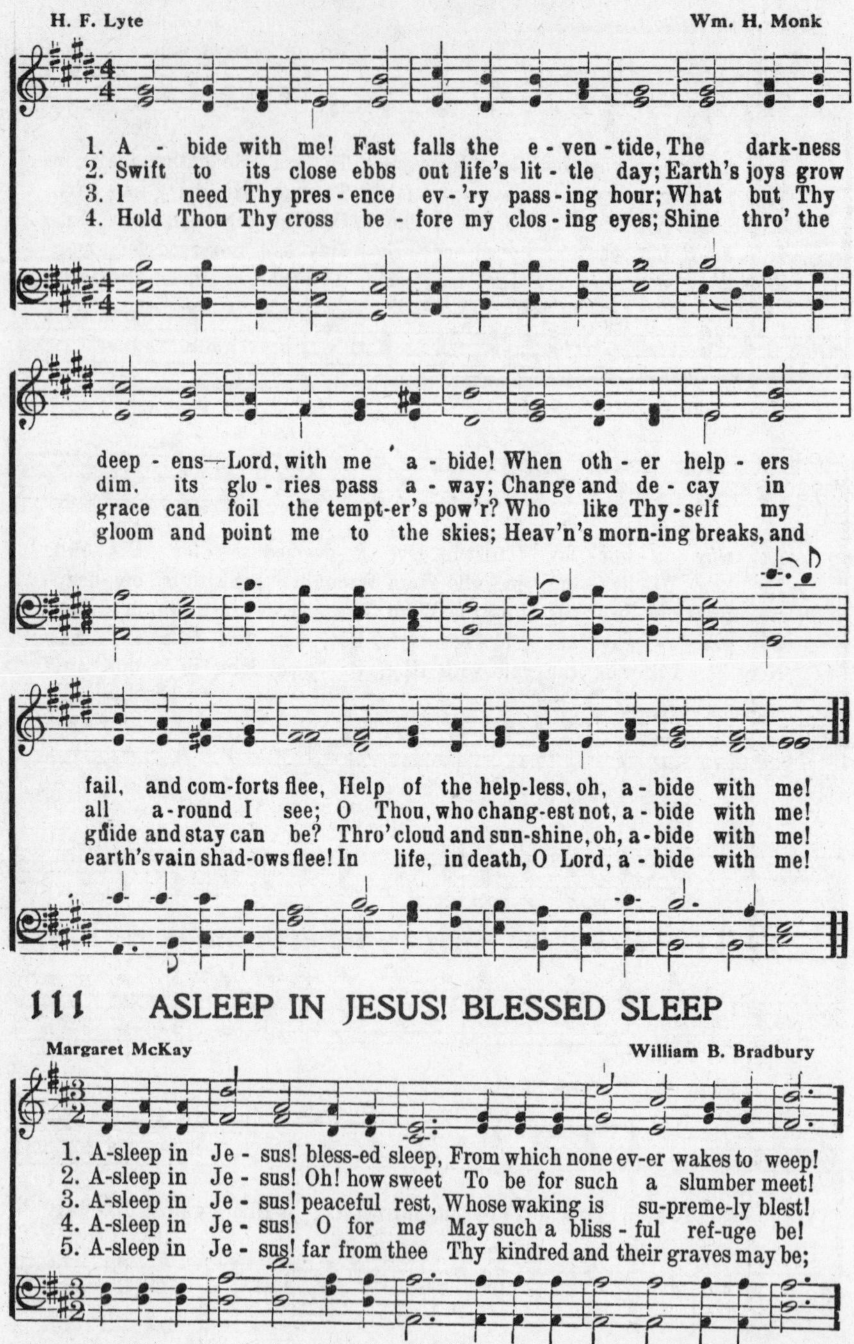
1. A - bide with me! Fast falls the e - ven - tide, The dark-ness
2. Swift to its close ebbs out life's lit - tle day; Earth's joys grow
3. I need Thy pres - ence ev - 'ry pass - ing hour; What but Thy
4. Hold Thou Thy cross be - fore my clos - ing eyes; Shine thro' the
deep - ens—Lord, with me a - bide! When oth - er help - ers
dim, its glo - ries pass a - way; Change and de - cay in
grace can foil the tempt - er's pow'r? Who like Thy - self my
gloom and point me to the skies; Heav'n's morn-ing breaks, and
fail, and com-forts flee, Help of the help-less, oh, a - bide with me!
all a - round I see; O Thou, who chang-est not, a - bide with me!
guide and stay can be? Thro' cloud and sun-shine, oh, a - bide with me!
earth's vain shad-ows flee! In life, in death, O Lord, a - bide with me!
111 ASLEEP IN JESUS! BLESSED SLEEP
Margaret McKay
William B. Bradbury
1. A-sleep in Je - sus! bless-ed sleep, From which none ev-er wakes to weep!
2. A-sleep in Je - sus! Oh! how sweet To be for such a slumber meet!
3. A-sleep in Je - sus! peaceful rest, Whose waking is su-preme-ly blest!
4. A-sleep in Je - sus! O for me May such a bliss - ful ref-uge be!
5. A-sleep in Je - sus! far from thee Thy kindred and their graves may be;

ASLEEP IN JESUS! BLESSED SLEEP

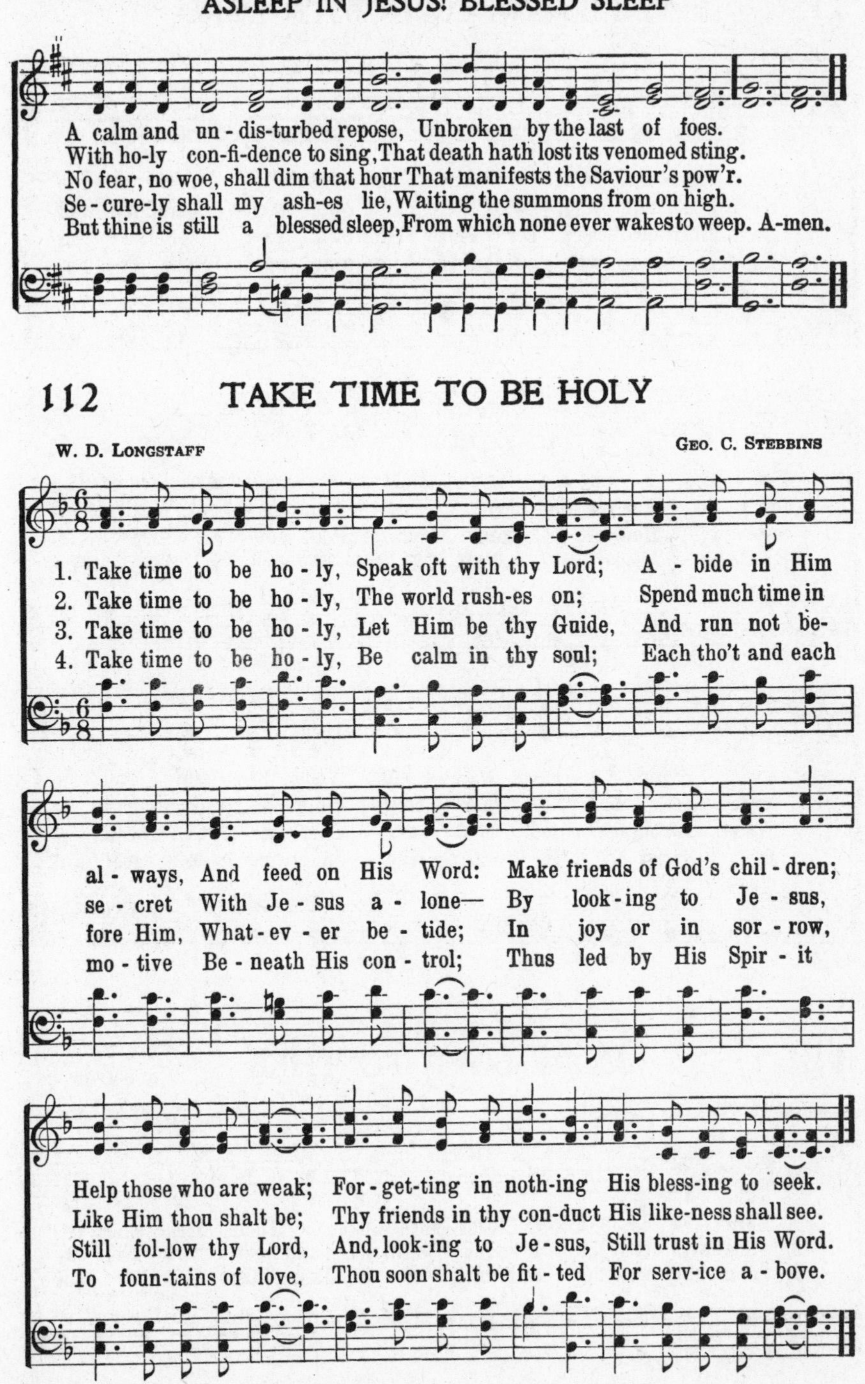
A calm and un-dis-turbed repose, Unbroken by the last of foes.
With ho-ly con-fi-dence to sing, That death hath lost its venomed sting.
No fear, no woe, shall dim that hour That manifests the Saviour's pow'r.
Se-cure-ly shall my ash-es lie, Waiting the summons from on high.
But thine is still a blessed sleep, From which none ever wakes to weep. A-men.
112 TAKE TIME TO BE HOLY
W. D. LONGSTAFF
GEO. C. STEBBINS
1. Take time to be ho-ly, Speak oft with thy Lord; A-bide in Him al-ways, And feed on His Word: Make friends of God's chil-dren; Help those who are weak; For-get-ting in noth-ing His bless-ing to seek.
2. Take time to be ho-ly, The world rush-es on; Spend much time in se-cret With Je-sus a-lone— By look-ing to Je-sus, Like Him thou shalt be; Thy friends in thy con-duct His like-ness shall see.
3. Take time to be ho-ly, Let Him be thy Guide, And run not be-fore Him, What-ev-er be-tide; In joy or in sor-row, Still fol-low thy Lord, And, look-ing to Je-sus, Still trust in His Word.
4. Take time to be ho-ly, Be calm in thy soul; Each tho't and each mo-tive Be-neath His con-trol; Thus led by His Spir-it To foun-tains of love, Thou soon shalt be fit-ted For serv-ice a-bove.

113 HAVE THINE OWN WAY, LORD

A. A. P. | Geo. C. Stebbins

Slowly

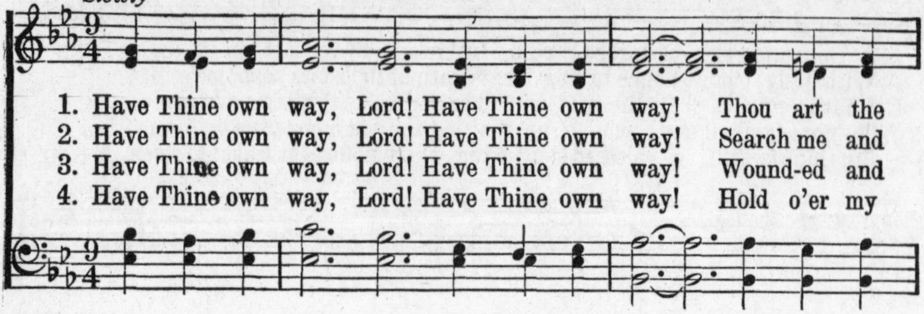

1. Have Thine own way, Lord! Have Thine own way! Thou art the
2. Have Thine own way, Lord! Have Thine own way! Search me and
3. Have Thine own way, Lord! Have Thine own way! Wound-ed and
4. Have Thine own way, Lord! Have Thine own way! Hold o'er my

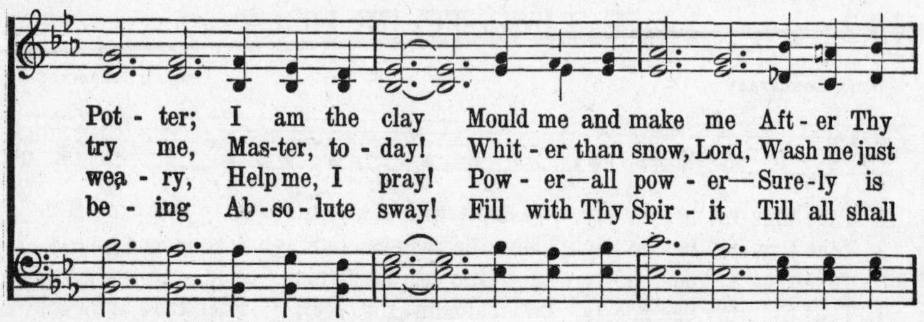

Pot - ter; I am the clay Mould me and make me Aft - er Thy
try me, Mas-ter, to - day! Whit - er than snow, Lord, Wash me just
wea - ry, Help me, I pray! Pow - er—all pow - er—Sure-ly is
be - ing Ab - so - lute sway! Fill with Thy Spir - it Till all shall

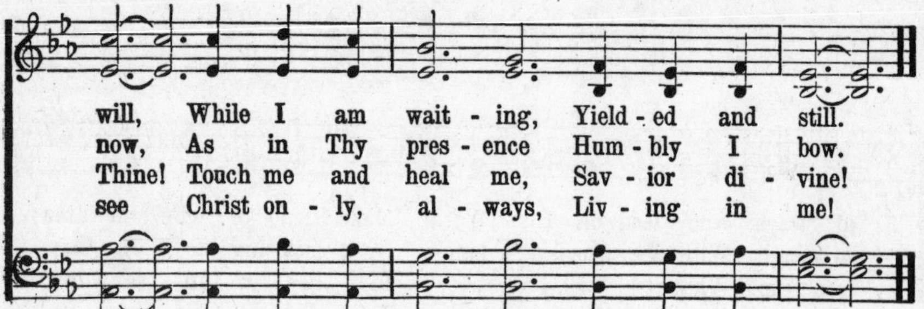

will, While I am wait - ing, Yield - ed and still.
now, As in Thy pres - ence Hum - bly I bow.
Thine! Touch me and heal me, Sav - ior di - vine!
see Christ on - ly, al - ways, Liv - ing in me!

114 MORE LOVE TO THEE

Elizabeth Prentiss | W. H. Doane

1. More love to Thee, O Christ, More love to Thee! Hear Thou the
2. Once earth - ly joy I craved, Sought peace and rest; Now Thee a-
3. Then shall my lat - est breath Whis - per Thy praise; This be the

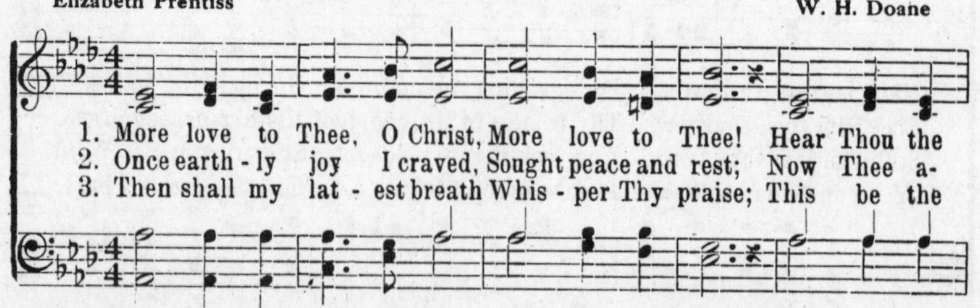

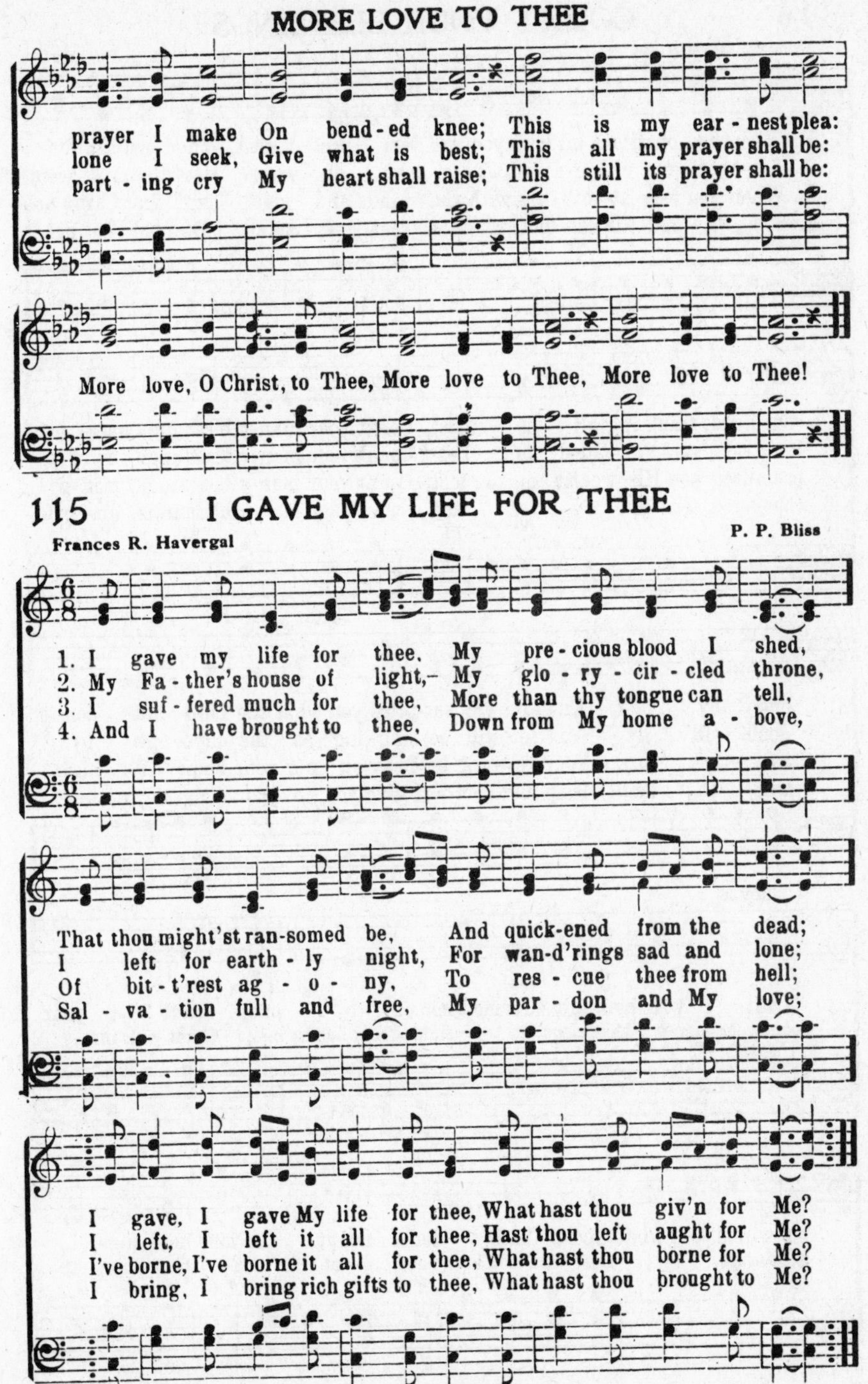
MORE LOVE TO THEE
prayer I make On bend-ed knee; This is my ear-nest plea:
lone I seek, Give what is best; This all my prayer shall be:
part-ing cry My heart shall raise; This still its prayer shall be:
More love, O Christ, to Thee, More love to Thee, More love to Thee!
115
I GAVE MY LIFE FOR THEE
Frances R. Havergal
P. P. Bliss
1. I gave my life for thee, My pre-cious blood I shed,
2. My Fa-ther's house of light,— My glo-ry-cir-cled throne,
3. I suf-fered much for thee, More than thy tongue can tell,
4. And I have brought to thee, Down from My home a-bove,
That thou might'st ran-somed be, And quick-ened from the dead;
I left for earth-ly night, For wan-d'rings sad and lone;
Of bit-t'rest ag-o-ny, To res-cue thee from hell;
Sal-va-tion full and free, My par-don and My love;
I gave, I gave My life for thee, What hast thou giv'n for Me?
I left, I left it all for thee, Hast thou left aught for Me?
I've borne, I've borne it all for thee, What hast thou borne for Me?
I bring, I bring rich gifts to thee, What hast thou brought to Me?

116 COUNT YOUR BLESSINGS

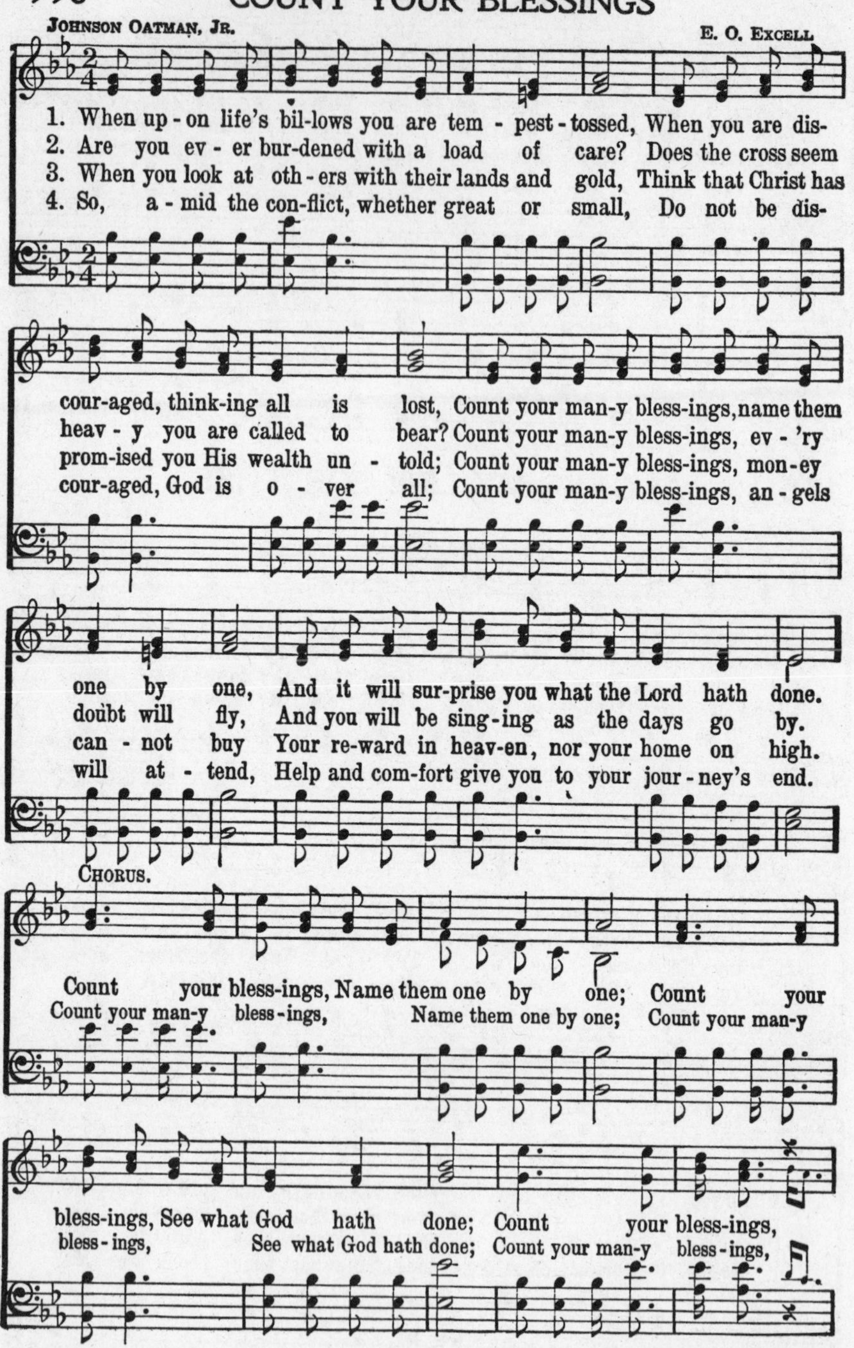
JOHNSON OATMAN, JR.
E. O. EXCELL
1. When up - on life's bil-lows you are tem - pest - tossed, When you are dis-
2. Are you ev - er bur-dened with a load of care? Does the cross seem
3. When you look at oth - ers with their lands and gold, Think that Christ has
4. So, a - mid the con-flict, whether great or small, Do not be dis-
cour-aged, think-ing all is lost, Count your man-y bless-ings, name them
heav - y you are called to bear? Count your man-y bless-ings, ev - 'ry
prom-ised you His wealth un - told; Count your man-y bless-ings, mon-ey
cour-aged, God is o - ver all; Count your man-y bless-ings, an - gels
one by one, And it will sur-prise you what the Lord hath done.
doubt will fly, And you will be sing-ing as the days go by.
can - not buy Your re-ward in heav-en, nor your home on high.
will at - tend, Help and com-fort give you to your jour - ney's end.
CHORUS.
Count your bless-ings, Name them one by one; Count your
Count your man-y bless-ings, Name them one by one; Count your man-y
bless-ings, See what God hath done; Count your bless-ings,
bless - ings, See what God hath done; Count your man-y bless - ings,

COUNT YOUR BLESSINGS

rit.
a tempo
Name them one by one; Count your man-y blessings, See what God hath done.

117 MY FAITH LOOKS UP TO THEE

RAY PALMER LOWELL MASON

1. My faith looks up to Thee, Thou Lamb of Cal-va-ry,
2. May Thy rich grace im-part Strength to my faint-ing heart,
3. While life's dark maze I tread, And griefs a-round me spread,
4. When ends life's tran-sient dream, When death's cold, sul-len stream

Sav-ior di-vine! Now hear me while I pray, Take all my
My zeal in-spire; As Thou hast died for me, O may my
Be Thou my Guide; Bid dark-ness turn to day, Wipe sor-row's
Shall o'er me roll; Blest Sav-ior, then, in love, Fear and dis-

guilt a-way, O let me from this day Be whol-ly Thine!
love to Thee Pure, warm, and changeless be, A liv-ing fire!
tears a-way, Nor let me ev-er stray From Thee a-side.
trust re-move; O bear me safe a-bove, A ran-somed soul!

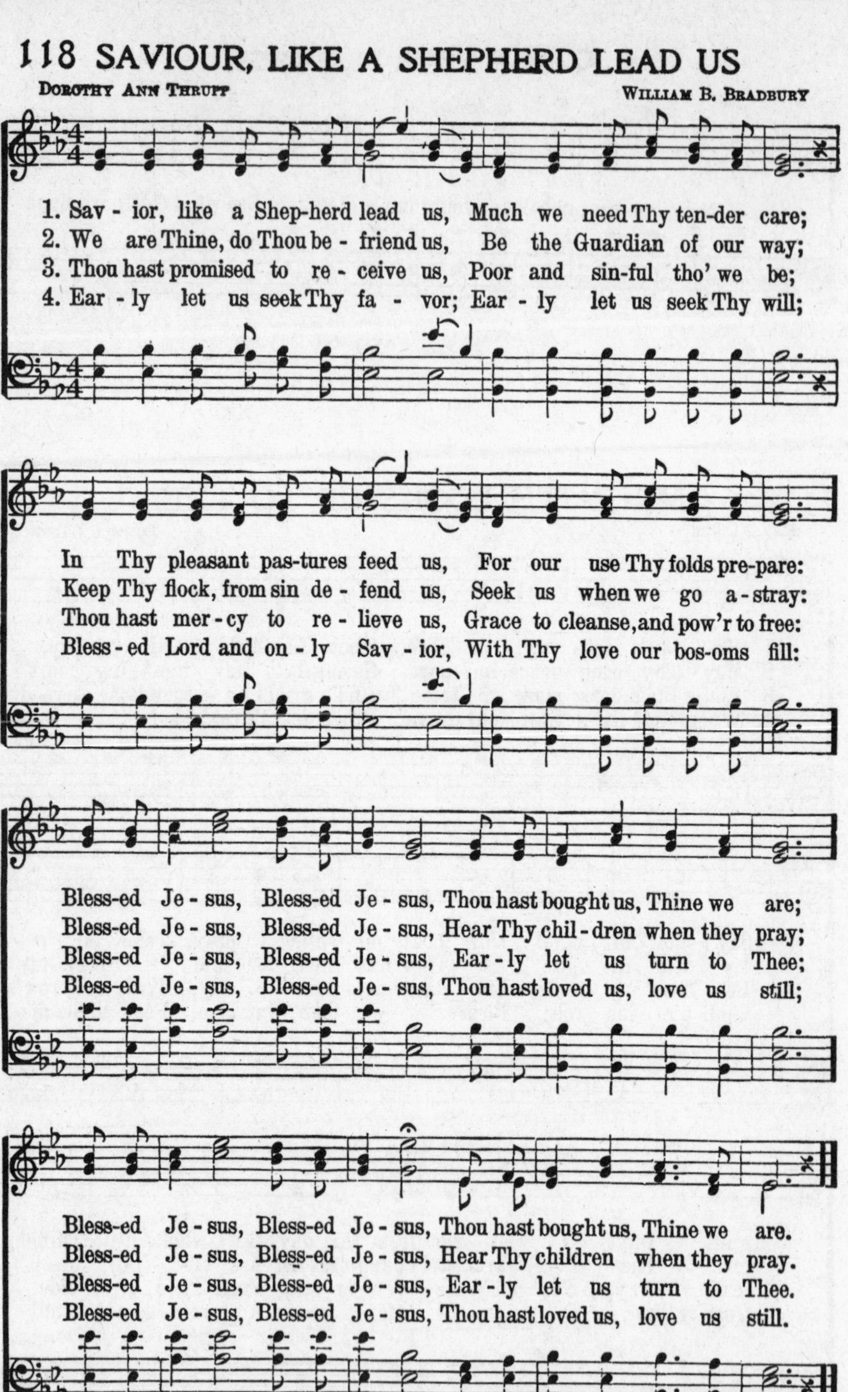
118 SAVIOUR, LIKE A SHEPHERD LEAD US
Dorothy Ann Thrupp
William B. Bradbury
1. Sav - ior, like a Shep-herd lead us, Much we need Thy ten-der care;
2. We are Thine, do Thou be - friend us, Be the Guardian of our way;
3. Thou hast promised to re - ceive us, Poor and sin-ful tho' we be;
4. Ear - ly let us seek Thy fa - vor; Ear - ly let us seek Thy will;
In Thy pleasant pas-tures feed us, For our use Thy folds pre-pare:
Keep Thy flock, from sin de - fend us, Seek us when we go a - stray:
Thou hast mer - cy to re - lieve us, Grace to cleanse, and pow'r to free:
Bless - ed Lord and on - ly Sav - ior, With Thy love our bos-oms fill:
Bless-ed Je - sus, Bless-ed Je - sus, Thou hast bought us, Thine we are;
Bless-ed Je - sus, Bless-ed Je - sus, Hear Thy chil - dren when they pray;
Bless-ed Je - sus, Bless-ed Je - sus, Ear - ly let us turn to Thee;
Bless-ed Je - sus, Bless-ed Je - sus, Thou hast loved us, love us still;
Bless-ed Je - sus, Bless-ed Je - sus, Thou hast bought us, Thine we are.
Bless-ed Je - sus, Bless-ed Je - sus, Hear Thy children when they pray.
Bless-ed Je - sus, Bless-ed Je - sus, Ear - ly let us turn to Thee.
Bless-ed Je - sus, Bless-ed Je - sus, Thou hast loved us, love us still.

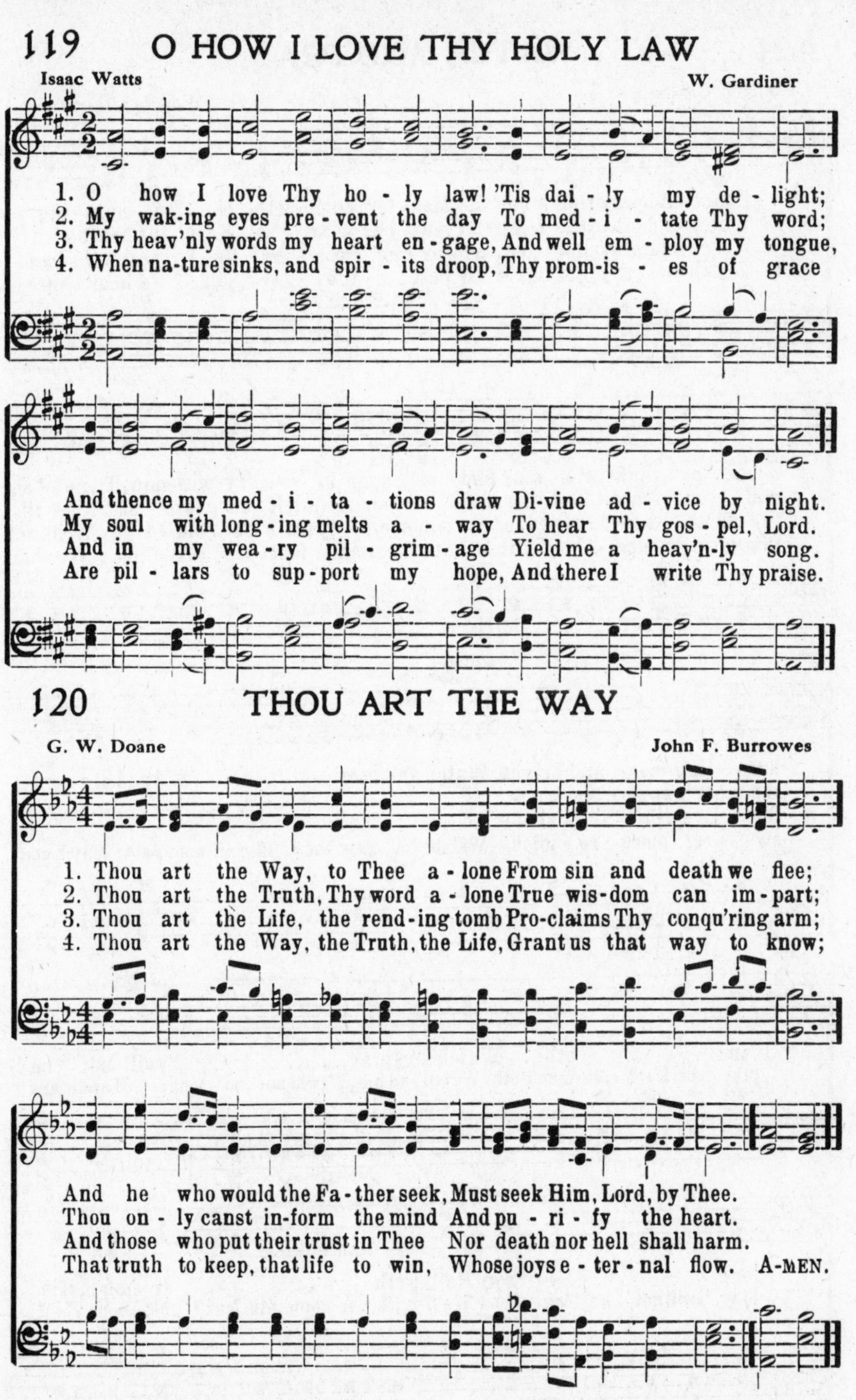
119 O HOW I LOVE THY HOLY LAW
Isaac Watts
W. Gardiner
1. O how I love Thy ho - ly law! 'Tis dai - ly my de - light;
2. My wak-ing eyes pre - vent the day To med - i - tate Thy word;
3. Thy heav'nly words my heart en - gage, And well em - ploy my tongue,
4. When na-ture sinks, and spir - its droop, Thy prom-is - es of grace
And thence my med - i - ta - tions draw Di-vine ad - vice by night.
My soul with long - ing melts a - way To hear Thy gos - pel, Lord.
And in my wea - ry pil - grim - age Yield me a heav'n-ly song.
Are pil - lars to sup - port my hope, And there I write Thy praise.
120 THOU ART THE WAY
G. W. Doane
John F. Burrowes
1. Thou art the Way, to Thee a - lone From sin and death we flee;
2. Thou art the Truth, Thy word a - lone True wis - dom can im - part;
3. Thou art the Life, the rend - ing tomb Pro-claims Thy conqu'ring arm;
4. Thou art the Way, the Truth, the Life, Grant us that way to know;
And he who would the Fa - ther seek, Must seek Him, Lord, by Thee.
Thou on - ly canst in-form the mind And pu - ri - fy the heart.
And those who put their trust in Thee Nor death nor hell shall harm.
That truth to keep, that life to win, Whose joys e - ter - nal flow. A-MEN.

121 WATCH AND PRAY

Fanny J. Crosby

Wm. J. Kirkpatrick

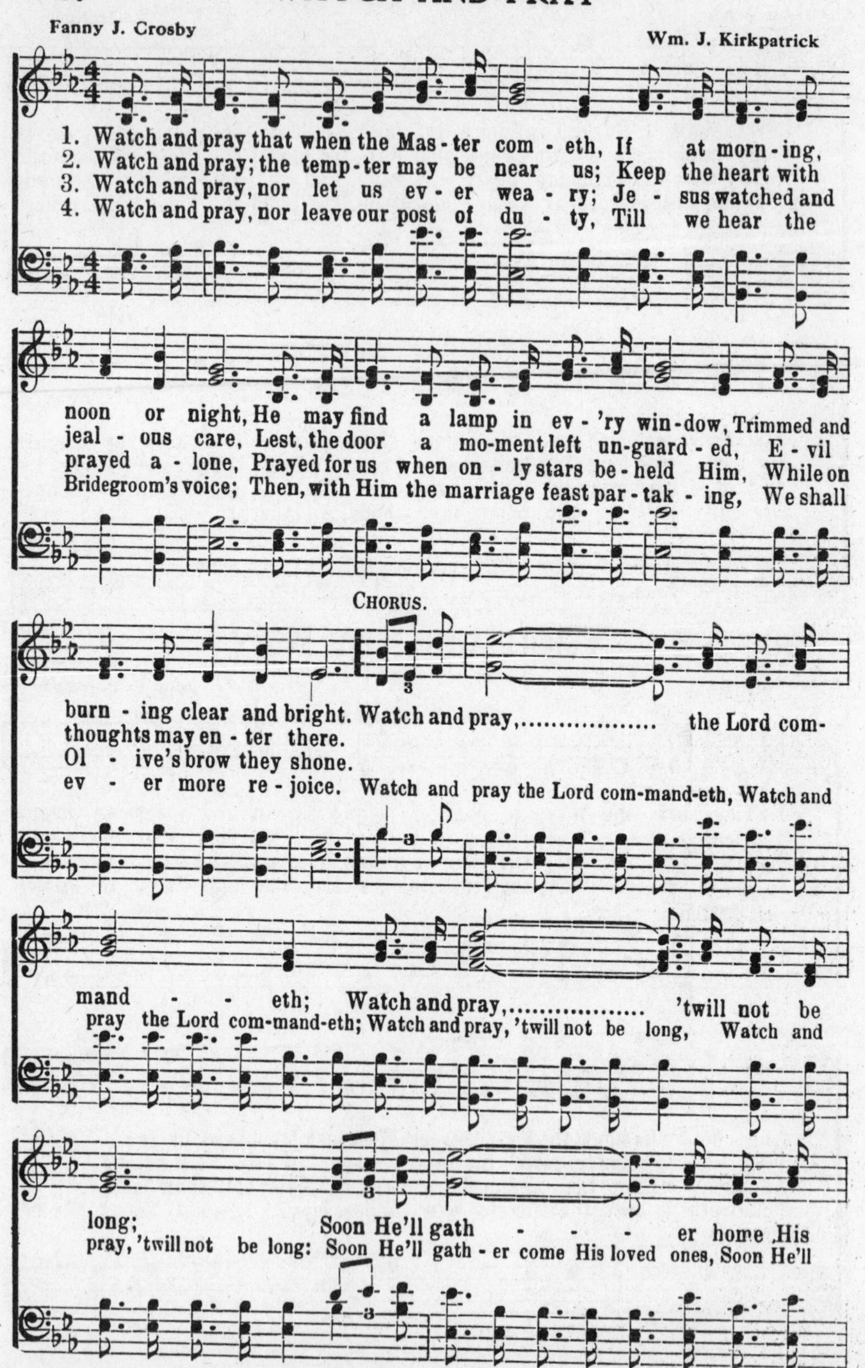
1. Watch and pray that when the Mas - ter com - eth, If at morn - ing,
2. Watch and pray; the temp - ter may be near us; Keep the heart with
3. Watch and pray, nor let us ev - er wea - ry; Je - sus watched and
4. Watch and pray, nor leave our post of du - ty, Till we hear the
noon or night, He may find a lamp in ev - 'ry win - dow, Trimmed and
jeal - ous care, Lest, the door a mo - ment left un - guard - ed, E - vil
prayed a - lone, Prayed for us when on - ly stars be - held Him, While on
Bridegroom's voice; Then, with Him the marriage feast par - tak - ing, We shall
CHORUS.
burn - ing clear and bright. Watch and pray,.................. the Lord com-
thoughts may en - ter there.
Ol - ive's brow they shone.
ev - er more re - joice. Watch and pray the Lord com-mand-eth, Watch and
mand - - eth; Watch and pray,.................. 'twill not be
pray the Lord com-mand-eth; Watch and pray, 'twill not be long, Watch and
long; Soon He'll gath - - - er home His
pray, 'twill not be long: Soon He'll gath - er come His loved ones, Soon He'll

loved ones To the hap - py vale of song (of song.)
gath - er home His loved ones To the hap - py vale of song, the vale of song.
122 WE'LL NEVER SAY GOOD-BY
Mrs. E. W. Chapman
J. H. Tenney
1. With friends on earth we meet in gladness, While swift the mo-ments fly,
2. How joy - ful is the hope that lingers, When loved ones cross death's sea,
3. No part - ing words shall e'er be spo-ken In yon - der home so fair,
Yet ev - er comes the tho't of sad-ness, That we must say, "Good-by."
That we, when all earth's toils are end-ed, With them shall ev - er be!
But songs of joy, and peace, and gladness, We'll sing for - ev - er there.
CHORUS.
We'll nev-er say good-by in heav'n, We'll nev-er say good - by, . . .
good-by,
For in that land of joy and song We'll nev - er say good - by.

123 THE LORD'S APOSTLES

H. B. O. A. L.

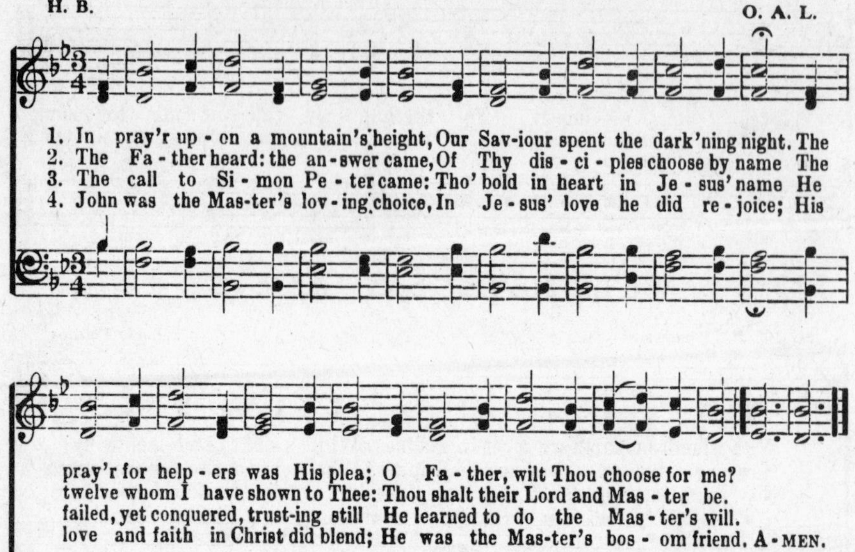
1. In pray'r up - on a mountain's height, Our Sav-iour spent the dark'ning night. The
2. The Fa - ther heard: the an - swer came, Of Thy dis - ci - ples choose by name The
3. The call to Si - mon Pe - ter came: Tho' bold in heart in Je - sus' name He
4. John was the Mas-ter's lov - ing choice, In Je - sus' love he did re - joice; His
pray'r for help - ers was His plea; O Fa - ther, wilt Thou choose for me?
twelve whom I have shown to Thee: Thou shalt their Lord and Mas - ter be.
failed, yet conquered, trust-ing still He learned to do the Mas - ter's will.
love and faith in Christ did blend; He was the Mas-ter's bos - om friend. A - MEN.

5. Then Andrew was the Master's choice,
In steadfast faith he did rejoice,
To help Him win the souls of men
And guide them back to heaven again.

6. He looked to James; the Master's plea,
Forsake the world, and follow me.
To Christ the Lord his soul was bound
Until a martyr's death he found.

7. And Philip sought and found the Lord
'Twas love and faith in one accord.
A deacon true,—great was his zeal.
His labors did his worth reveal.

8. Bartholomew was Jesus' friend.
This willing worker Christ did send
With others of Apostle band
To harvest souls in distant lands.

9. In Matthew did the Saviour find
A publican of humble mind.
Forsook the tax collector's part
And gave to Christ a willing heart.

10. In fear, dismay, and doubtful mind
In Thomas we example find.
The risen Christ did faith afford,
Then Thomas cried, "My God, and Lord."

11. In James, the son of Alphaeus,
A helper true and virtuous,
The Saviour found a worthy hand
To fill the dear Apostle band.

12. And Simon, called the Canaanite,
The Lord did bring to truth and light.
'Tis true his record is not plain;
Yet true to Christ he did remain.

13. Thaddaeus, called by Christ the Lord
Obeyed the Master's voice and Word.
A true Apostle did he prove.
And labored on in faith and love.

14. How sad a lot, we fain would tell
That Judas by transgression fell,
By his betrayal,—crucified,
Our Saviour languished, bled and died.

15. Matthias now the ranks to fill
Was chosen by the Father's will.
The holy band was thus supplied,
By God's own choice and sanctified.

16. The chief of sinners once was Paul,
Though he was chosen last of all;
Repenting, pardoned,—labored most,
He's numbered with the heavenly host.

124 READY

S. E. L. Charlie D. Tillman

1. Read-y to suf-fer grief or pain, Read-y to stand the test;
2. Read-y to go, read-y to bear, Read-y to watch and pray;
3. Read-y to speak, read-y to think, Read-y with heart and brain;
4. Read-y to speak, read-y to warn, Read-y o'er souls to yearn;

Read-y to stay at home and send Oth-ers, if He sees best.
Read-y to stand a - side and give, Till He shall clear the way.
Read-y to stand where He sees fit, Read-y to stand the strain.
Read-y in life, read-y in death, Read-y for His re - turn.

CHORUS

Read-y to go, read-y to stay, Read-y my place to fill;

Read-y for serv - ice, low-ly or great, Read-y to do His will.

125 WE SHALL SLEEP BUT NOT FOREVER

Mary A. Kidder

Silas J. Vail

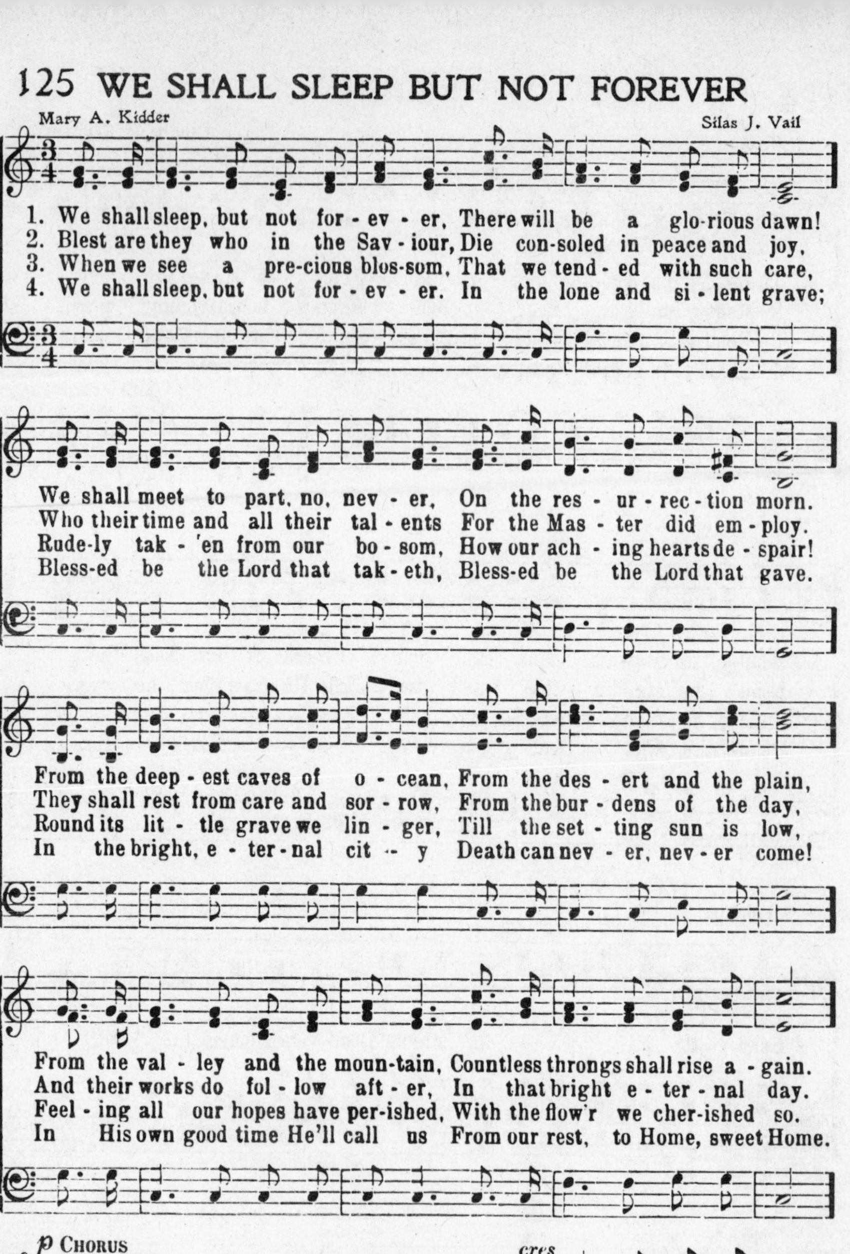
1. We shall sleep, but not for-ev-er, There will be a glo-rious dawn!
2. Blest are they who in the Sav-iour, Die con-soled in peace and joy,
3. When we see a pre-cious blos-som, That we tend-ed with such care,
4. We shall sleep, but not for-ev-er. In the lone and si-lent grave;
We shall meet to part, no, nev-er, On the res-ur-rec-tion morn.
Who their time and all their tal-ents For the Mas-ter did em-ploy.
Rude-ly tak-'en from our bo-som, How our ach-ing hearts de-spair!
Bless-ed be the Lord that tak-eth, Bless-ed be the Lord that gave.
From the deep-est caves of o-cean, From the des-ert and the plain,
They shall rest from care and sor-row, From the bur-dens of the day,
Round its lit-tle grave we lin-ger, Till the set-ting sun is low,
In the bright, e-ter-nal cit-y Death can nev-er, nev-er come!
From the val-ley and the moun-tain, Countless throngs shall rise a-gain.
And their works do fol-low aft-er, In that bright e-ter-nal day.
Feel-ing all our hopes have per-ished, With the flow'r we cher-ished so.
In His own good time He'll call us From our rest, to Home, sweet Home.

p CHORUS *cres*

We shall sleep, but not for-ev-er, There will be a glo-rious dawn;

WE SHALL SLEEP BUT NOT FOREVER

We shall meet to part, no, nev - er, On the res - ur - rec - tion morn!
126
ANTICIPATION
1. O Je - ru - sa - lem, the gold-en, Where God's praises ev - er ring;
Heav'nly choir to Thee be-hold-en, "Ho - ly, ho - ly, ho-ly" sing.
2. In this pil-grim hab - i - ta-tion, In the heat of trials se - vere,
Ere our suff-'ring finds ces-sa-tion, Pain and strife as - sail us here.
3. Ah, how much I long to meet Thee, Je - sus, my soul's bos-om Friend.
There on Sa-lem's peaceful pastures, Where our tears and sighs will end;
4. Come and lead us full of glad-ness, Gen-tle Shep-herd, by Thy hand,
Aft - er all this pain and sad-ness In - to that true Fa-ther - land,
O when will God grant to me, Thy glad cit - i- zen to be! Thy glad cit - i - zen to be!
But the Lord gives hope and strength, To pre - vail thru faith at length. To pre - vail thru faith at length.
Where in glo - ry, light and grace, We shall see God face to face. We shall see God face to face.
Where the liv - ing wa - ters free, Quench our thirst e - ter - nal - ly. Quench our thirst e - ter - nal - ly.

127 NEVER ALONE

1. How man - y times, dis - cour - aged, We sink be - side the way;
2. Oh, soul, hast thou for - got - en The ten - der word and sweet
3. Take cour-age, way-worn pil - grim! Tho' mists and shad-ows hide
A - bout us all is dark - ness, We hard - ly dare to pray.
Of Him who left be - hind Him The print of bleed - ing feet?
The face of Him thou lov - est, He's ev - er at thy side.
Then, thro' the mists and shad - ows, The sweet - est voice e'er known
"I nev - er will for - sake thee, Oh, child, so wea - ry grown;
Reach out thy hand and find Him, And lo, the clouds have flown;
Says, "Child, am I not with thee, Nev - er to leave thee a - lone?"
Re - mem - ber, I have prom - ised Nev - er to leave thee a - lone."
He smiles on thee who prom - ised Nev - er to leave thee a - lone.

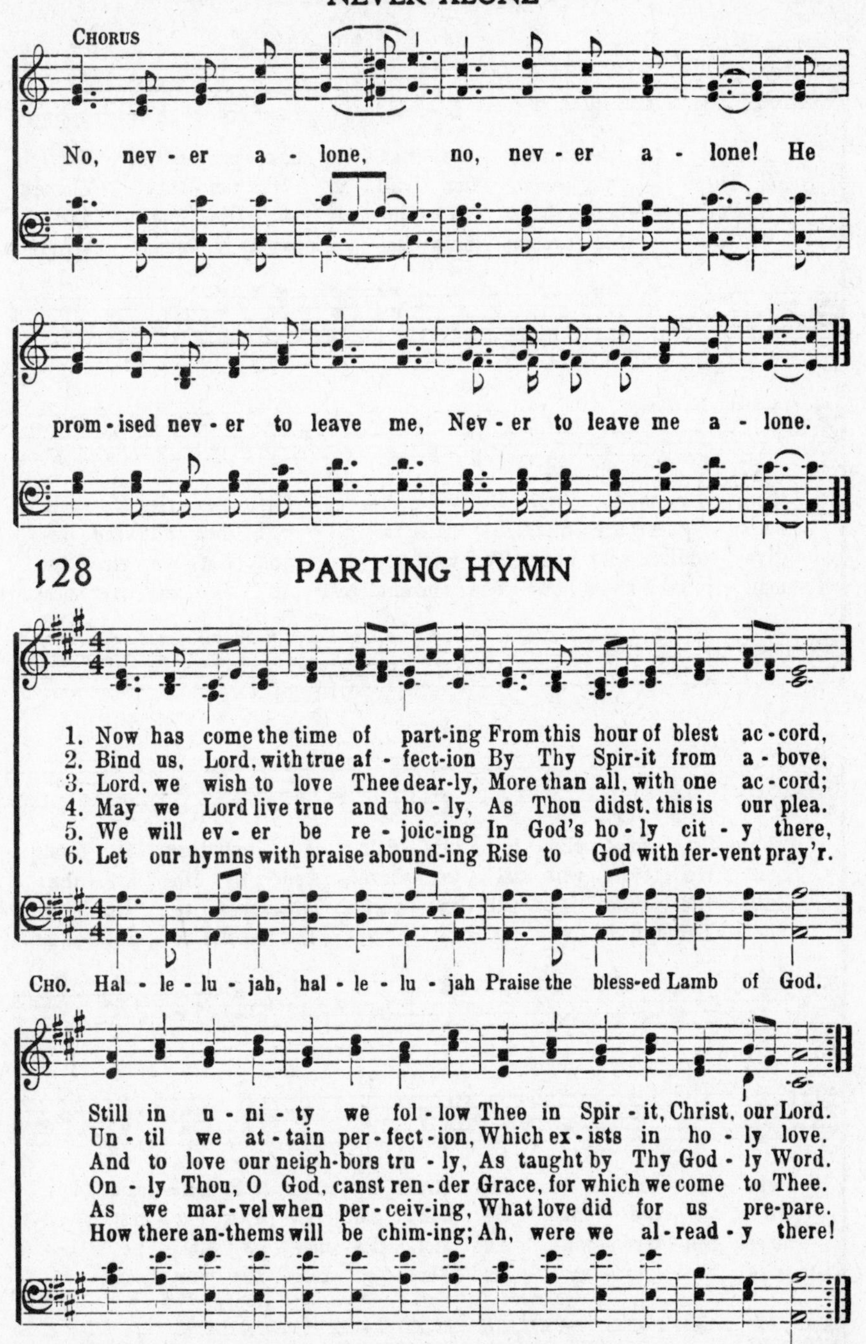
NEVER ALONE
CHORUS
No, nev - er a - lone, no, nev - er a - lone! He
prom - ised nev - er to leave me, Nev - er to leave me a - lone.
128
PARTING HYMN
1. Now has come the time of part-ing From this hour of blest ac - cord,
2. Bind us, Lord, with true af - fect-ion By Thy Spir-it from a - bove,
3. Lord, we wish to love Thee dear-ly, More than all, with one ac - cord;
4. May we Lord live true and ho - ly, As Thou didst, this is our plea.
5. We will ev - er be re - joic-ing In God's ho - ly cit - y there,
6. Let our hymns with praise abound-ing Rise to God with fer-vent pray'r.
CHO. Hal - le - lu - jah, hal - le - lu - jah Praise the bless-ed Lamb of God.
Still in u - ni - ty we fol - low Thee in Spir - it, Christ, our Lord.
Un - til we at - tain per - fect - ion, Which ex - ists in ho - ly love.
And to love our neigh-bors tru - ly, As taught by Thy God - ly Word.
On - ly Thou, O God, canst ren - der Grace, for which we come to Thee.
As we mar - vel when per - ceiv-ing, What love did for us pre-pare.
How there an-thems will be chim-ing; Ah, were we al - read - y there!
Hal - le - lu - jah, hal - le - lu - jah, Praise the bless - ed Lamb of God!

129 YET THERE IS ROOM

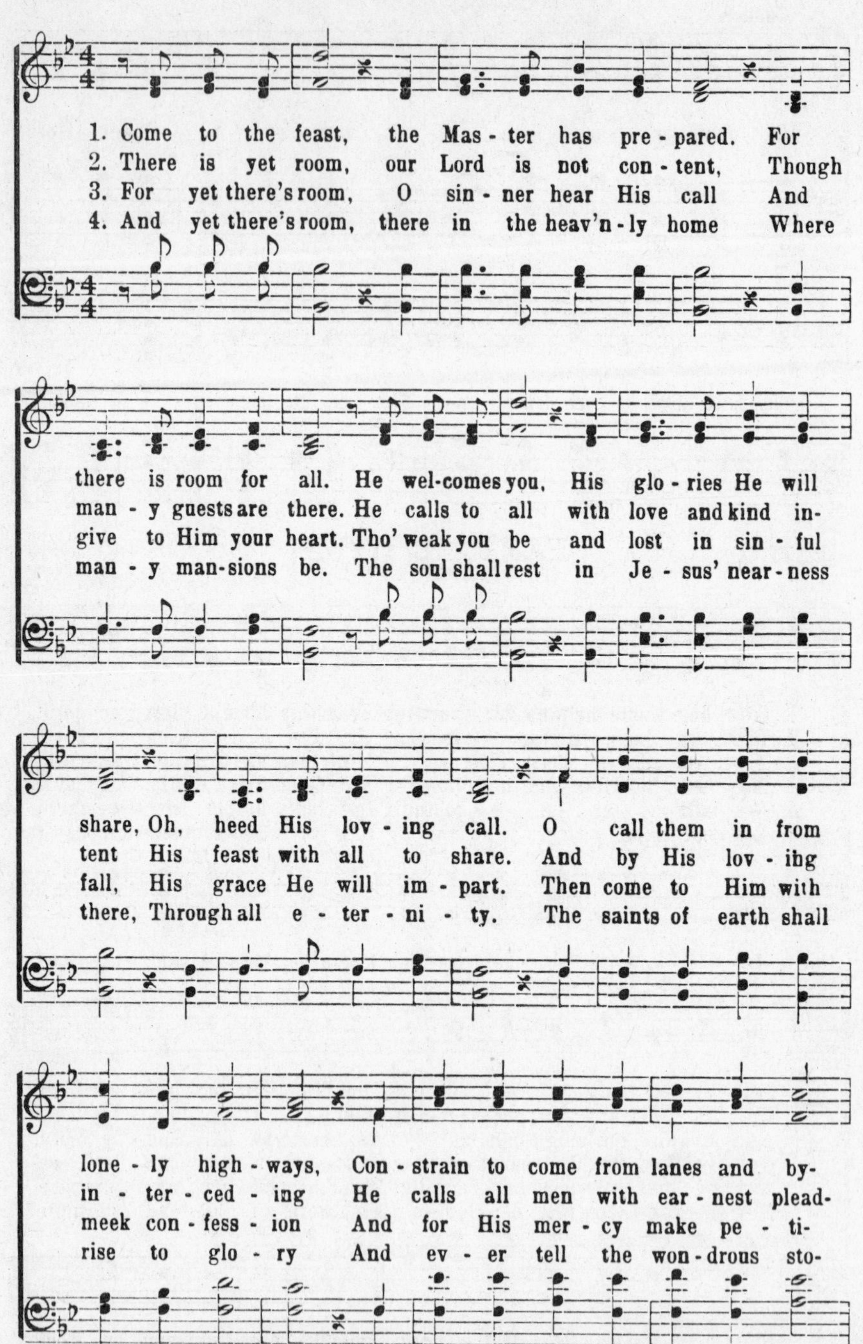
1. Come to the feast, the Mas - ter has pre - pared. For
2. There is yet room, our Lord is not con - tent, Though
3. For yet there's room, O sin - ner hear His call And
4. And yet there's room, there in the heav'n - ly home Where
there is room for all. He wel-comes you, His glo - ries He will
man - y guests are there. He calls to all with love and kind in-
give to Him your heart. Tho' weak you be and lost in sin - ful
man - y man-sions be. The soul shall rest in Je - sus' near - ness
share, Oh, heed His lov - ing call. O call them in from
tent His feast with all to share. And by His lov - ibg
fall, His grace He will im - part. Then come to Him with
there, Through all e - ter - ni - ty. The saints of earth shall
lone - ly high - ways, Con - strain to come from lanes and by-
in - ter - ced - ing He calls all men with ear - nest plead-
meek con - fess - ion And for His mer - cy make pe - ti-
rise to glo - ry And ev - er tell the won - drous sto-

YET THERE IS ROOM

ways, For there is room, for there is room.
ing. For yet there's room, for yet there's room.
tion To cleanse your heart, to cleanse your heart.
ry That there was room, that there was room.
130
HIS YOKE IS EASY
1. The Lord is my Shep-herd, I shall not want; He mak-eth me down to
2. My soul cri-eth out: "Re-store me a-gain, And give me the strength to
3. Yea, tho' I should walk the val-ley of death, Yet why should I fear from
lie In pas-tures green, He lead-eth me The qui-et wa-ters by.
take The nar-row path of right-eous-ness, E'en for His own name's sake."
ill? For Thou art with me, and Thy rod And staff me com-fort still.
CHORUS
His yoke is eas-y, His bur-den is light, I've found it so, I've found it so;
He lead-eth me by day and by night, Where liv-ing wa-ters flow.

131 O WHAT IS MORTAL

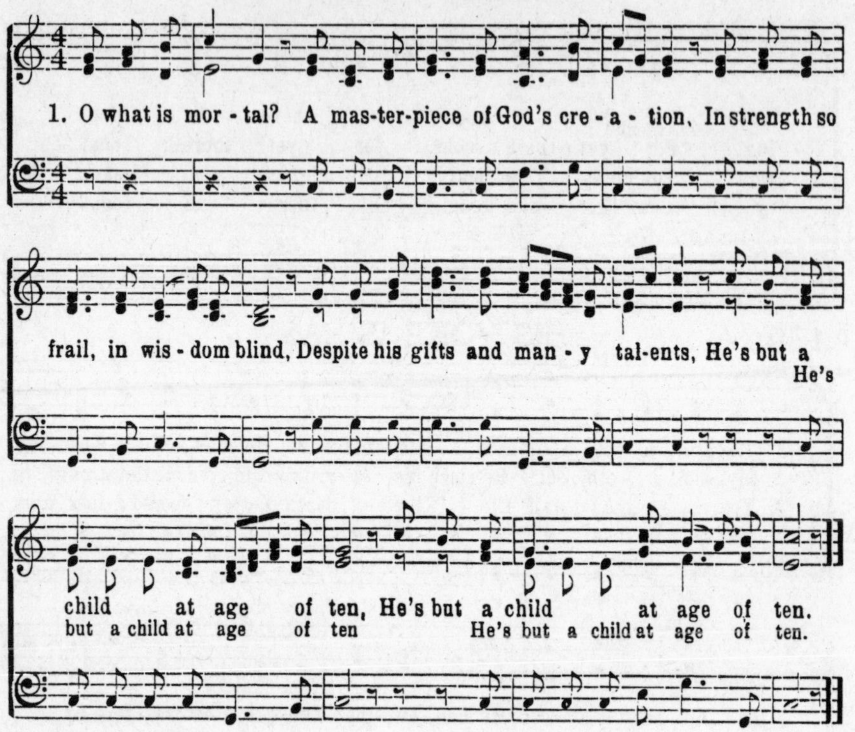
1. O what is mor - tal? A mas-ter-piece of God's cre - a - tion, In strength so
frail, in wis - dom blind, Despite his gifts and man - y tal-ents, He's but a
He's
child at age of ten, He's but a child at age of ten.
but a child at age of ten He's but a child at age of ten.

2. O what is twenty? The age when
youth buds forth with vigor
To reach accountability;
Then fear thy God, self-will subduing,
That innocence might go with thee.

3. O what is thirty? The age of manhood's understanding,
Advanced in mind he may employ
Himself with things of most importance
That life for him might hold true joy.

4. O what is forty? In life this is a time
most joyous
When children bring his heart delight,
And if good fortune is attendant
His children he can rear aright.

5. O what is fifty? The time when as a
happy father
Man can his family life review,
His heart is filled with satisfaction,
As on life's course he doth persue.

6. O what is sixty? The fact to him becomes apparent
That his old age has now begun,
But now he reaps what with welldoing
He for his latter years has won.

7. O what is seventy? Then in the midst
of his grandchildren,
Whom he so fondly can caress,
He does review past life so fleeting
Which brought to him this happiness.

8. O what is eighty? His body now becomes enfeebled,
He unto God does daily pray
That death for him be sweet and easy,
But clings to life while yet he may.

9. O what is ninety? He finds that life
runs in a cycle
And as a child he is again;
But if in God he lives a hundred
Long life will not have been in vain.

10. O what is hundred? This age to few
is e'er allotted;
O man do strive for virtues pure,
And lay thy treasures up in heaven
And make your own election sure!

132 SWEETER THAN ALL

Johnson Oatman, Jr. — Howard Entwisle

1. Christ will me His aid af-ford, Nev-er to fall, nev-er to fall;
While I find my pre-cious Lord Sweet-er than all, sweet-er than all.
2. I will fol-low all the way, Hearing Him call, hearing Him call;
Find-ing Him from day to day Sweet-er than all, sweet-er than all.
3. Though a ves-sel I may be, Bro-ken and small, bro-ken and small;
Yet His bless-ings fall on me, Sweet-er than all, sweet-er than all.
4. When I reach the crys-tal sea, Voic-es will call, voic-es will call;
But my Sav-iour's voice will be, Sweet-er than all, sweet-er than all.
CHORUS
Je-sus is now and ev-er will be Sweet-er than all the world to me;
Since I heard His lov-ing call, Sweet-er than all, sweet-er than all.

133 LEAD ME GENTLY HOME, FATHER

W. L. T. Will L. Thompson

1. Lead me gen-tly home, Fa-ther, Lead me gen - tly home, When life's toils are end - ed, And part-ing days have come; Sin no more shall tempt me, Ne'er from Thee I'll roam, If Thou'lt on - ly lead me, Fa-ther, Lead me gen-tly home.
2. Lead me gen-tly home, Fa-ther, Lead me gen - tly home, In life's dark-est hours, Father, When life's troubles come, Keep my feet from wand'ring, Lest from Thee I roam, Lest I fall up-on the way-side, Lead me gen-tly home.
rit.
p
REFRAIN.
Lead me gen - tly home, Fa - ther, Lead me gen - tly,
Lead me gen-tly home, Fa-ther, Lead me gen - tly home, Fa - ther,
Lest I fall up - on the way-side, Lead me gen - tly home.
gen - tly home.

134 THERE WILL BE PEACE

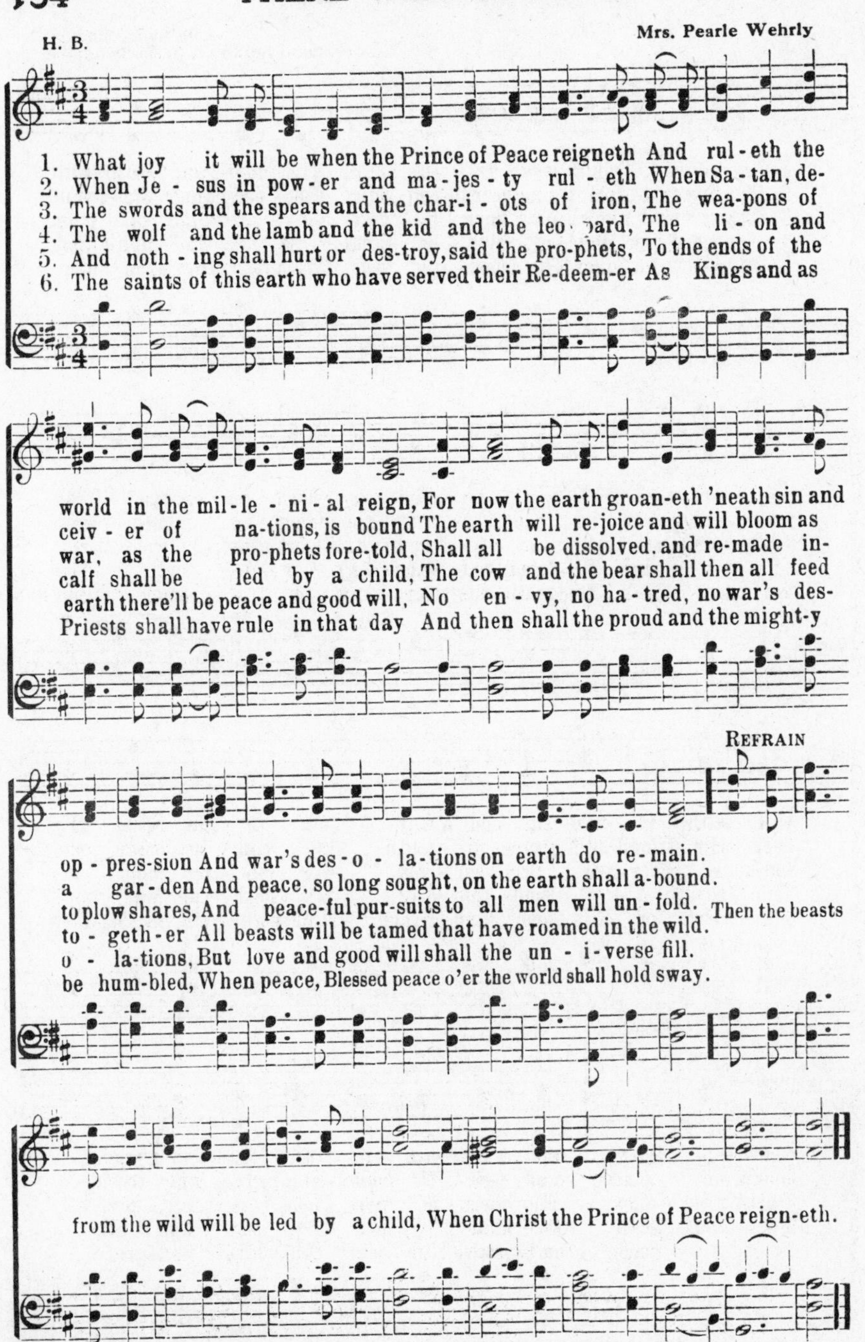
H. B.
Mrs. Pearle Wehrly
1. What joy it will be when the Prince of Peace reigneth And rul-eth the
2. When Je-sus in pow-er and ma-jes-ty rul-eth When Sa-tan, de-
3. The swords and the spears and the char-i-ots of iron, The wea-pons of
4. The wolf and the lamb and the kid and the leo-pard, The li-on and
5. And noth-ing shall hurt or des-troy, said the pro-phets, To the ends of the
6. The saints of this earth who have served their Re-deem-er As Kings and as
world in the mil-le-ni-al reign, For now the earth groan-eth 'neath sin and
ceiv-er of na-tions, is bound The earth will re-joice and will bloom as
war, as the pro-phets fore-told, Shall all be dissolved. and re-made in-
calf shall be led by a child, The cow and the bear shall then all feed
earth there'll be peace and good will, No en-vy, no ha-tred, no war's des-
Priests shall have rule in that day And then shall the proud and the might-y
REFRAIN
op-pres-sion And war's des-o-la-tions on earth do re-main.
a gar-den And peace, so long sought, on the earth shall a-bound.
to plow shares, And peace-ful pur-suits to all men will un-fold. Then the beasts
to-geth-er All beasts will be tamed that have roamed in the wild.
o-la-tions, But love and good will shall the un-i-verse fill.
be hum-bled, When peace, Blessed peace o'er the world shall hold sway.
from the wild will be led by a child, When Christ the Prince of Peace reign-eth.

135 YOUTH

H. B.

Old Swiss Melody
Harmonized by M. L. McLaughlin

1. In days of youth seek ye the Lord, His love and truth with
2. The flowers of spring time bright and fair Dis - perse their fra - grance
3. Thy strength and vig - or hope - ful view, Thy zeal and tal - ents
4. You need not hon - or, rich - es, fame This life a - bun - dant
5. In youth-ful days His bless - ing seek, With heart that's ten - der
one ac - cord, Go of - fer Him thy youth - ful days and
sweet and rare, So con - se - crate the bloom of youth, and
vir - tue true, Go of - fer them in Christ's em - ploy His
to at - tain, Oh heed the Mas - ter's lov - ing call Give
true and meek, And while the years draw on a - pace, You'll
walk with - in the Sav - iour's ways. Go of - fer Him thy
seek His friend - ship, grace and truth. So con - se - crate the
bless - ed near - ness to en - joy. Go of - fer them in
Him thy bod - y, soul and all. Go heed the Mas - ter's
praise Him for His love and grace. And while the years draw
youth - ful days and walk with - in the Sav - iour's ways.
bloom of youth, and seek His friend - ship, grace and truth.
Christ's em - ploy His bless - ed near - ness to en - joy.
lov - ing call Give Him thy bod - y, soul and all.
on a - pace, You'll praise Him for His love and grace.

136 ALL WILL BE WELL

Welsh Air

1. Thro' the love of God, our Sav - iour, All will be well;
2. Tho' we pass thro' trib - u - la - tion, All will be well;
3. We ex - pect a bright to - mor - row, All will be well;

Free and change-less is His fa - vor, All, all is well.
Ours is such a full sal - va - tion, All, all is well;
Faith can sing thro' days of sor - row, All, all is well.

Pre-cious is the blood that healed us; Per-fect is the grace that sealed us;
Hap-py still in God con-fid - ing; Fruit-ful, if in Christ a - bid - ing;
On our Fa-ther's love re - ly - ing, Je - sus ev - 'ry need sup - ply - ing;

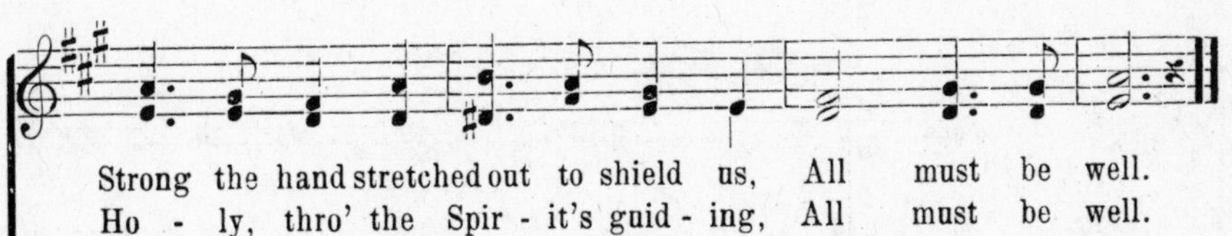

Strong the hand stretched out to shield us, All must be well.
Ho - ly, thro' the Spir - it's guid - ing, All must be well.
Or in liv - ing, or in dy - ing, All must be well.

137 TREAD SOFTLY

Fanny J. Crosby | W. H. Doane

Gently
p
1. Be si - lent, be si - lent, A whis - per is heard; Be
2. Be si - lent, be si - lent, For ho - ly this place; This
3. Be si - lent, be si - lent, His mer - cy re - cord; Be
si - lent, and list - en, O treas - ure each word!
al - tar that ech - oes The mes - sage of grace.
si - lent, be si - lent, And wait on the Lord.
CHORUS
Tread soft - ly, tread soft - ly, The Mas - ter is here; Tread
Tread soft - ly here, tread soft - ly here, Tread
p
p
rit.
soft - ly tread soft - ly, He bids us draw near.
soft - ly here, tread soft - ly here,

138 GOD WILL TAKE CARE OF YOU

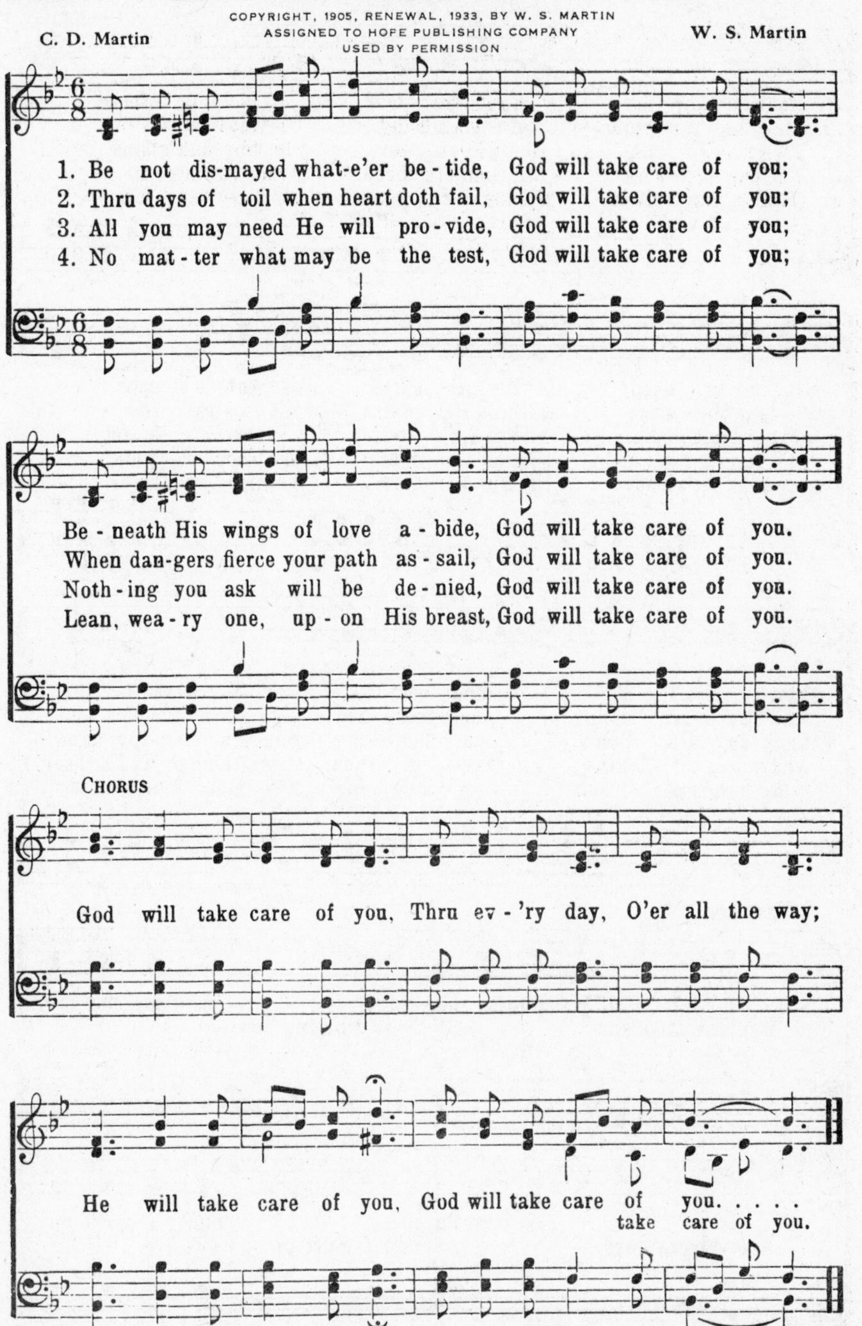
C. D. Martin
COPYRIGHT, 1905, RENEWAL, 1933, BY W. S. MARTIN
ASSIGNED TO HOPE PUBLISHING COMPANY
USED BY PERMISSION
W. S. Martin
1. Be not dis-mayed what-e'er be-tide, God will take care of you;
2. Thru days of toil when heart doth fail, God will take care of you;
3. All you may need He will pro-vide, God will take care of you;
4. No mat-ter what may be the test, God will take care of you;
Be-neath His wings of love a-bide, God will take care of you.
When dan-gers fierce your path as-sail, God will take care of you.
Noth-ing you ask will be de-nied, God will take care of you.
Lean, wea-ry one, up-on His breast, God will take care of you.
CHORUS
God will take care of you, Thru ev-'ry day, O'er all the way;
He will take care of you, God will take care of you. . . . .
take care of you.

139 A BEAUTIFUL LIFE

Wm. M. Golden

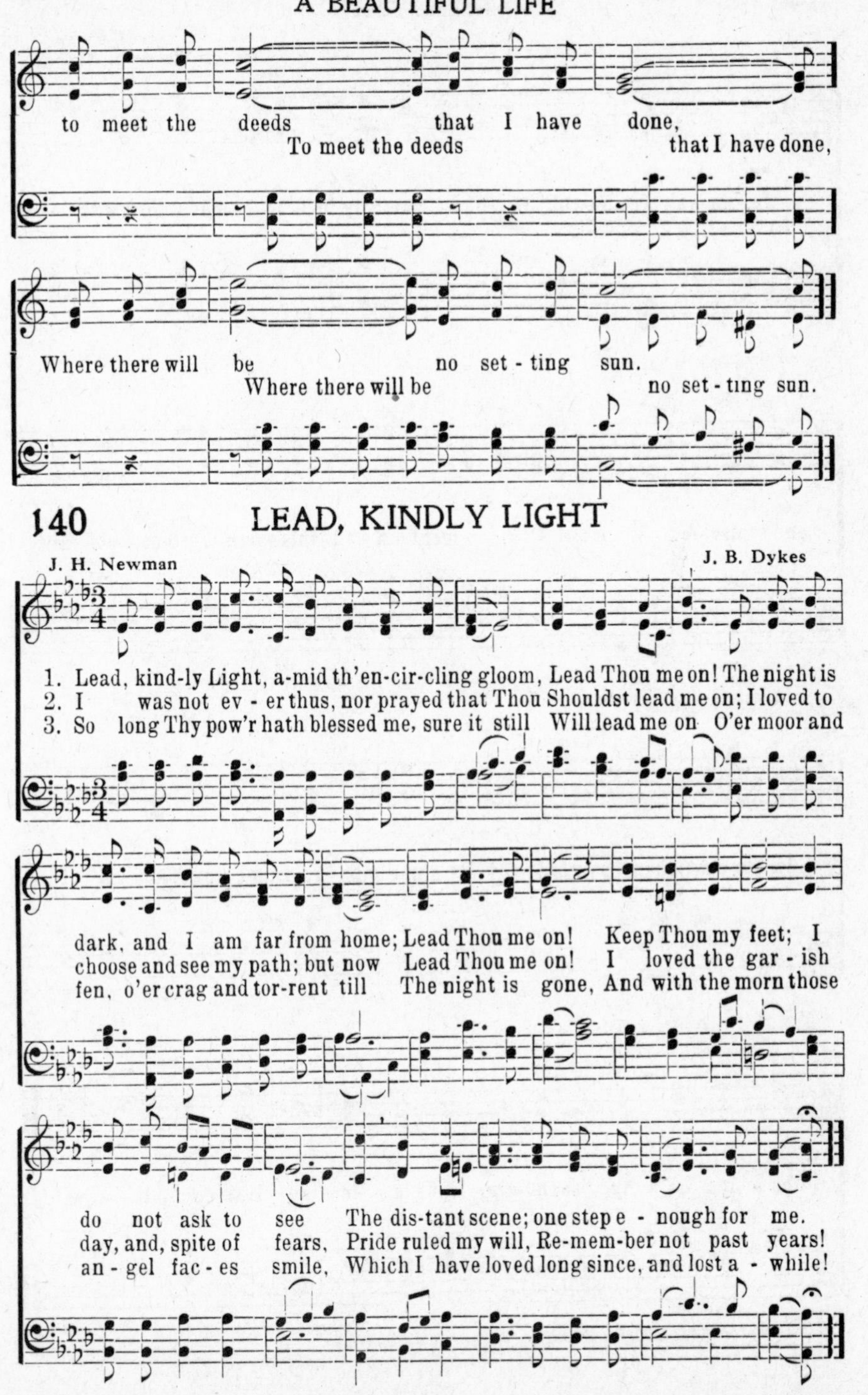
A BEAUTIFUL LIFE
to meet the deeds that I have done,
To meet the deeds that I have done,
Where there will be no set - ting sun.
Where there will be no set - ting sun.
140
LEAD, KINDLY LIGHT
J. H. Newman
J. B. Dykes
1. Lead, kind-ly Light, a-mid th'en-cir-cling gloom, Lead Thou me on! The night is
2. I was not ev - er thus, nor prayed that Thou Shouldst lead me on; I loved to
3. So long Thy pow'r hath blessed me, sure it still Will lead me on O'er moor and
dark, and I am far from home; Lead Thou me on! Keep Thou my feet; I
choose and see my path; but now Lead Thou me on! I loved the gar - ish
fen, o'er crag and tor-rent till The night is gone, And with the morn those
do not ask to see The dis-tant scene; one step e - nough for me.
day, and, spite of fears, Pride ruled my will, Re-mem-ber not past years!
an - gel fac - es smile, Which I have loved long since, and lost a - while!

141 JEHOVAH

M. Y. R.
Arr. by Walter E. Yoder

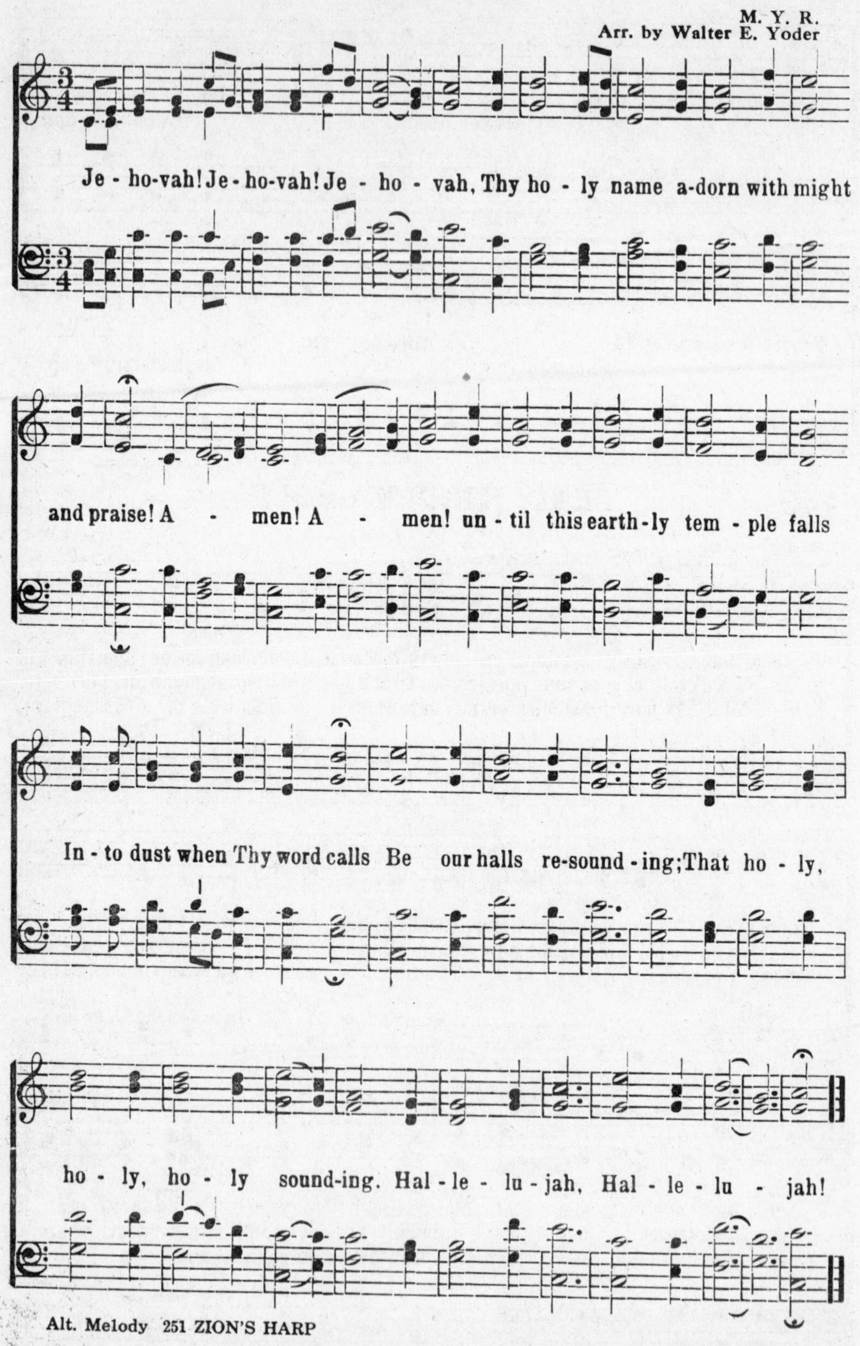
Je - ho-vah! Je - ho-vah! Je - ho - vah, Thy ho - ly name a-dorn with might
and praise! A - men! A - men! un - til this earth-ly tem - ple falls
In - to dust when Thy word calls Be our halls re-sound - ing; That ho - ly,
ho - ly, ho - ly sound-ing. Hal - le - lu - jah, Hal - le - lu - jah!

Alt. Melody 251 ZION'S HARP

142 TWILIGHT IS STEALING

Aldine S. Kieffer

B. C. Unseld

1. Twi - light is steal - ing O - ver the sea, Shad - ows are fall - ing
2. Voic - es of loved ones Songs of the past! Still lin - ger round me,
3. Come in the twi - light, Come, come to me! Bring - ing some mes - sage
Dark on the lea; Borne on the night winds, Voic - es of yore,
While life shall last; Lone - ly I wan - der, Sad - ly I roam,
O - ver the sea; Cheer - ing my path - way While here I roam,
Come from the far off shore.
Seek - ing that far off home.
Seek - ing that far off home.
CHORUS
Far a - way be-
yond the star - lit skies, Where the love - light nev - er, nev - er dies,
Gleam - eth a man - sion filled with de-light, Sweet hap - py home so bright.

143

BEFORE THE DAWN

M. Y. R.

1. All is o'er, the pain, the sor-row, Hu-man taunts and Sa-tan's spite; Death shall be de-spoiled to-mor-row Of the prey he grasps to-night. Yet once more His own to save Christ must sleep with-in the grave.
2. Fierce and dead-ly was the an-guish Of the bit-ter cross He bore. How did soul and bod-y lan-guish, Till the toil of life was o'er. But that toil, so fierce and dread, Bruised and crushed the ser-pent's head.
3. Close and still the tomb that holds Him, While in brief re-pose He lies. Deep the slum-ber that en-folds Him Veiled a while from mor-tal eyes. Slum-ber such as needs must be Af-ter hard won vic-to-ry.
4. Near this tomb with voice of sad-ness Chant the an-them soft and low; Lof-tier strains of joy and glad-ness From to-mor-row's hearts shall flow. Death and hell at length are slain, Christ hath tri-umphed, Christ doth reign.
Yet once more

144 REST FOR THE WEARY

S. Y. Harmer

Wm. McDonald

1. In the Chris-tian's home in glo - ry, There re-mains a land of rest;
2. He is fit - ting up my man-sion, Which e - ter - nal - ly shall stand,
3. Sing, Oh! sing, ye heirs of glo - ry! Shout your tri - umph as you go;
There my Sav-iour's gone be - fore me, To ful - fil my soul's re-quest,
For my stay shall not be tran-sient, In that ho - ly, hap - py land.
Zi - on's gate will o - pen for you, You shall find an en-trance through.
CHORUS
There is rest for the wea - ry, There is rest for the wea - ry,
On the oth-er side of Jor - dan, In the sweet fields of E - den,
There is rest for the wea - ry, There is rest for you.
Where the tree of life is bloom-ing, There is rest for you.

145 COME NOW SAITH THE LORD

W. W. D. James McGranahan

1. Come souls that are long - ing for pleas - ure, Our Sav - iour has pleas-ures to give; Come find in His love the rare treas - ure, That makes ev - 'ry true pleas - ure live.
2. The pleas - ures of sin are de - ceiv - ing, They've noth - ing for yes - ter-day's pain, But hope of to - mor - row re- ceiv - ing, And then, it's to - mor - row a - gain.
3. The pleas - ures of sin are all fleet - ing, They van - ish with life's pass - ing morn; Like dew-drops the morn - ing sun greet - ing, They glis - ten and then they are gone.
4. Then all who are long - ing for pleas - ure, Ye wea - ry, and all who are worn; Come find in the Lord a sure treas - ure, That from you shall nev - er be torn.
5. Of Je - sus, thy choice be now mak - ing, Re- deem - er, and Sav - iour, and Lord; And soon in the glo - ry a- wak - ing, You'll share in the Saint's blest re - ward.
CHORUS
Come now saith the Lord, let us rea-son, Come now and your pur-pose de - clare;
It is pleas-ures of sin for a sea-son, Or pleas-ures the glo - ri-fied share?

146 GO BURY THY SORROW

Mary A. Bachelor
P. P. Bliss
1. Go bur - y thy sor - row, The world hath its share;
2. Go tell it to Je - sus, He know - eth thy grief;
3. Hearts grow-ing a - wea - ry With heav - i - er woe
Go bur - y it deep - ly, Go hide it with care,
Go tell it to Je - sus, He'll send thee re - lief,
Now droop 'mid the dark - ness Go com - fort them, go!
Go think of it calm - ly, When cur - tained by night,
Go gath - er the sun - shine He sheds on the way;
Go bur - y thy sor - rows, Let oth - ers be blest;
rit.
Go tell it to Je - sus, And all will be right.
He'll light - en thy bur - den, Go, wea - ry one, pray.
Go give them the sun - shine; Tell Je - sus the rest.

147 'TIS SO SWEET TO TRUST IN JESUS

LOUISA M. R. STEAD — WM. J. KIRKPATRICK

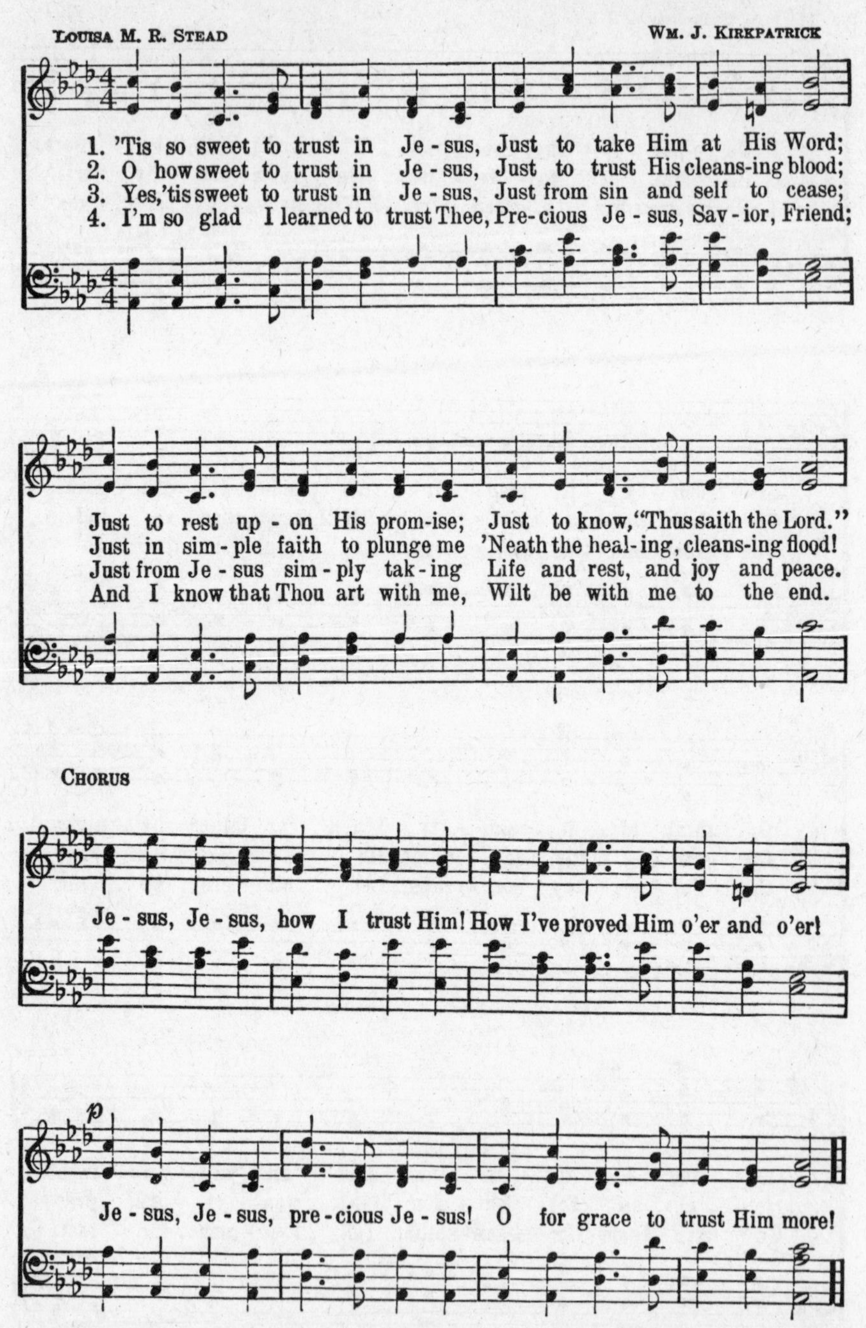

HEAR THOU MY PRAYER

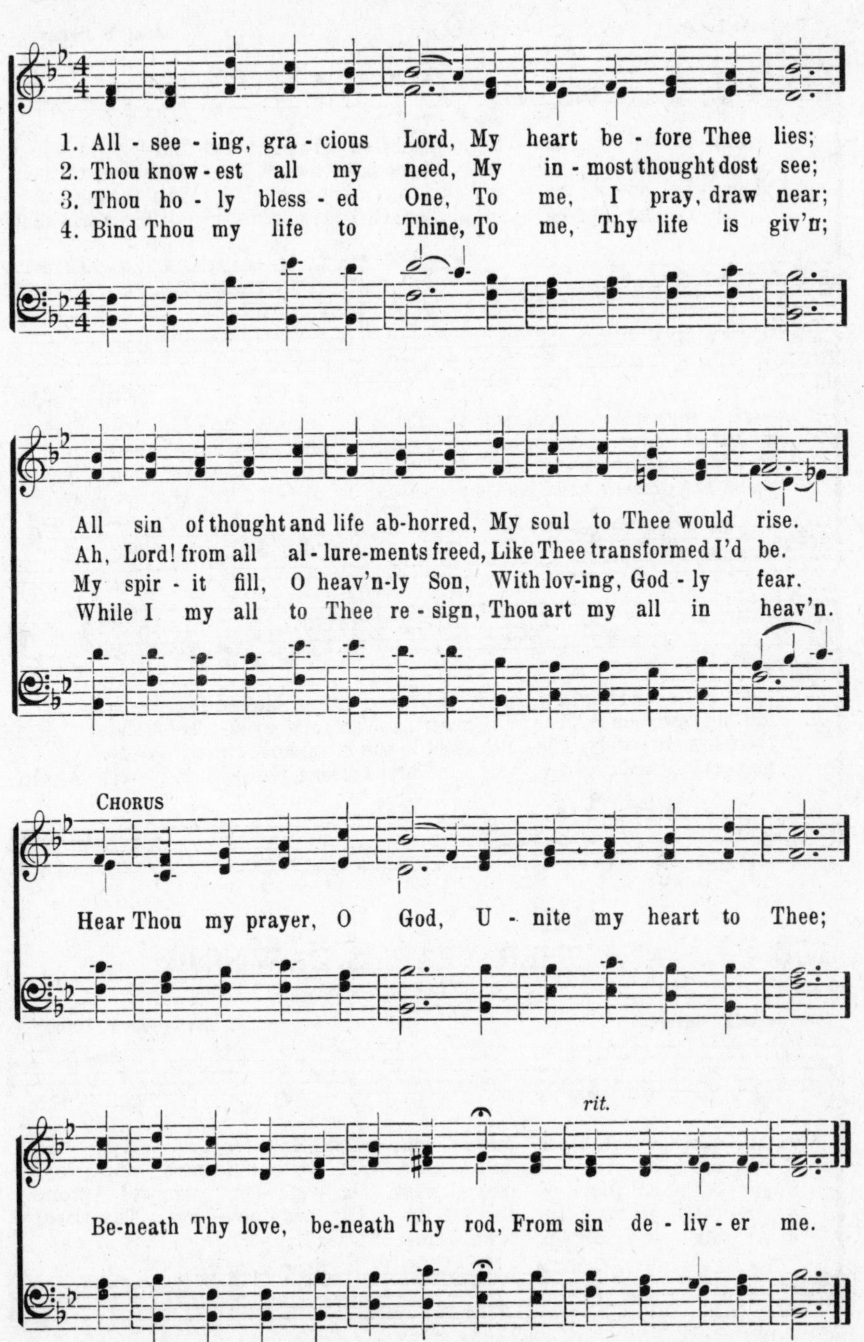
1. All - see - ing, gra - cious Lord, My heart be - fore Thee lies;
2. Thou know - est all my need, My in - most thought dost see;
3. Thou ho - ly bless - ed One, To me, I pray, draw near;
4. Bind Thou my life to Thine, To me, Thy life is giv'n;
All sin of thought and life ab-horred, My soul to Thee would rise.
Ah, Lord! from all al - lure-ments freed, Like Thee transformed I'd be.
My spir - it fill, O heav'n-ly Son, With lov-ing, God - ly fear.
While I my all to Thee re - sign, Thou art my all in heav'n.
CHORUS
Hear Thou my prayer, O God, U - nite my heart to Thee;
rit.
Be-neath Thy love, be-neath Thy rod, From sin de - liv - er me.

149 HOLY, HOLY, HOLY, LORD GOD ALMIGHTY

NICÆA 11. 12. 12. 10

Reginald Heber — **John B. Dykes**

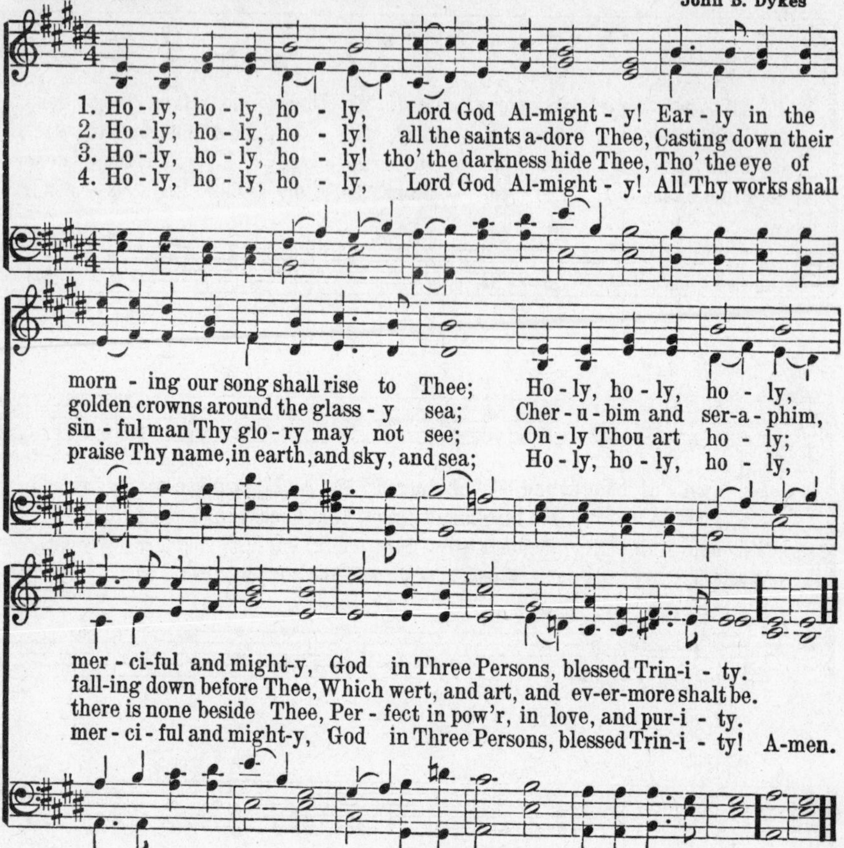

1. Ho-ly, ho-ly, ho-ly, Lord God Al-might-y! Ear-ly in the morn-ing our song shall rise to Thee; Ho-ly, ho-ly, ho-ly, mer-ci-ful and might-y, God in Three Persons, blessed Trin-i-ty.
2. Ho-ly, ho-ly, ho-ly! all the saints a-dore Thee, Casting down their golden crowns around the glass-y sea; Cher-u-bim and ser-a-phim, fall-ing down before Thee, Which wert, and art, and ev-er-more shalt be.
3. Ho-ly, ho-ly, ho-ly! tho' the darkness hide Thee, Tho' the eye of sin-ful man Thy glo-ry may not see; On-ly Thou art ho-ly; there is none beside Thee, Per-fect in pow'r, in love, and pur-i-ty.
4. Ho-ly, ho-ly, ho-ly, Lord God Al-might-y! All Thy works shall praise Thy name, in earth, and sky, and sea; Ho-ly, ho-ly, ho-ly, mer-ci-ful and might-y, God in Three Persons, blessed Trin-i-ty! A-men.

150 ANOTHER YEAR IS DAWNING

CARMINA 7. 6. 7. 6.

Frances R. Havergal — **Arr. from F. Flotow**

1. An-oth-er year is dawn-ing, Dear Mas-ter, let it be,
2. An-oth-er year of mer-cies, Of faith-ful-ness and grace.
3. An-oth-er year of pro-gress, An-oth-er year of praise,
4. An-oth-er year of serv-ice, Of wit-ness for Thy love;
5. An-oth-er year is dawn-ing, Dear Mas-ter, let it be,

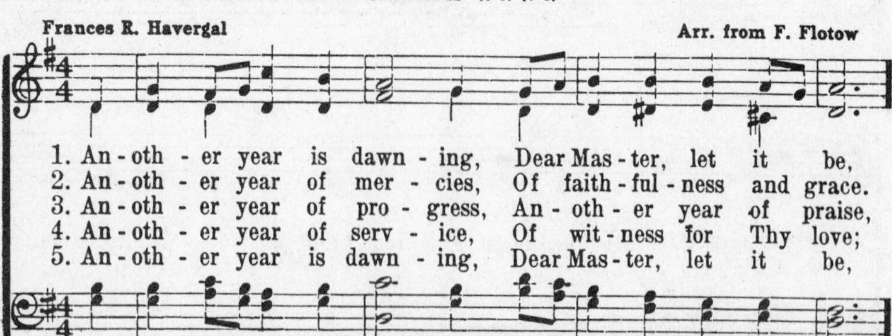

ANOTHER YEAR IS DAWNING

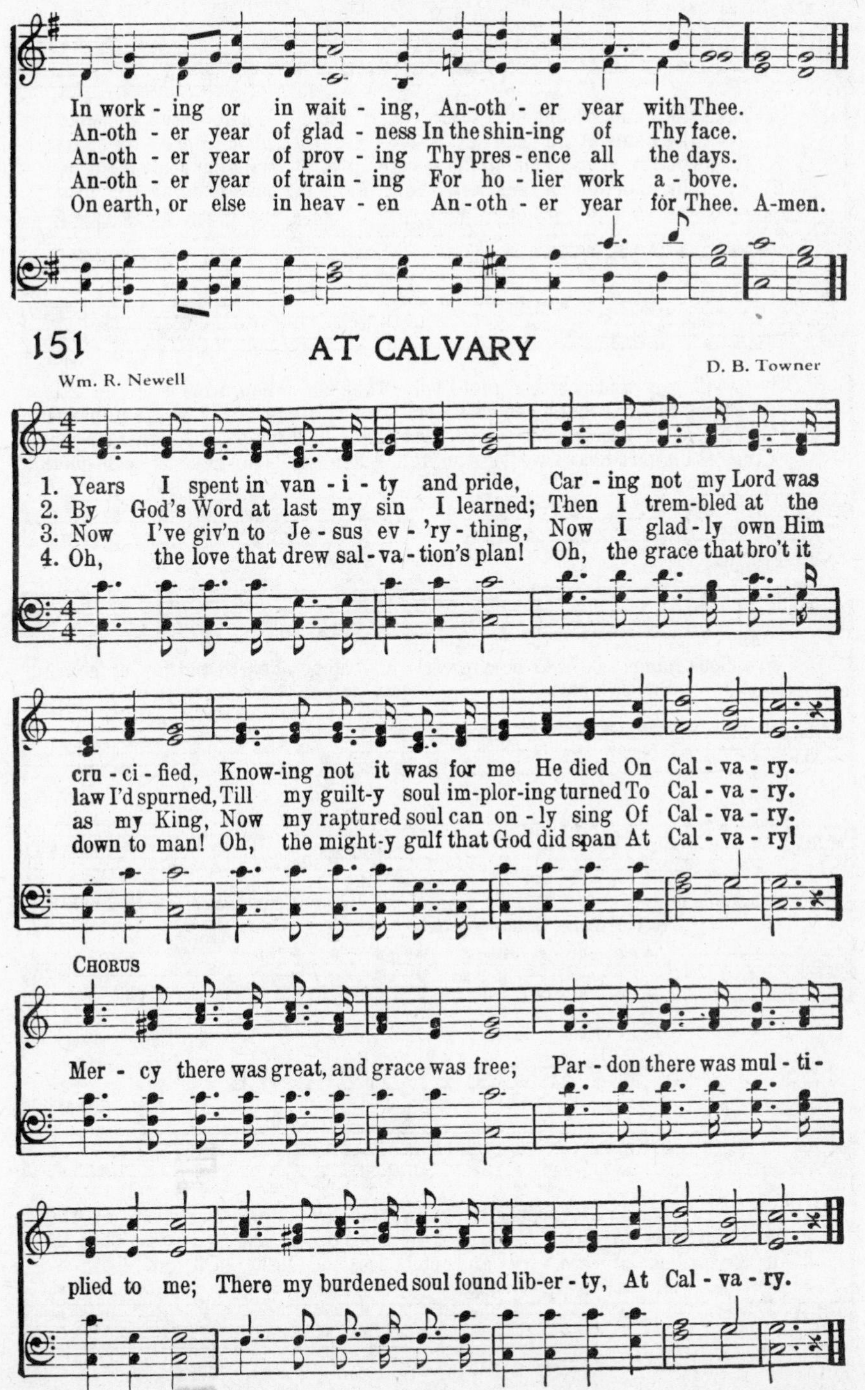

In work - ing or in wait - ing, An-oth - er year with Thee.
An-oth - er year of glad - ness In the shin-ing of Thy face.
An-oth - er year of prov - ing Thy pres - ence all the days.
An-oth - er year of train - ing For ho - lier work a - bove.
On earth, or else in heav - en An - oth - er year for Thee. A-men.
151
AT CALVARY
Wm. R. Newell
D. B. Towner
1. Years I spent in van - i - ty and pride, Car - ing not my Lord was cru - ci - fied, Know-ing not it was for me He died On Cal - va - ry.
2. By God's Word at last my sin I learned; Then I trem-bled at the law I'd spurned, Till my guilt-y soul im-plor-ing turned To Cal - va - ry.
3. Now I've giv'n to Je - sus ev - 'ry - thing, Now I glad - ly own Him as my King, Now my raptured soul can on - ly sing Of Cal - va - ry.
4. Oh, the love that drew sal - va - tion's plan! Oh, the grace that bro't it down to man! Oh, the might-y gulf that God did span At Cal - va - ry!
Chorus
Mer - cy there was great, and grace was free; Par - don there was mul - ti - plied to me; There my burdened soul found lib-er - ty, At Cal - va - ry.

152 TAKE THE NAME OF JESUS WITH YOU
Mrs. Lydia Baxter
W. H. Doane
1. Take the name of Je - sus with you, Child of sor-row and of woe;
2. Take the name of Je - sus ev - er, As a shield from ev-'ry snare;
3. O the pre-cious name of Je - sus! How it thrills our souls with joy,
4. At the name of Je-sus bow - ing, Fall - ing pros-trate at His feet,
It will joy and com-fort give you, Take it, then, wher-e'er you go.
If temp-ta-tions round you gath - er, Breathe that ho - ly name in prayer.
When His lov-ing arms re-ceive us, And His songs our tongues em-ploy!
King of kings in heav'n we'll crown Him, When our jour-ney is com-plete.
CHORUS
Pre-cious name, O how sweet! Hope of earth and joy of heav'n;
Pre-cious name, O how sweet!
Pre-cious name, O how sweet! Hope of earth and joy of heav'n.
Precious name, O how sweet, how sweet!
153 MY JESUS, I LOVE THEE
Anonymous
A. J. Gordon
1. My Je - sus, I love Thee, I know Thou art mine, For Thee all the
2. I'll love Thee in life, I will love Thee in death, And praise Thee as
3. In mansions of glo - ry and end - less de - light, I'll ev - er a -

MY JESUS, I LOVE THEE

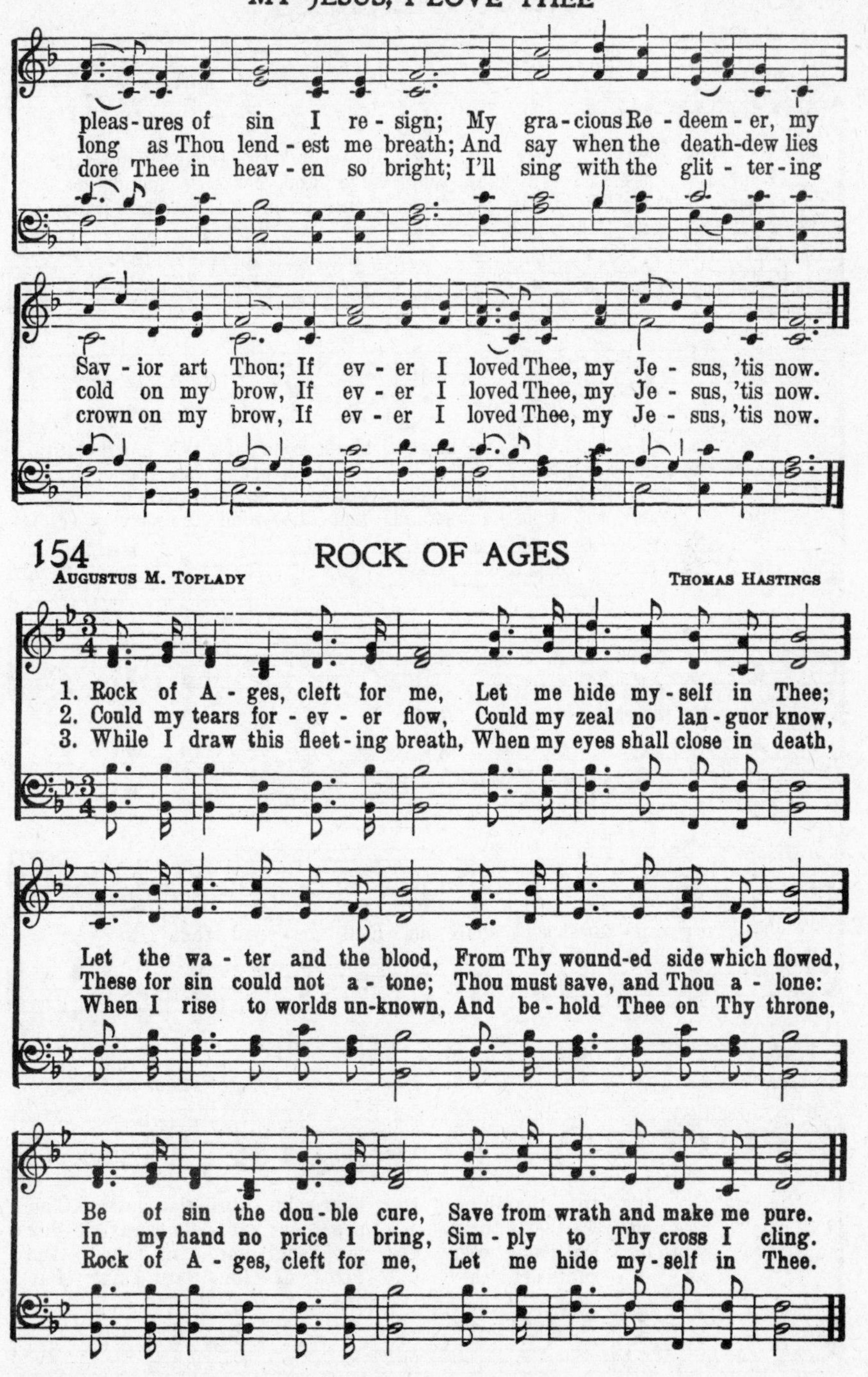

155 NEAR THE CROSS
Fanny J. Crosby
William H. Doane
1. Je - sus, keep me near the cross, There a pre - cious foun - tain
2. Near the cross, a trem-bling soul, Love and mer - cy found me;
3. Near the cross! O Lamb of God, Bring its scenes be - fore me;
4. Near the cross I'll watch and wait, Hop - ing, trust - ing ev - er,
Free to all— a heal - ing stream, Flows from Cal-v'ry's moun - tain.
There the Bright and Morn - ing Star Sheds its beams a - round me.
Help me walk from day to day, With its shad - ows o'er me.
Till I reach the gold - en strand, Just be - yond the riv - er.
CHORUS
In the cross, in the cross, Be my glo - ry ev - er;
Till my rap - tured soul shall find Rest be - yond the riv - er.
156 BLEST BE THE TIE
John Fawcett
Hans G. Naegeli
1. Blest be the tie that binds Our hearts in Chris-tian love; The
2. Be - fore our Fa-ther's throne, We pour our ar - dent prayers; Our
3. We share our mu - tual woes, Our mu - tual bur - dens bear; And
4. When we a - sun - der part, It gives us in - ward pain; But

BLEST BE THE TIE

158 GUIDE ME, O THOU GREAT JEHOVAH

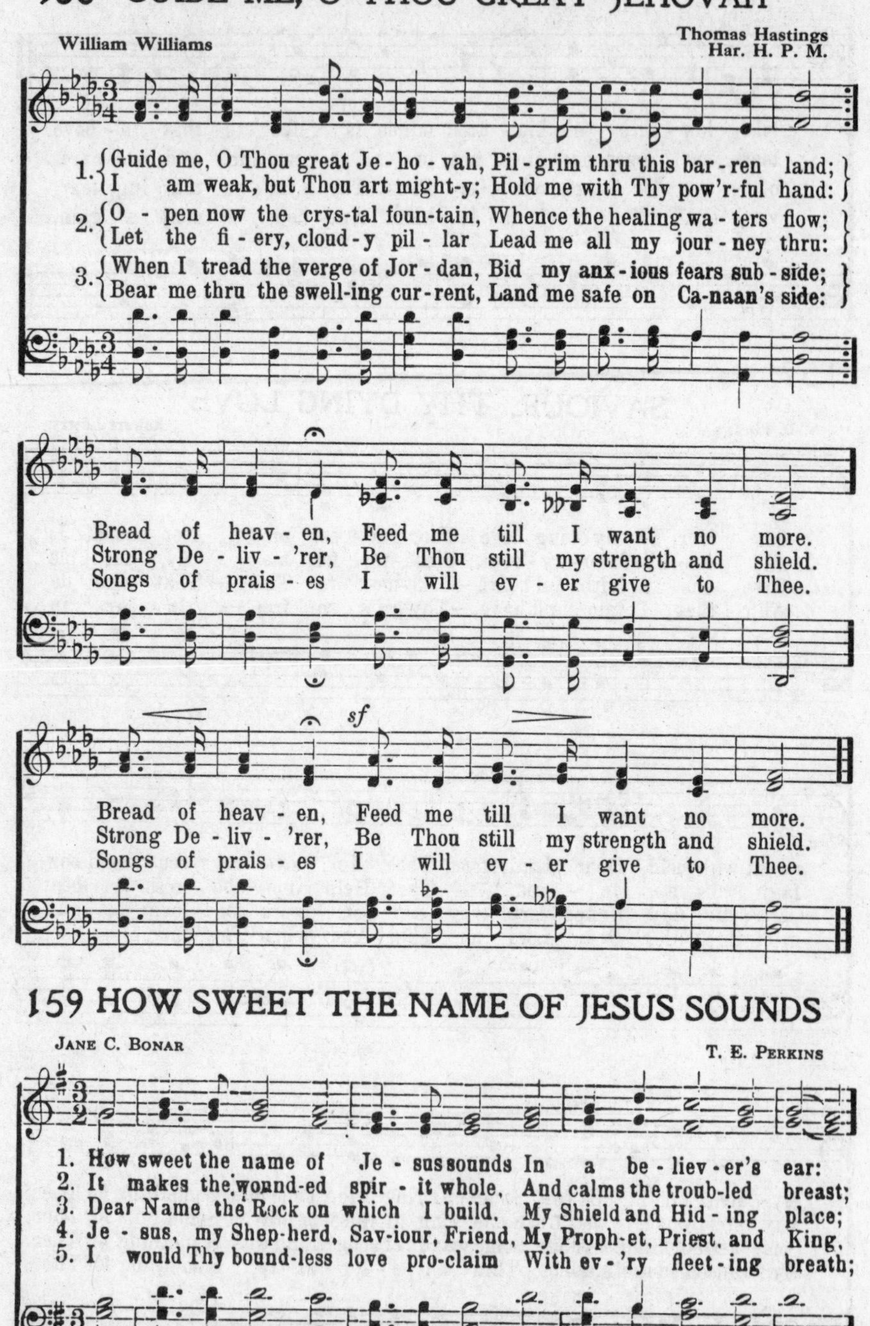

HOW SWEET THE NAME OF JESUS SOUNDS
It soothes his sor - rows, heals his wounds, And drives a - way his fear.
'Tis man - na to the hun - gry soul, And to the wea - ry, rest.
My nev - er fail - ing treas - ury, filled, With boundless stores of grace.
My Lord, my Life, my Way, my End, Ac - cept the praise I bring.
So shall the mu - sic of Thy name Re - fresh my soul in death.
160
THE SWEET STORY OF OLD
Mrs. Jemima Luke
J. C. Englebrecht
1. I think when I read that sweet sto - ry of old When Je - sus was here
2. I wish that His hands had been placed on my head, That His arm had been thrown
3. Yet still to His foot - stool in prayer I may go, And ask for a share
4. In that beau - ti - ful place He is gone to pre - pare, For all that are washed
a - mong men, How He called lit - tle chil - dren as lambs to His fold, I should
a - round me; And that I might have seen His kind look when He said, "Let the
in His love; And if I now ear - nest - ly seek Him be - low, I shall
and for - given; And man - y dear chil - dren are gath - er - ing there, For "Of
Fine
Refrain
D. S.
like to have been with them then. I should like to have been with them then;
lit - tle ones come un - to Me." "Let the lit - tle ones come un - to Me;"
see Him and hear Him a - bove. I shall see Him and hear Him a - bove;
such is the king - dom of heaven." For "Of such is the king - dom of heaven;"

161 WHAT A FRIEND

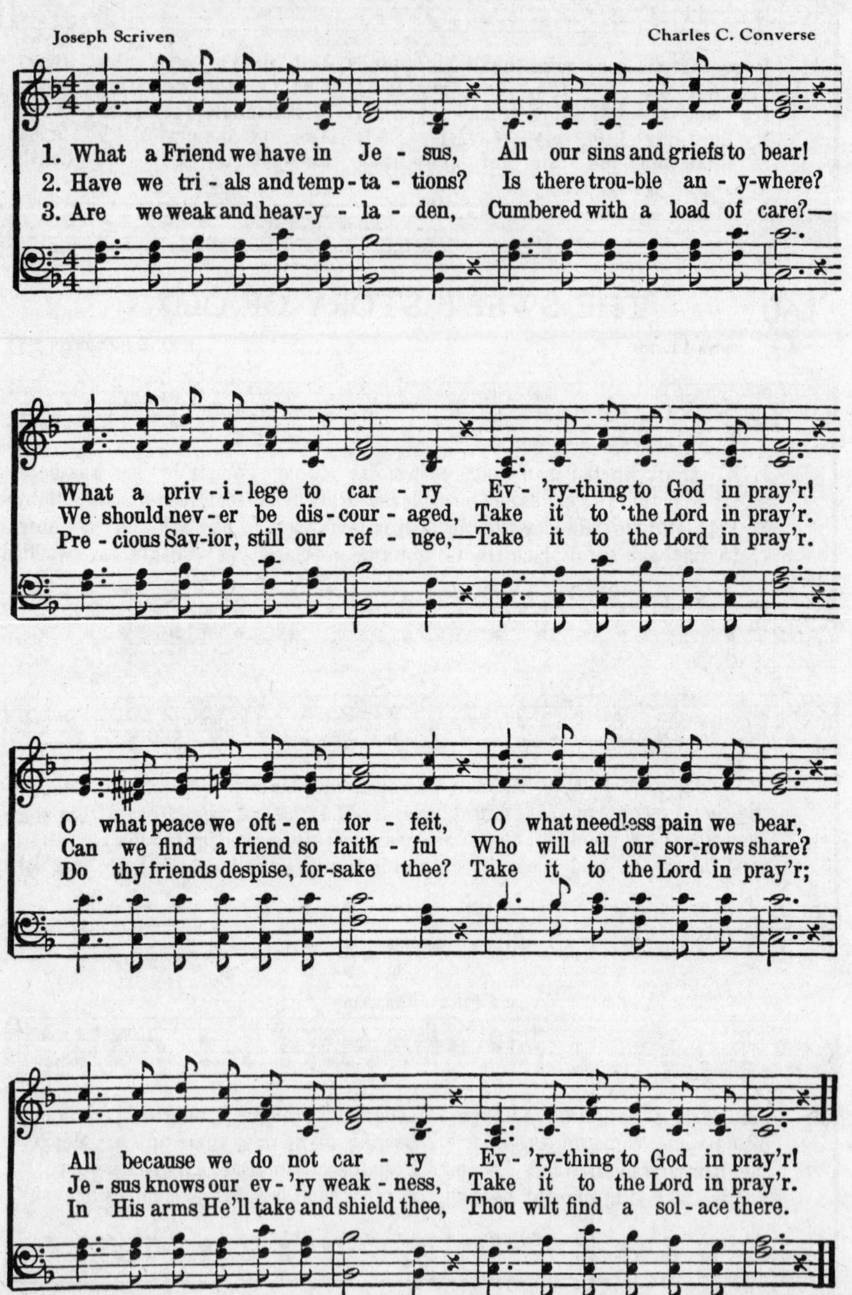
Joseph Scriven
Charles C. Converse
1. What a Friend we have in Je - sus, All our sins and griefs to bear!
2. Have we tri - als and temp - ta - tions? Is there trou-ble an - y-where?
3. Are we weak and heav-y - la - den, Cumbered with a load of care?—
What a priv - i - lege to car - ry Ev - 'ry-thing to God in pray'r!
We should nev - er be dis - cour - aged, Take it to the Lord in pray'r.
Pre - cious Sav-ior, still our ref - uge,—Take it to the Lord in pray'r.
O what peace we oft - en for - feit, O what needless pain we bear,
Can we find a friend so faith - ful Who will all our sor-rows share?
Do thy friends despise, for-sake thee? Take it to the Lord in pray'r;
All because we do not car - ry Ev - 'ry-thing to God in pray'r!
Je - sus knows our ev - 'ry weak - ness, Take it to the Lord in pray'r.
In His arms He'll take and shield thee, Thou wilt find a sol - ace there.

162 HE LEADETH ME

Joseph H. Gilmore — William B. Bradbury

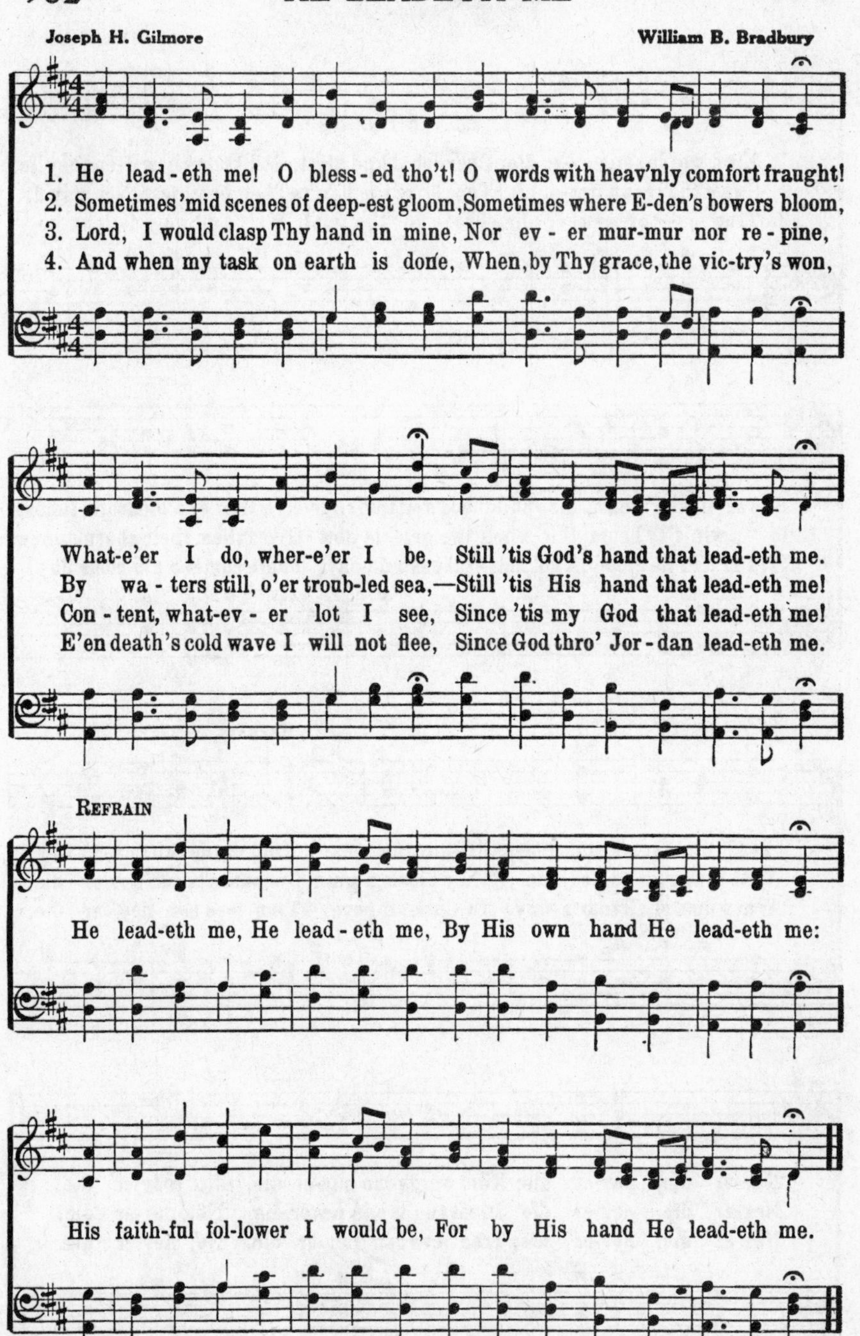
1. He lead-eth me! O bless-ed tho't! O words with heav'nly comfort fraught!
2. Sometimes 'mid scenes of deep-est gloom, Sometimes where E-den's bowers bloom,
3. Lord, I would clasp Thy hand in mine, Nor ev - er mur-mur nor re - pine,
4. And when my task on earth is done, When, by Thy grace, the vic-try's won,
What-e'er I do, wher-e'er I be, Still 'tis God's hand that lead-eth me.
By wa - ters still, o'er troub-led sea,—Still 'tis His hand that lead-eth me!
Con - tent, what-ev - er lot I see, Since 'tis my God that lead-eth me!
E'en death's cold wave I will not flee, Since God thro' Jor-dan lead-eth me.
Refrain
He lead-eth me, He lead - eth me, By His own hand He lead-eth me:
His faith-ful fol-lower I would be, For by His hand He lead-eth me.

163 KIND WORDS

Abby Hutchinson

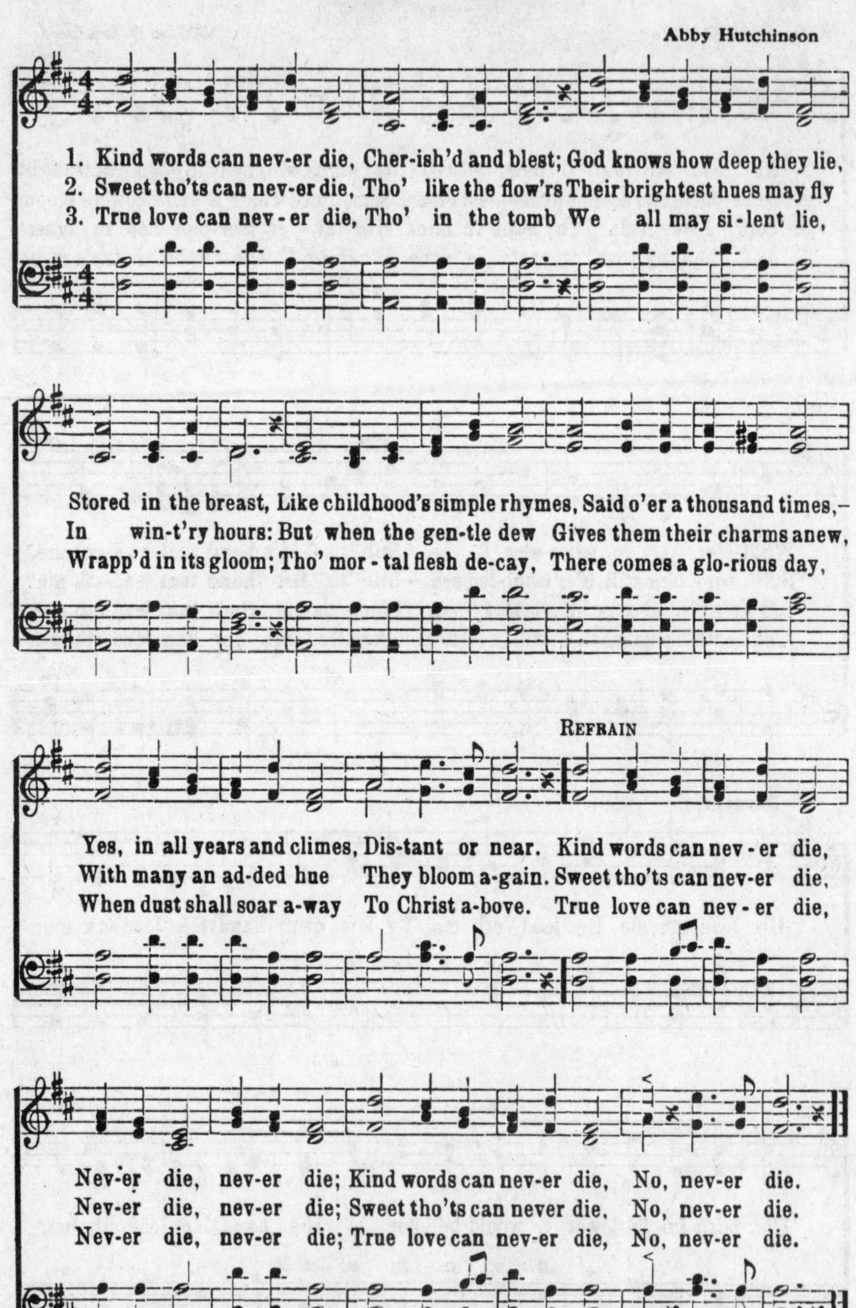
1. Kind words can nev-er die, Cher-ish'd and blest; God knows how deep they lie,
2. Sweet tho'ts can nev-er die, Tho' like the flow'rs Their brightest hues may fly
3. True love can nev - er die, Tho' in the tomb We all may si-lent lie,
Stored in the breast, Like childhood's simple rhymes, Said o'er a thousand times,–
In win-t'ry hours: But when the gen-tle dew Gives them their charms anew,
Wrapp'd in its gloom; Tho' mor - tal flesh de-cay, There comes a glo-rious day,
Refrain
Yes, in all years and climes, Dis-tant or near. Kind words can nev - er die,
With many an ad-ded hue They bloom a-gain. Sweet tho'ts can nev-er die,
When dust shall soar a-way To Christ a-bove. True love can nev - er die,
Nev-er die, nev-er die; Kind words can nev-er die, No, nev-er die.
Nev-er die, nev-er die; Sweet tho'ts can never die, No, nev-er die.
Nev-er die, nev-er die; True love can nev-er die, No, nev-er die.

164 ARISE, MY SOUL

CHARLES WESLEY | LENOX 6. 6. 6. 6. 8. 8 | LEWIS EDSON

1. A - rise, my soul, a - rise; Shake off thy guilt - y fears;
2. He ev - er lives a - bove, For me to in - ter - cede;
3. Five bleed - ing wounds He bears, Re - ceived on Cal - va - ry;
4. The Fa - ther hears Him pray, His dear a - noint - ed One;
5. My God is rec - on - ciled; His par - d'ning voice I hear;
The bleed - ing Sac - ri - fice In my be - half ap - pears:
His all - re - deem - ing love, His pre - cious blood, to plead;
They pour ef - fec - tual prayers, They strong - ly plead for me:
He can - not turn a - way The pres - ence of His Son;
He owns me for His child, I can no lon - ger fear:
Be - fore the throne my Sure - ty stands, Be - fore the throne my
His blood a - toned for all our race, His blood a - toned for
"For - give Him, O for - give," they cry, "For - give Him, O for -
His Spir - it an - swers to the blood, His Spir - it an - swers
With con - fi - dence I now draw nigh, With con - fi - dence I
Sure - ty stands, My name is writ - ten on His hands.
all our race, And sprin - kles now the throne of grace.
give," they cry, "Nor let that ran - somed sin - ner die!"
to the blood, And tells me I am born of God.
now draw nigh, And, "Fa - ther, Ab - ba, Fa - ther," cry. A - MEN.

165 SOME TIME WE'LL UNDERSTAND

MAXWELL N. CORNELIUS | JAMES MCGRANAHAN

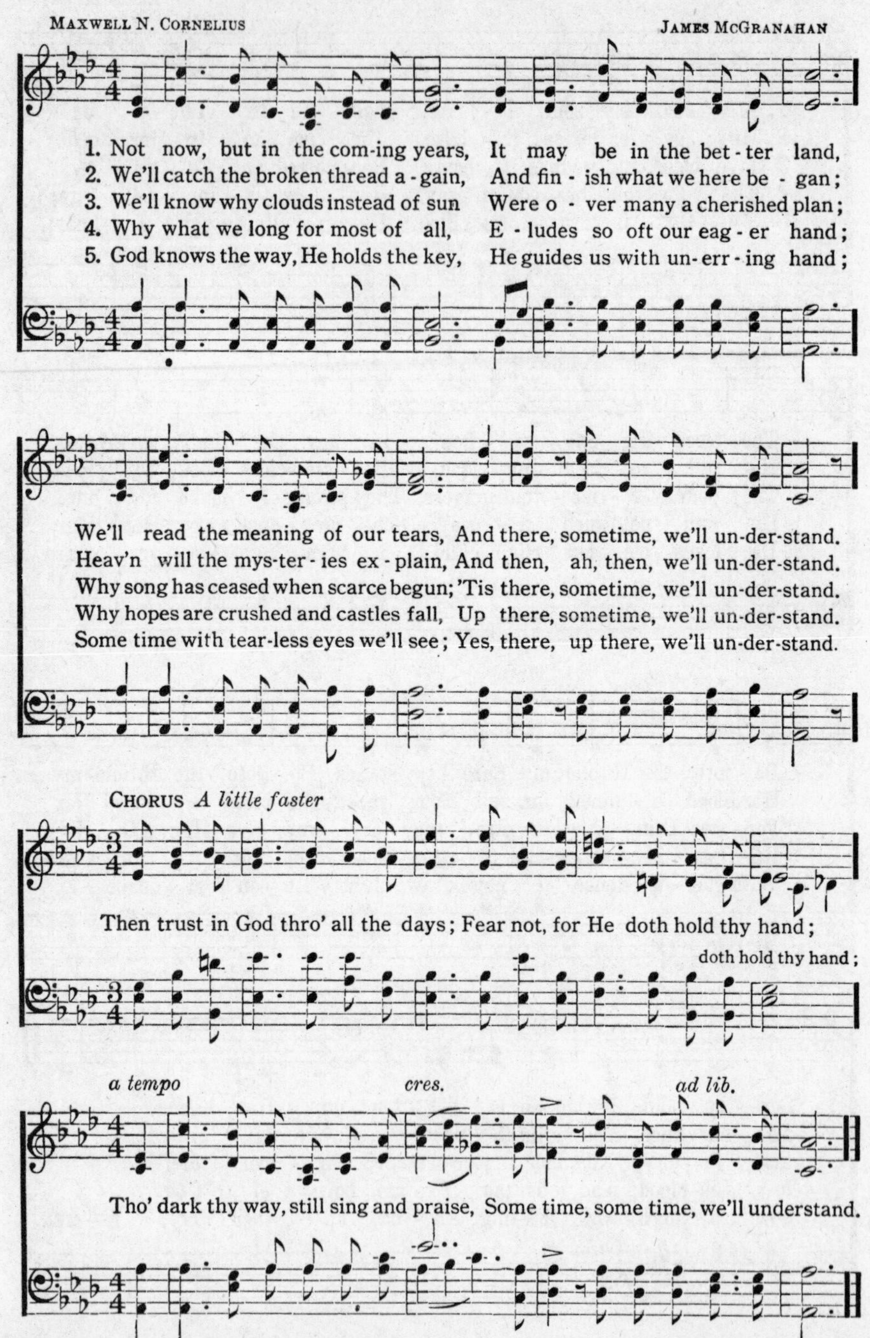
1. Not now, but in the com-ing years, It may be in the bet-ter land,
2. We'll catch the broken thread a-gain, And fin-ish what we here be-gan;
3. We'll know why clouds instead of sun Were o-ver many a cherished plan;
4. Why what we long for most of all, E-ludes so oft our eag-er hand;
5. God knows the way, He holds the key, He guides us with un-err-ing hand;
We'll read the meaning of our tears, And there, sometime, we'll un-der-stand.
Heav'n will the mys-ter-ies ex-plain, And then, ah, then, we'll un-der-stand.
Why song has ceased when scarce begun; 'Tis there, sometime, we'll un-der-stand.
Why hopes are crushed and castles fall, Up there, sometime, we'll un-der-stand.
Some time with tear-less eyes we'll see; Yes, there, up there, we'll un-der-stand.
CHORUS A little faster
Then trust in God thro' all the days; Fear not, for He doth hold thy hand;
doth hold thy hand;
a tempo
cres.
ad lib.
Tho' dark thy way, still sing and praise, Some time, some time, we'll understand.

166 YIELD NOT TO TEMPTATION

H. R. P. Dr. H. R. Palmer

1. Yield not to temp-ta-tion, For yield-ing is sin; Each vic-t'ry will
2. Shun e-vil com-pan-ions, Bad lan-guage dis-dain; God's name hold in
3. To him that o'er-com-eth, God giv-eth a crown; Thro' faith we will
help you Some oth-er to win; Fight man-ful-ly on-ward,
rev-'rence, Nor take it in vain; Be thought-ful and ear-nest,
con-quer, Tho' oft-en cast down; He who is our Sav-ior,
Dark pas-sions sub-due; Look ev-er to Je-sus, He'll car-ry you through.
Kind-heart-ed and true; Look ev-er to Je-sus, He'll car-ry you through.
Our strength will re-new; Look ev-er to Je-sus, He'll car-ry you through.
CHORUS
Ask the Sav-ior to help you, Com-fort, strength-en, and keep you;
He is will-ing to aid you, He will car-ry you through.

167 THE WAY OF THE CROSS LEADS HOME

JESSIE BROWN POUNDS — CHAS. H. GABRIEL

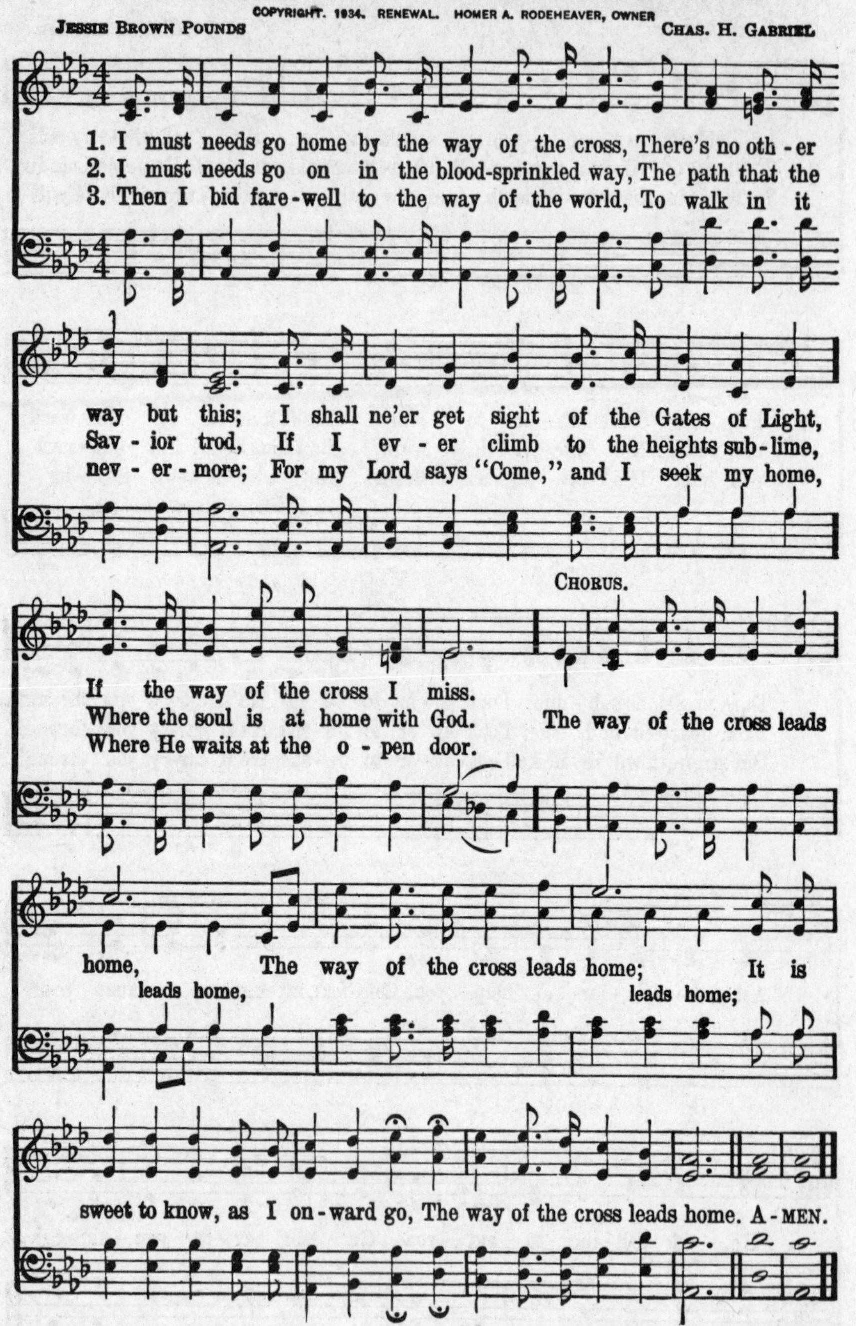
1. I must needs go home by the way of the cross, There's no oth - er way but this; I shall ne'er get sight of the Gates of Light, If the way of the cross I miss.
2. I must needs go on in the blood-sprinkled way, The path that the Sav - ior trod, If I ev - er climb to the heights sub-lime, Where the soul is at home with God.
3. Then I bid fare-well to the way of the world, To walk in it nev - er - more; For my Lord says "Come," and I seek my home, Where He waits at the o - pen door.
CHORUS.
The way of the cross leads home, leads home, The way of the cross leads home; leads home; It is sweet to know, as I on-ward go, The way of the cross leads home. A-MEN.

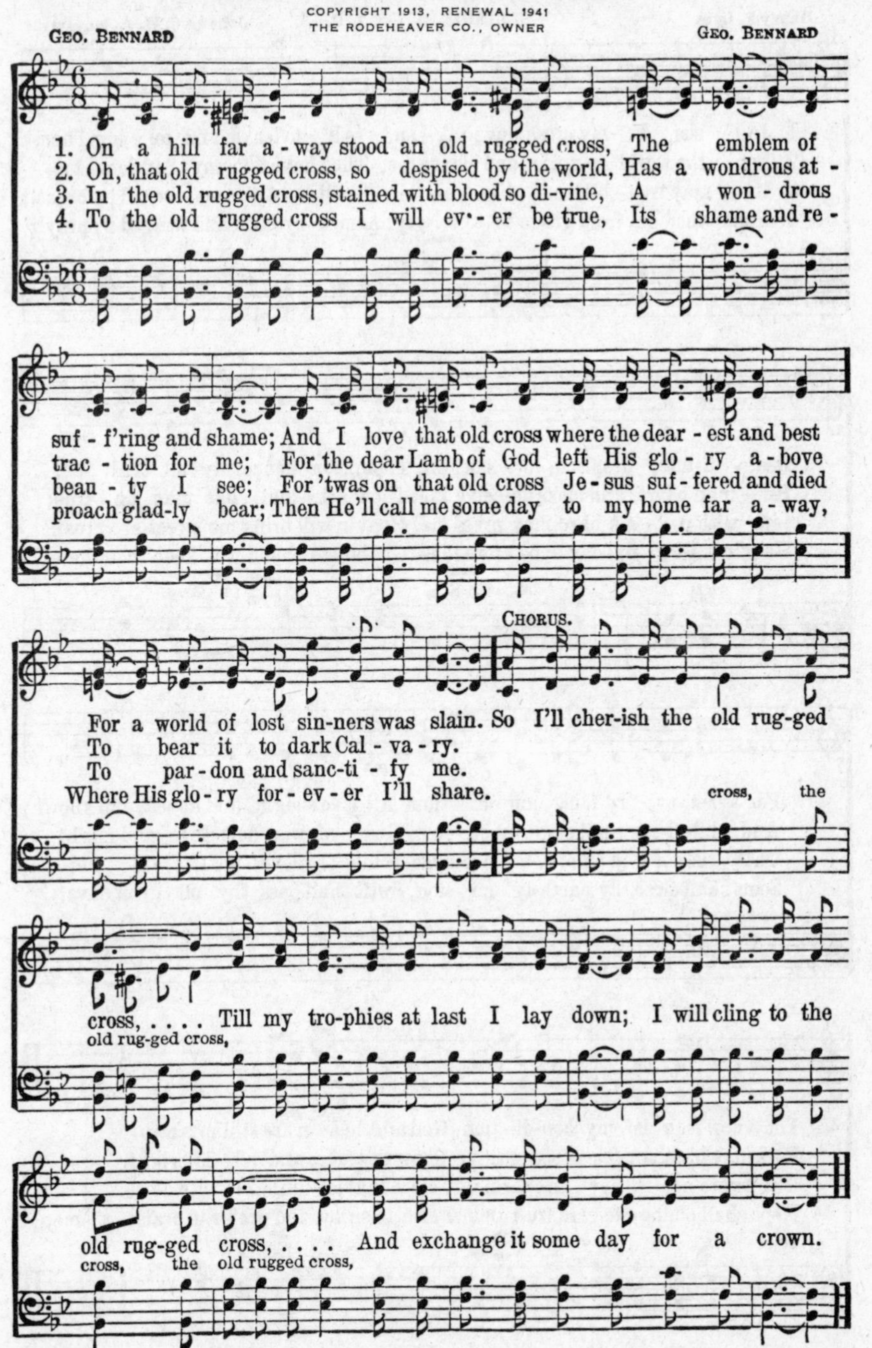
168 THE OLD RUGGED CROSS
COPYRIGHT 1913, RENEWAL 1941
THE RODEHEAVER CO., OWNER
GEO. BENNARD
GEO. BENNARD
1. On a hill far a-way stood an old rugged cross, The emblem of suf-f'ring and shame; And I love that old cross where the dear-est and best For a world of lost sin-ners was slain.
2. Oh, that old rugged cross, so despised by the world, Has a wondrous at-trac-tion for me; For the dear Lamb of God left His glo-ry a-bove To bear it to dark Cal-va-ry.
3. In the old rugged cross, stained with blood so di-vine, A won-drous beau-ty I see; For 'twas on that old cross Je-sus suf-fered and died To par-don and sanc-ti-fy me.
4. To the old rugged cross I will ev-er be true, Its shame and re-proach glad-ly bear; Then He'll call me some day to my home far a-way, Where His glo-ry for-ev-er I'll share.
CHORUS.
So I'll cher-ish the old rug-ged cross, . . . Till my tro-phies at last I lay down; I will cling to the old rug-ged cross, . . . And exchange it some day for a crown.
cross, the old rug-ged cross,
cross, the old rugged cross,

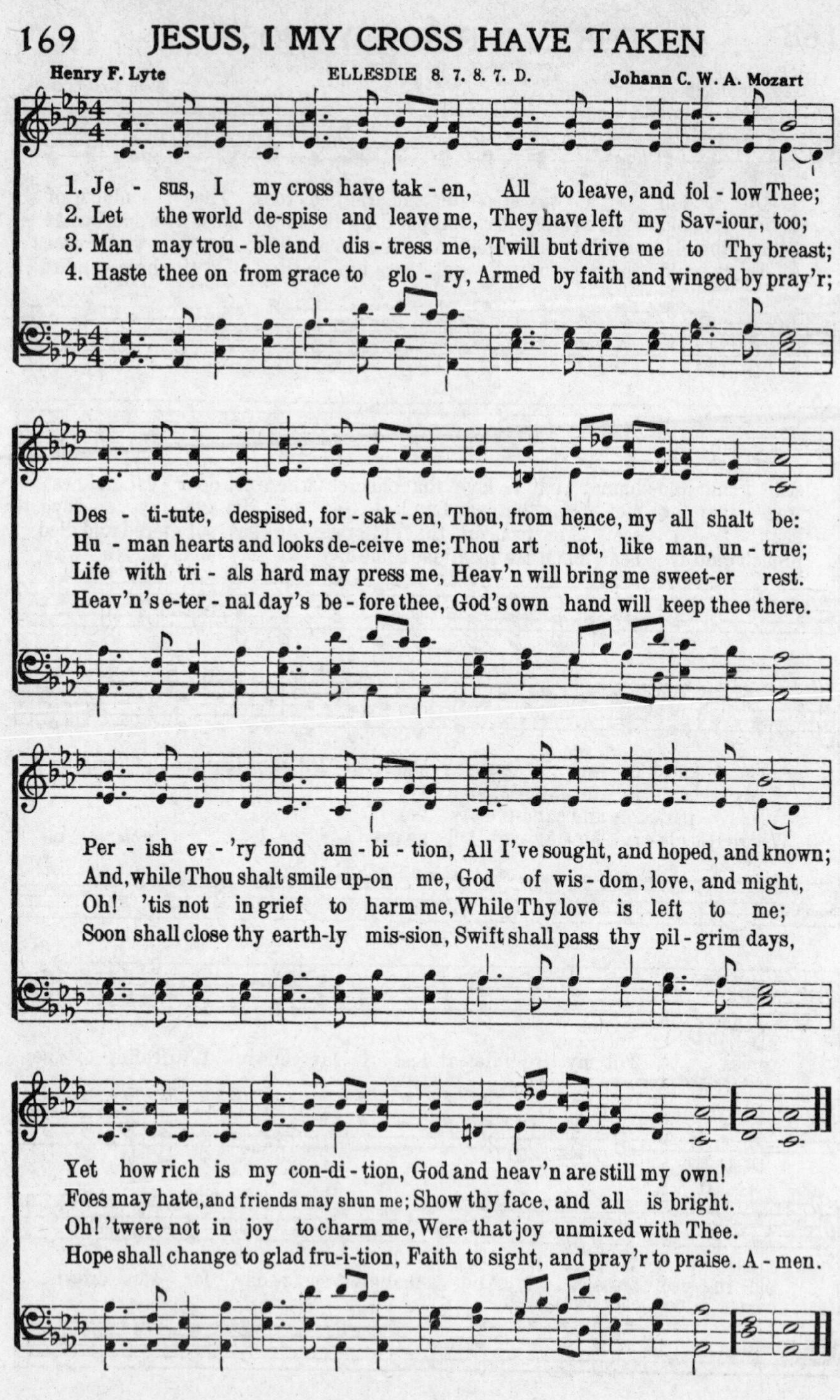
169 JESUS, I MY CROSS HAVE TAKEN
Henry F. Lyte
ELLESDIE 8. 7. 8. 7. D.
Johann C. W. A. Mozart
1. Je - sus, I my cross have tak - en, All to leave, and fol - low Thee;
2. Let the world de-spise and leave me, They have left my Sav-iour, too;
3. Man may trou - ble and dis - tress me, 'Twill but drive me to Thy breast;
4. Haste thee on from grace to glo - ry, Armed by faith and winged by pray'r;
Des - ti-tute, despised, for - sak - en, Thou, from hence, my all shalt be:
Hu - man hearts and looks de-ceive me; Thou art not, like man, un - true;
Life with tri - als hard may press me, Heav'n will bring me sweet-er rest.
Heav'n's e-ter - nal day's be - fore thee, God's own hand will keep thee there.
Per - ish ev - 'ry fond am - bi - tion, All I've sought, and hoped, and known;
And, while Thou shalt smile up-on me, God of wis - dom, love, and might,
Oh! 'tis not in grief to harm me, While Thy love is left to me;
Soon shall close thy earth-ly mis-sion, Swift shall pass thy pil - grim days,
Yet how rich is my con-di - tion, God and heav'n are still my own!
Foes may hate, and friends may shun me; Show thy face, and all is bright.
Oh! 'twere not in joy to charm me, Were that joy unmixed with Thee.
Hope shall change to glad fru-i-tion, Faith to sight, and pray'r to praise. A - men.

170 I AM THINE, O LORD

Fanny J. Crosby
W. H. Doane
1. I am Thine, O Lord, I have heard Thy voice, And it told Thy love to me; But I long to rise in the arms of faith, And be clos - er drawn to Thee.
2. Con - se - crate me now to Thy serv - ice, Lord, By the pow'r of grace di - vine; Let my soul look up with a stead-fast hope, And my will be lost in Thine.
3. O the pure de - light of a sin - gle hour That be- fore Thy throne I spend, When I kneel in prayer, and with Thee, my God, I com-mune as friend with friend!
4. There are depths of love that I can - not know Till I cross the nar - row sea; There are heights of joy that I may not reach Till I rest in peace with Thee.
REFRAIN
Draw me near - er,
near - er, near - er,
near-er, bless-ed Lord, To the cross where Thou hast died; Draw me
near-er, near - er, near - er, bless-ed Lord, To Thy precious, bleed-ing side.

171 OPEN THE WELLS OF SALVATION

E. A. Hoffman
Chas. Edw. Pollock
1. Lord, I am fond-ly, ear-nest-ly long-ing In-to Thy
2. Dead to the world would I be, O Fa-ther! Dead un-to
3. I would be Thine, and serve Thee for-ev-er, Filled with Thy
ho-ly like-ness to grow; Thirst-ing for more and deep-er com-
sin, a-live un-to Thee; Cru-ci-fy all the earth-ly with-
Spir-it, lost in Thy love; Come to my heart, Lord, come with a-
mun-ion, Yearn-ing Thy love more ful-ly to know.
in me, Emp-tied of sin and self may I be.
noint-ing, Show-ers of grace send down from a-bove.
Refrain
O-pen the
wells of grace and sal-va-tion, Pour the rich
O-pen the wells of grace and sal-va-tion,
streams deep in-to my heart; Cleanse and re-fine my
Pour the rich streams deep in-to my heart; Cleanse and re-fine my

OPEN THE WELLS OF SALVATION

tho't and af - fec - tion, Seal me and make me pure as Thou art.
tho't and af - fec - tion, Seal me and make me pure as Thou art.

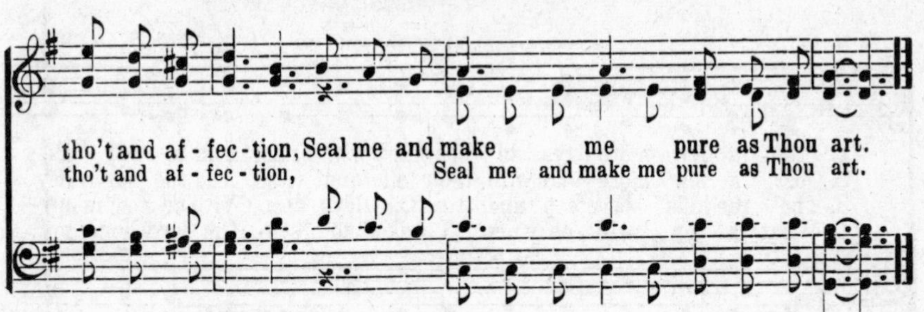

172 BEYOND THE SUNSET

Virgil P. Brock | Blanche Kerr Brock

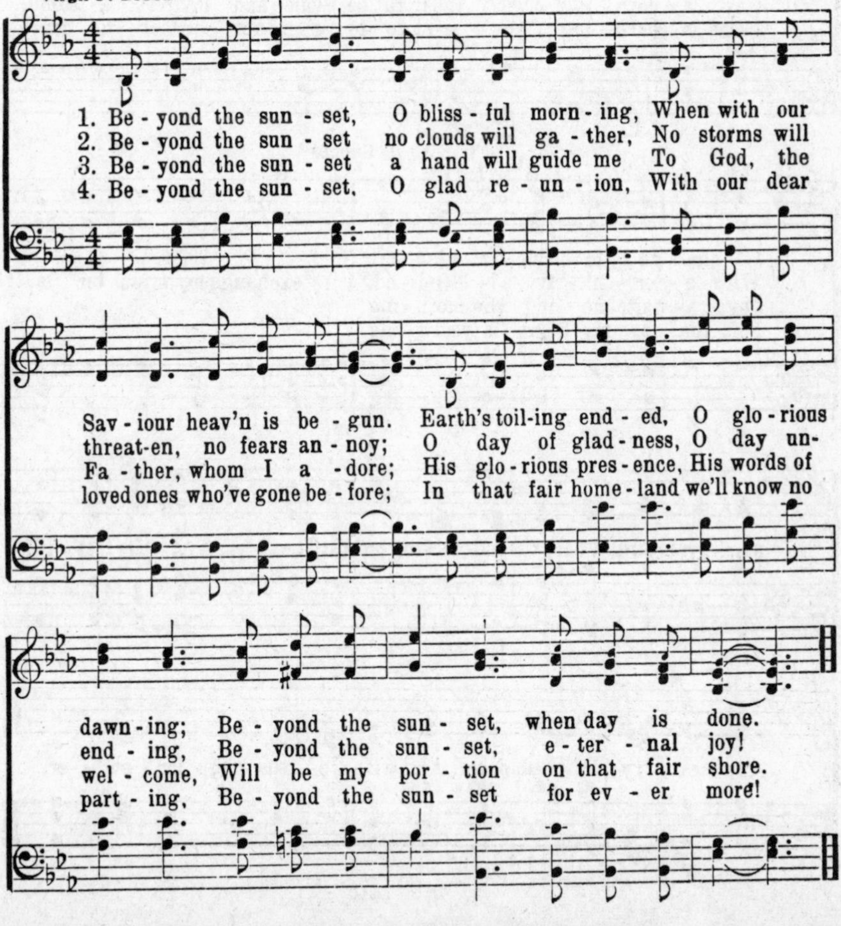

1. Be - yond the sun - set, O bliss - ful morn - ing, When with our
2. Be - yond the sun - set no clouds will ga - ther, No storms will
3. Be - yond the sun - set a hand will guide me To God, the
4. Be - yond the sun - set, O glad re - un - ion, With our dear
Sav - iour heav'n is be - gun. Earth's toil - ing end - ed, O glo - rious
threat - en, no fears an - noy; O day of glad - ness, O day un-
Fa - ther, whom I a - dore; His glo - rious pres - ence, His words of
loved ones who've gone be - fore; In that fair home - land we'll know no
dawn - ing; Be - yond the sun - set, when day is done.
end - ing, Be - yond the sun - set, e - ter - nal joy!
wel - come, Will be my por - tion on that fair shore.
part - ing, Be - yond the sun - set for ev - er more!

173 WHERE THE GATES SWING OUTWARD NEVER

C. H. G. CHAS. H. GABRIEL

1. Just a few more days to be filled with praise, And to tell the
2. Just a few more years with their toil and tears, And the jour - ney
3. Tho' the hills be steep and the val - leys deep, With no flow'rs my
4. What a joy 'twill be when I wake to see Him for whom my
old, old sto - ry; Then, when twi - light falls, and my Sav - ior calls,
will be end - ed; Then I'll be with Him, where the tide of time
way a - dorn - ing; Tho' the night be lone and my rest a stone,
heart is burn - ing! Nev - er-more to sigh, nev - er-more to die—
I shall go to Him in glo - ry.
With e - ter - ni - ty is blend - ed.
Joy a - waits me in the morn - ing.
For that day my heart is yearn - ing.
CHORUS
I'll exchange my cross for a
star - ry crown, Where the gates swing outward nev - er; At His feet I'll
lay ev - 'ry bur - den down, And with Je - sus reign for - ev - er.

174 MY SAVIOUR'S LOVE

C. H. G. Chas. H. Gabriel

1. I stand a-mazed in the pres-ence Of Je-sus the Naz-a-rene,
2. For me it was in the gar-den He pray'd; "Not My will, but Thine,"
3. In pit-y an-gels be-held Him, And came from the world of light
4. He took my sins and my sor-rows, He made them His ver-y own;
5. When with the ran-som'd in glo-ry His face I at last shall see,

And won-der how He could love me, A sin-ner condem'd, un-clean.
He had no tears for His own griefs, But sweat-drops of blood for mine.
To com-fort Him in the sor-rows He bore for my soul that night.
He bore the bur-den to Cal-v'ry, And suf-fer'd, and died a-lone.
'Twill be my joy thro' the a-ges To sing of His love for me.

CHORUS

How mar-vel-ous! how won-der-ful! And my song shall ev-er be:
Oh, how mar-vel-ous! oh, how won-der-ful!

How mar-vel-ous! how won-der-ful Is my Sav-iour's love for me!
Oh, how mar-vel-ous! oh, how won-der-ful

175 NEAR TO THE HEART OF GOD
COPYRIGHT, 1931, RENEWAL. THE LORENZ PUB. CO., OWNER
C. B. McAfee
1. There is a place of qui - et rest, Near to the heart of God,
2. There is a place of com - fort sweet, Near to the heart of God,
3. There is a place of full re - lease, Near to the heart of God,
A place where sin can - not mo - lest, Near to the heart of God.
A place where we our Sav - ior meet, Near to the heart of God.
A place where all is joy and peace, Near to the heart of God.
REFRAIN
O Je - sus, blest Re - deem - er, Sent from the heart of God,
Hold us, who wait be - fore Thee, Near to the heart of God.
176 JESUS LOVES ME
Anna B. Warner
Wm. B. Bradbury
1. Je - sus loves me! this I know, For the Bi - ble tells me so: Lit - tle
2. Je - sus from His throne on high, Came in-to this world to die; That I
3. Je - sus loves me! He who died Heaven's gate to o - pen wide! He will
4. Je - sus, take this heart of mine; Make it pure, and whol-ly Thine: Thou hast

JESUS LOVES ME

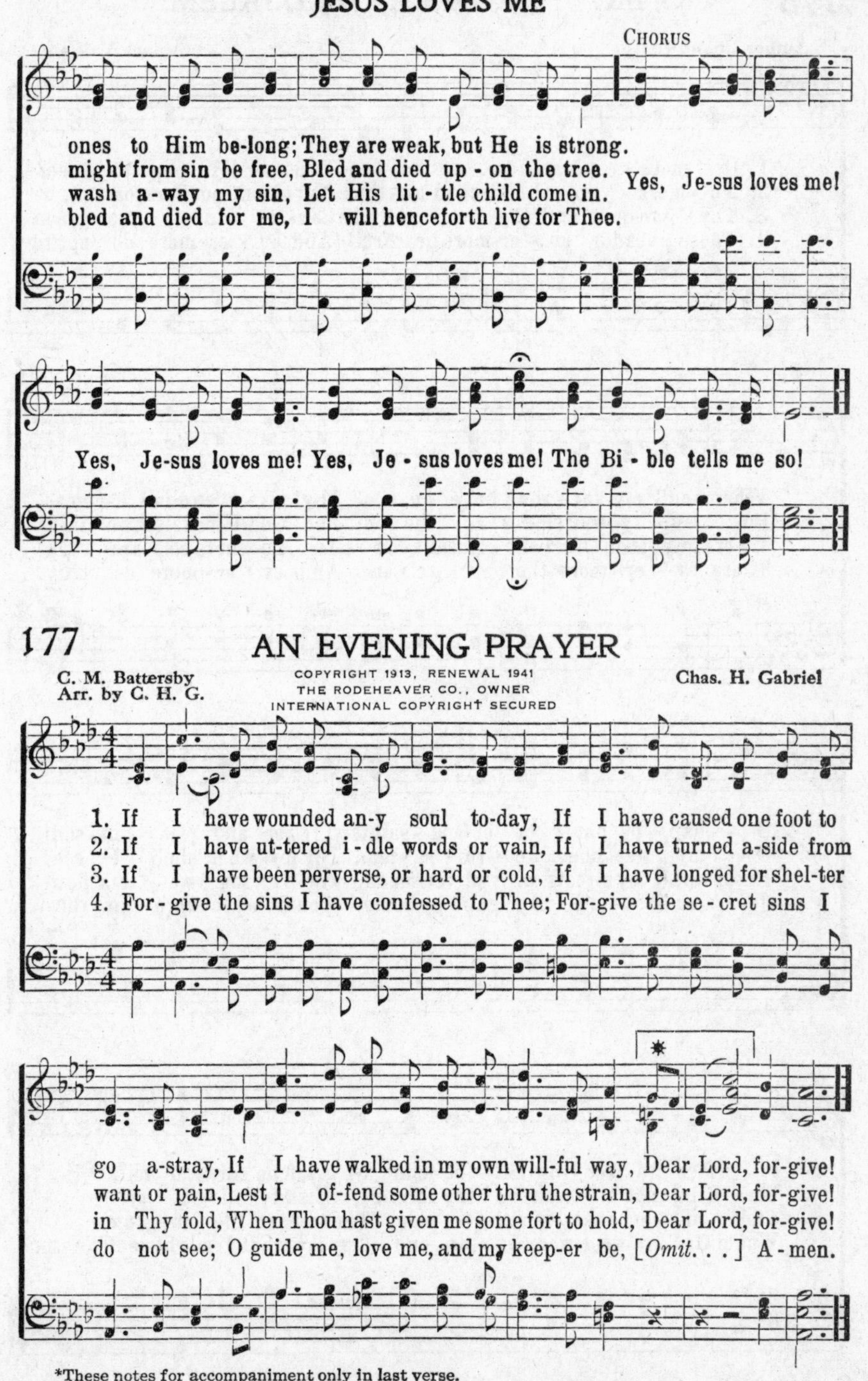
CHORUS
ones to Him be-long; They are weak, but He is strong.
might from sin be free, Bled and died up - on the tree.
wash a-way my sin, Let His lit - tle child come in.
bled and died for me, I will henceforth live for Thee.
Yes, Je-sus loves me!
Yes, Je-sus loves me! Yes, Je - sus loves me! The Bi - ble tells me so!
177 AN EVENING PRAYER
C. M. Battersby
Arr. by C. H. G.
COPYRIGHT 1913, RENEWAL 1941
THE RODEHEAVER CO., OWNER
INTERNATIONAL COPYRIGHT SECURED
Chas. H. Gabriel
1. If I have wounded an-y soul to-day, If I have caused one foot to
2. If I have ut-tered i - dle words or vain, If I have turned a-side from
3. If I have been perverse, or hard or cold, If I have longed for shel-ter
4. For - give the sins I have confessed to Thee; For-give the se - cret sins I
go a-stray, If I have walked in my own will-ful way, Dear Lord, for-give!
want or pain, Lest I of-fend some other thru the strain, Dear Lord, for-give!
in Thy fold, When Thou hast given me some fort to hold, Dear Lord, for-give!
do not see; O guide me, love me, and my keep-er be, [Omit. . .] A-men.
*These notes for accompaniment only in last verse.

178 O MOTHER DEAR, JERUSALEM!

Author Unknown — Samuel A. Ward

1. O moth - er dear, Je - ru - sa - lem! When shall I come to thee?
2. No murk - y cloud o'er-shad-ows thee, Nor gloom, nor darksome night;
3. Thy gar-dens and thy good - ly walks Con - tin - ual - ly are green,
4. Those trees for ev - er-more bear fruit, And ev - er-more do spring:
When shall my sor - rows have an end? Thy joys when shall I see?. . .
But ev - 'ry soul shines as the sun; For God Him-self gives light. .
Where grow such sweet and pleasant flow'rs As no-where else are seen. . .
There ev - er-more the an - gels are, And ev - er-more do sing. . .
O hap - py har - bor of God's saints! O sweet and pleas - ant soil! . .
O my sweet home, Je - ru - sa - lem, Thy joys when shall I see? . .
Right thro' thy streets, with sil-ver sound, The liv - ing wa - ters flow, . .
Je - ru - sa - lem, my hap - py home, Would God I were in thee! . .
In thee no sor - row may be found, No grief, no care, no toil.
The King that sit - teth on thy throne In His fe - li - ci - ty?
And on the banks, on eith - er side, The trees of life do grow.
Would God my woes were at an end, Thy joys that I might see! A-MEN.

179 ANYWHERE WITH JESUS

Jessie H. Brown D. B. Towner

1. An - y-where with Je - sus I can safe - ly go; An - y - where He leads me in this world be - low; An - y-where with-out Him dear - est joys would fade; An - y-where with Je - sus I am not a - fraid.
2. An - y-where with Je - sus I need fear no ill, Tho' temp-ta - tions gath - er 'round my path-way still; He Him-self was tempt-ed that He might help me; An - y-where with Je - sus I may vic - tor be.
3. An - y-where with Je - sus I am not a - lone; Oth - er friends may fail me, He is still my own; Tho' His hand may lead me o - ver drear - y ways, An - y-where with Je - sus is a house of praise.
4. An - y-where with Je - sus o - ver land or sea; Tell - ing souls in dark - ness of sal - va - tion free; Read - y as He sum-mons me to go or stay, An - y-where with Je - sus when He points the way.
5. An - y-where with Je - sus I can go to sleep, When the dark-'ning shad-ows 'round a - bout me creep; Know-ing I shall wak - en, nev - er more to roam, An - y-where with Je - sus will be home, sweet home.
CHORUS
An - y - where! an - y - where! Fear I can not know; An - y - where with Je - sus I can safe - ly go.

180 SEEKING THE LOST

W. A. O.
W. A. Ogden
1. Seek-ing the lost, yes, kind-ly en-treat-ing Wan-der-ers on the
2. Seek-ing the lost, and point-ing to Je-sus Souls that are weak and
3. Thus would I go, for Je-sus hath called me, Him would I fol-low
moun-tains a-stray, "Come un-to me," His mes-sage re-peat-ing, Words of the
hearts that are sore, Lead-ing them forth in ways of sal-va-tion, Show-ing the
day un-to day; Care for the dy-ing, raise up the fall-en, Point-ing the
Mas-ter speak-ing to-day.
path to life ev-er-more.
lost to Je-sus the way.
CHORUS with Bass Solo obligato.
Go-ing a-far, a-
Go-ing a-far.................. up-on the
far up-on the moun-tain, Bring-ing the wan-d'rers, the
moun-tain,...... Bring-ing the wan - - - d'rers back a-
wan'drers back a-gain, In-to the fold, the fold of my Redeemer,
gain,.............. In-to the fold.............. of my Re-deem-er,........

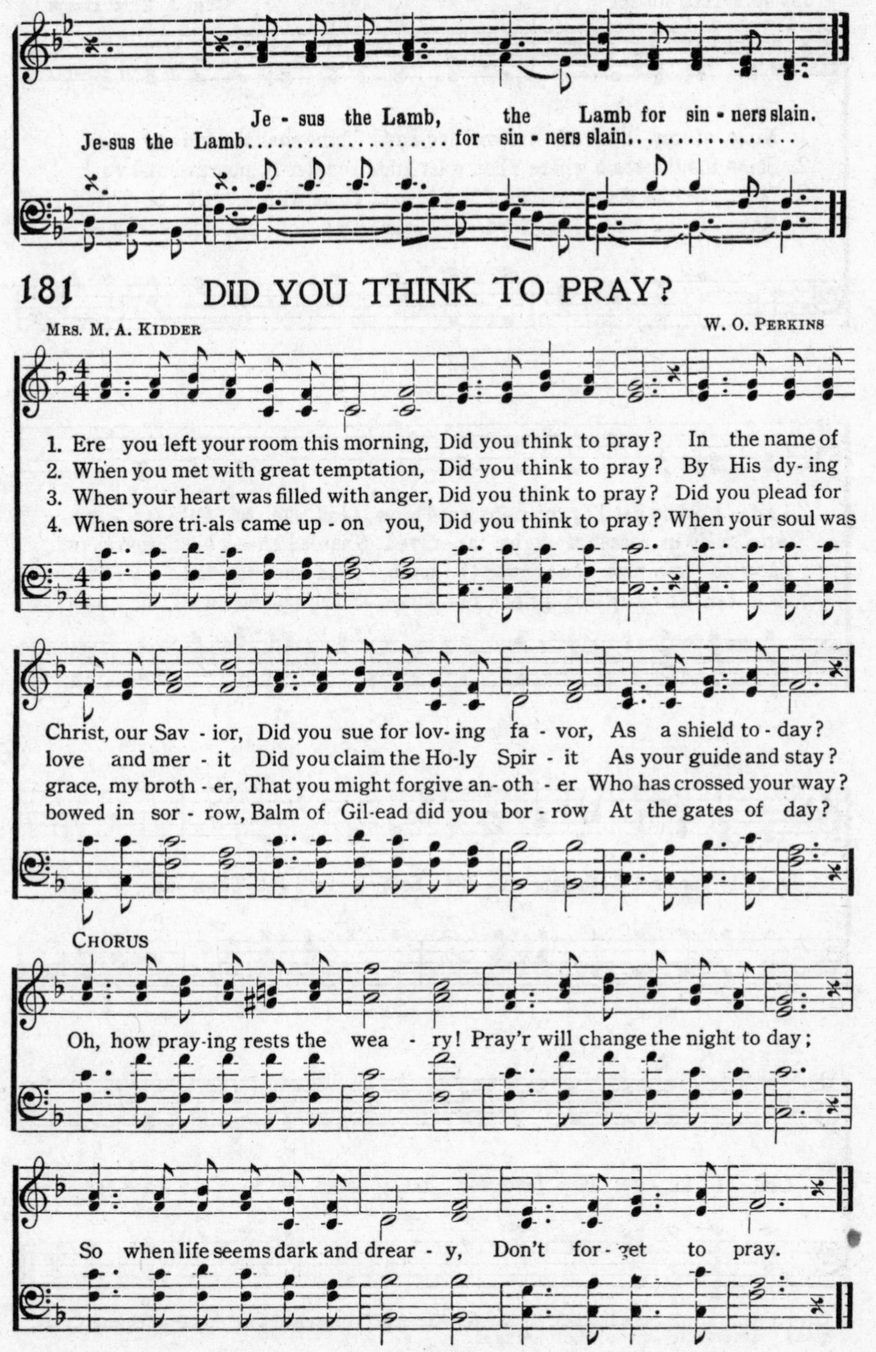
Je - sus the Lamb, the Lamb for sin - ners slain.
Je-sus the Lamb............. for sin - ners slain...............
181
DID YOU THINK TO PRAY?
Mrs. M. A. Kidder
W. O. Perkins
1. Ere you left your room this morning, Did you think to pray? In the name of
2. When you met with great temptation, Did you think to pray? By His dy- ing
3. When your heart was filled with anger, Did you think to pray? Did you plead for
4. When sore tri-als came up - on you, Did you think to pray? When your soul was
Christ, our Sav - ior, Did you sue for lov- ing fa - vor, As a shield to - day?
love and mer - it Did you claim the Ho-ly Spir - it As your guide and stay?
grace, my broth - er, That you might forgive an- oth - er Who has crossed your way?
bowed in sor - row, Balm of Gil-ead did you bor - row At the gates of day?
Chorus
Oh, how pray-ing rests the wea - ry! Pray'r will change the night to day;
So when life seems dark and drear - y, Don't for- get to pray.

182 LEAD ME TO CALVARY

JENNIE EVELYN HUSSEY | WM. J. KIRKPATRICK

1. King of my life, I crown Thee now, Thine shall the glo - ry be;
2. Show me the tomb where Thou wast laid, Ten-der-ly mourned and wept;
3. Let me like Ma - ry, thro' the gloom, Come with a gift to Thee;
4. May I be will - ing, Lord, to bear Dai - ly my cross for Thee;

Lest I for - get Thy thorn-crowned brow, Lead me to Cal - va - ry.
An - gels in robes of light ar - rayed Guarded Thee whilst Thou slept.
Show to me now the emp - ty tomb, Lead me to Cal - va - ry.
E - ven Thy cup of grief to share, Thou hast borne all for me.

CHORUS

Lest I for - get Geth-sem - a - ne; Lest I for - get Thine ag - o - ny;

Lest I for - get Thy love for me, Lead me to Cal - va - ry.

183 SAFELY THROUGH ANOTHER WEEK

John Newton

Lowell Mason

1. Safe - ly through an - oth - er week God has brought us on our way;
2. While we pray for par-d'ning grace, Thro' the dear Re-deem-er's name,
3. Here we come Thy name to praise, Let us feel Thy pres-ence near;
4. May Thy gos-pel's joy - ful sound Con-quer sin-ners, com-fort saints;
Let us now a bless-ing seek, Wait-ing in His courts to - day;
Show Thy rec - on - cil - ed face; Take a - way our sin and shame:
May Thy glo - ry meet our eyes, While we in Thy house ap - pear:
Make the fruits of grace a - bound, Bring re - lief for all com-plaints:
Day of all the week the best, Em-blem of e - ter - nal rest: Day of
From our world-ly cares set free, May we rest this day in Thee: From our
Here af - ford us, Lord, a taste Of our ev - er - last - ing feast: Here af-
Thus may all our Sab-baths prove, Till we join the Church a - bove: Thus may
all the week the best, Em - blem of e - ter - nal rest.
world-ly cares set free, May we rest this day in Thee.
ford us, Lord, a taste Of our ev - er - last - ing feast.
all our Sab-baths prove, Till we join the Church a - bove. A - men.

184 JESUS TOOK MY HEART

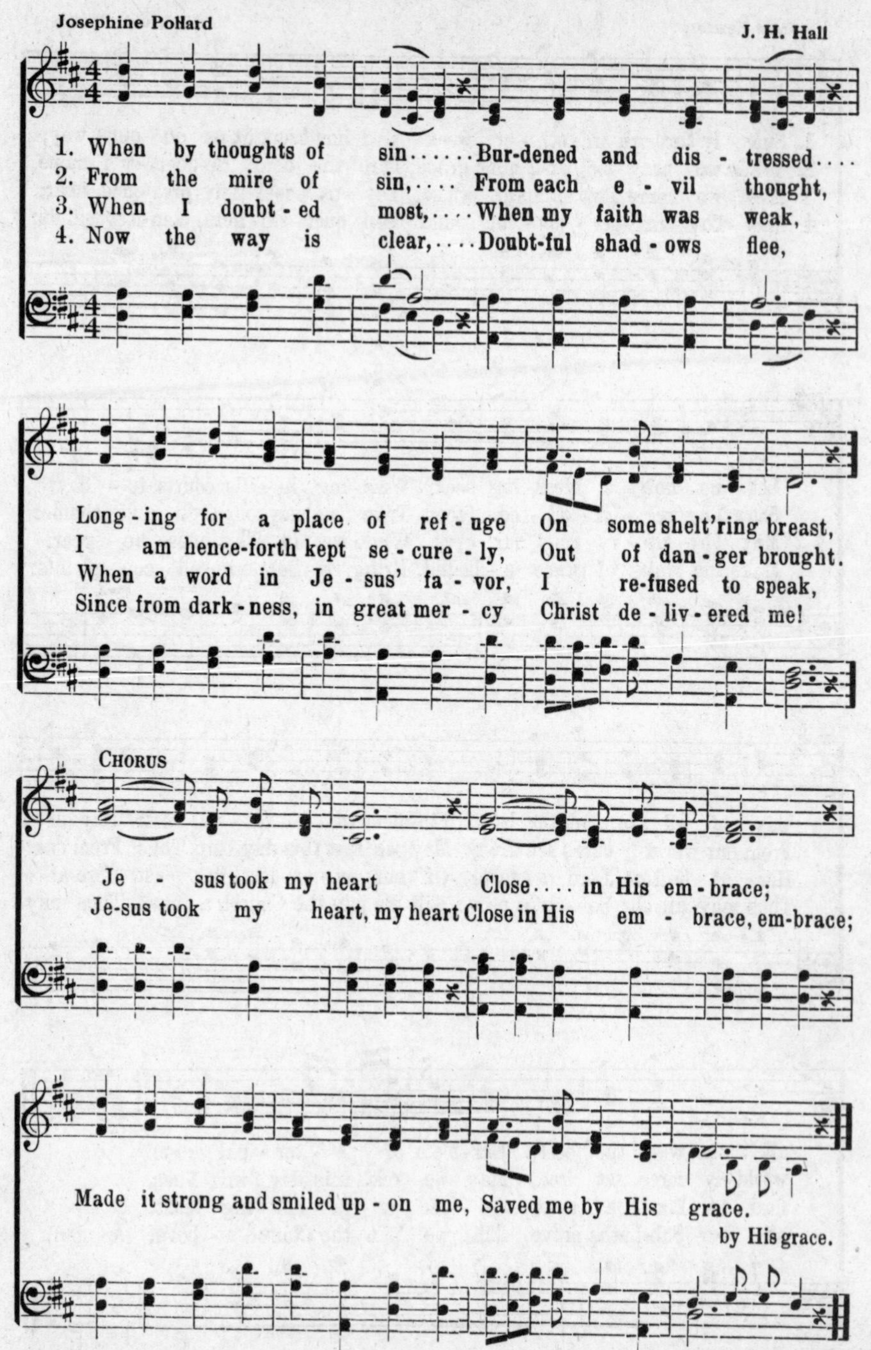
Josephine Pollard
J. H. Hall
1. When by thoughts of sin...... Bur-dened and dis - tressed....
2. From the mire of sin,.... From each e - vil thought,
3. When I doubt - ed most,.... When my faith was weak,
4. Now the way is clear,.... Doubt-ful shad - ows flee,
Long - ing for a place of ref - uge On some shelt'ring breast,
I am hence-forth kept se - cure - ly, Out of dan - ger brought.
When a word in Je - sus' fa - vor, I re-fused to speak,
Since from dark - ness, in great mer - cy Christ de - liv - ered me!
CHORUS
Je - sus took my heart Close.... in His em - brace;
Je-sus took my heart, my heart Close in His em - brace, em-brace;
Made it strong and smiled up - on me, Saved me by His grace.
by His grace.

185 LOVE DIVINE

CHARLES WESLEY

JOHN ZUNDEL

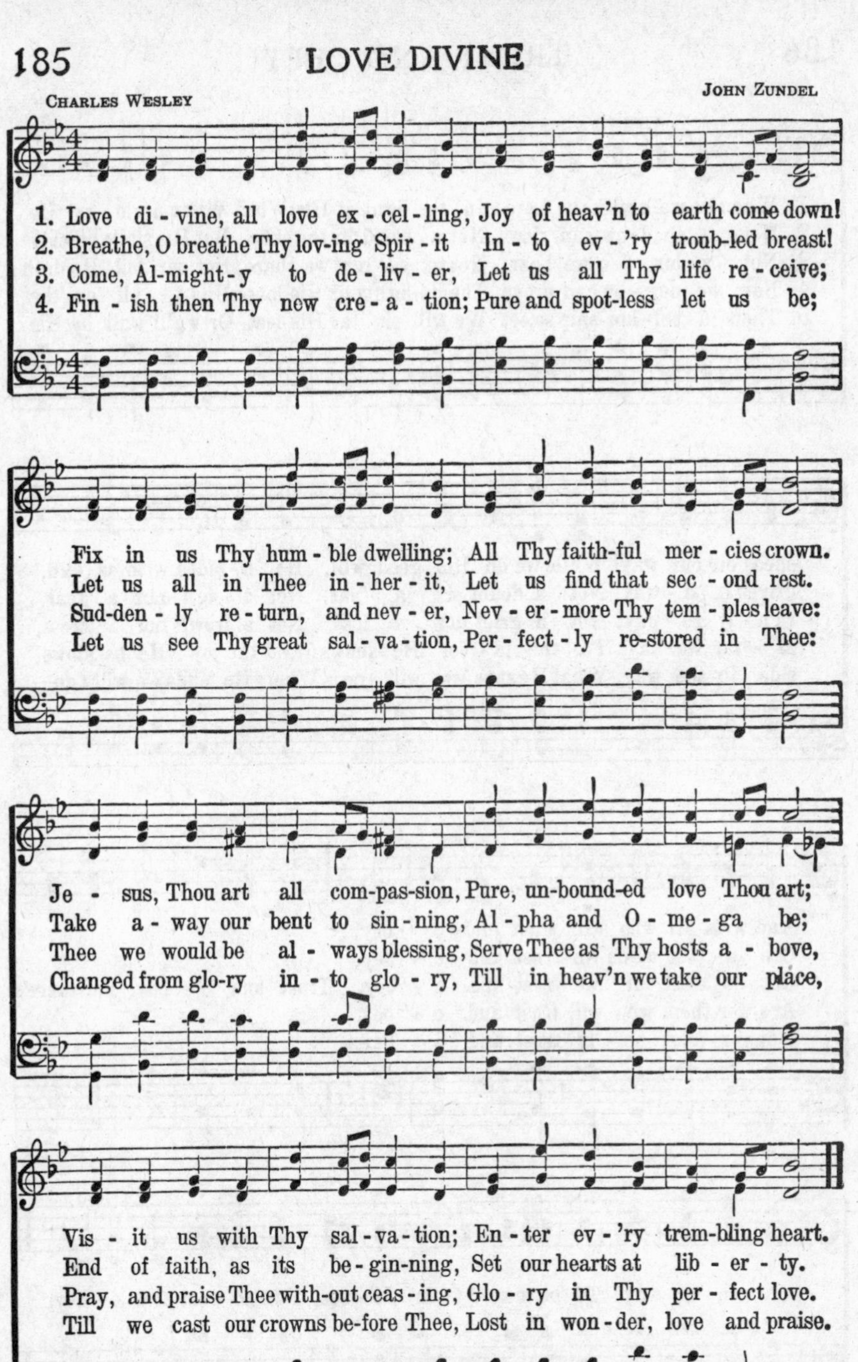
1. Love di - vine, all love ex - cel - ling, Joy of heav'n to earth come down!
2. Breathe, O breathe Thy lov-ing Spir - it In - to ev - 'ry troub-led breast!
3. Come, Al-might - y to de - liv - er, Let us all Thy life re - ceive;
4. Fin - ish then Thy new cre - a - tion; Pure and spot-less let us be;
Fix in us Thy hum - ble dwelling; All Thy faith-ful mer - cies crown.
Let us all in Thee in - her - it, Let us find that sec - ond rest.
Sud-den - ly re - turn, and nev - er, Nev - er - more Thy tem - ples leave:
Let us see Thy great sal - va - tion, Per - fect - ly re-stored in Thee:
Je - sus, Thou art all com-pas-sion, Pure, un-bound-ed love Thou art;
Take a - way our bent to sin - ning, Al - pha and O - me - ga be;
Thee we would be al - ways blessing, Serve Thee as Thy hosts a - bove,
Changed from glo-ry in - to glo - ry, Till in heav'n we take our place,
Vis - it us with Thy sal - va - tion; En - ter ev - 'ry trem-bling heart.
End of faith, as its be - gin-ning, Set our hearts at lib - er - ty.
Pray, and praise Thee with-out ceas - ing, Glo - ry in Thy per - fect love.
Till we cast our crowns be-fore Thee, Lost in won - der, love and praise.

186 TRUST AND OBEY

John H. Sammis D. B. Towner

1. When we walk with the Lord In the light of His Word What a glo - ry He
2. Not a shad - ow can rise, Not a cloud in the skies, But His smile quickly
3. Not a bur - den we bear, Not a sor - row we share, But our toil He doth
4. But we nev - er can prove The de - lights of His love Un - til all on the
5. Then in fel - low - ship sweet We will sit at His feet, Or we'll walk by His
sheds on our way! While we do His good will, He a - bides with us still,
drives it a - way; Not a doubt or a fear, Not a sigh nor a tear,
rich - ly re - pay; Not a grief nor a loss, Not a frown nor a cross,
al - tar we lay; For the fa - vor He shows, And the joy He be - stows,
side in the way; What He says we will do, Where He sends we will go—
CHORUS
And with all who will trust and o - bey.
Can a - bide while we trust and o - . bey.
But is blest if we trust and o - bey. Trust and o - bey, For there's
Are for them who will trust and o - bey.
Nev - er fear, on - ly trust and o - bey.
no oth - er way To be hap - py in Je - sus, But to trust and o - bey.

187 WHAT DID HE DO?

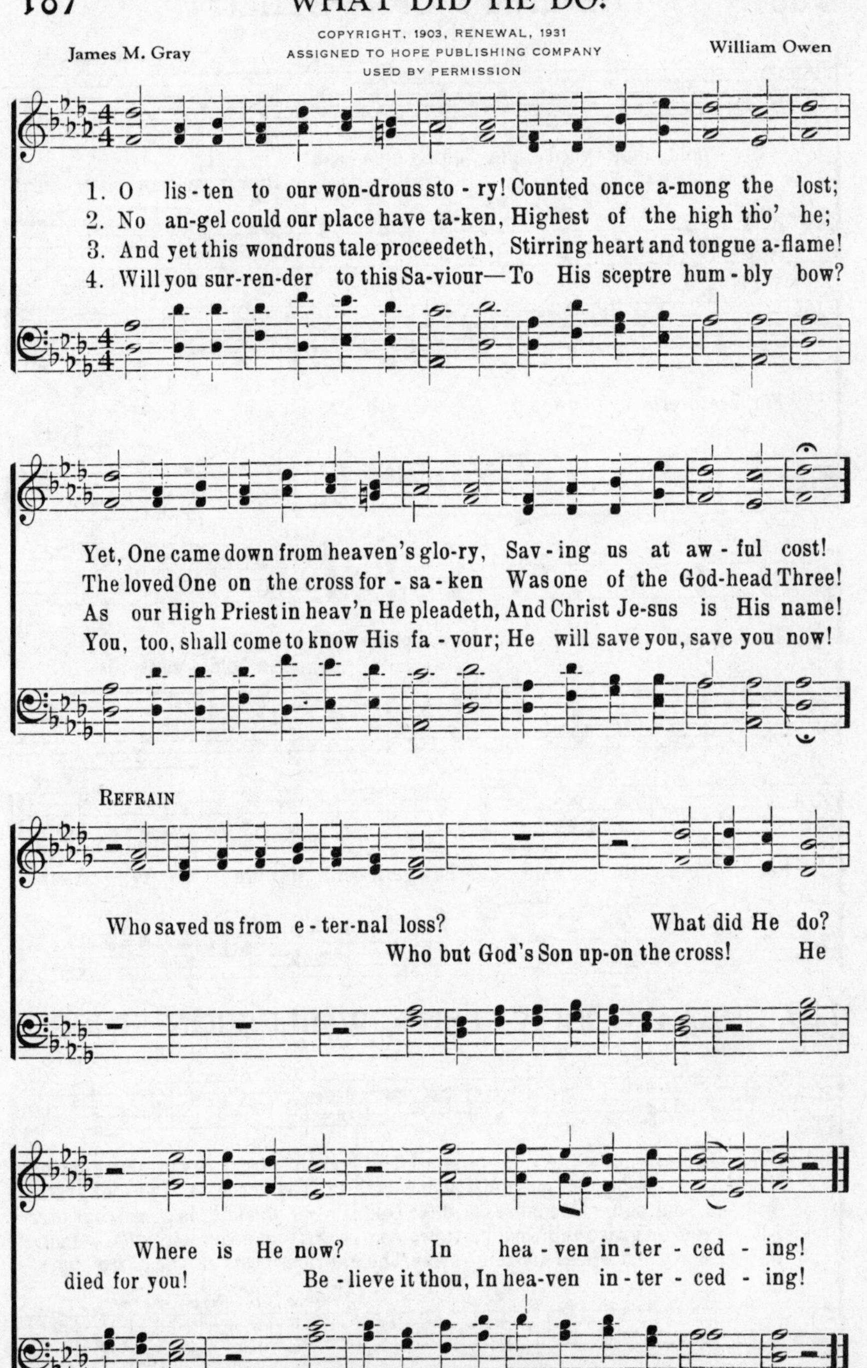
COPYRIGHT, 1903, RENEWAL, 1931
ASSIGNED TO HOPE PUBLISHING COMPANY
USED BY PERMISSION
James M. Gray
William Owen
1. O lis-ten to our won-drous sto-ry! Counted once a-mong the lost;
2. No an-gel could our place have ta-ken, Highest of the high tho' he;
3. And yet this wondrous tale proceedeth, Stirring heart and tongue a-flame!
4. Will you sur-ren-der to this Sa-viour—To His sceptre hum-bly bow?
Yet, One came down from heaven's glo-ry, Sav-ing us at aw-ful cost!
The loved One on the cross for-sa-ken Was one of the God-head Three!
As our High Priest in heav'n He pleadeth, And Christ Je-sus is His name!
You, too, shall come to know His fa-vour; He will save you, save you now!
Refrain
Who saved us from e-ter-nal loss?
Who but God's Son up-on the cross!
What did He do?
He died for you!
Where is He now?
Be-lieve it thou,
In hea-ven in-ter-ced-ing!
In hea-ven in-ter-ced-ing!

188 THE UNITY OF BRETHERN

Psa. 133: 1

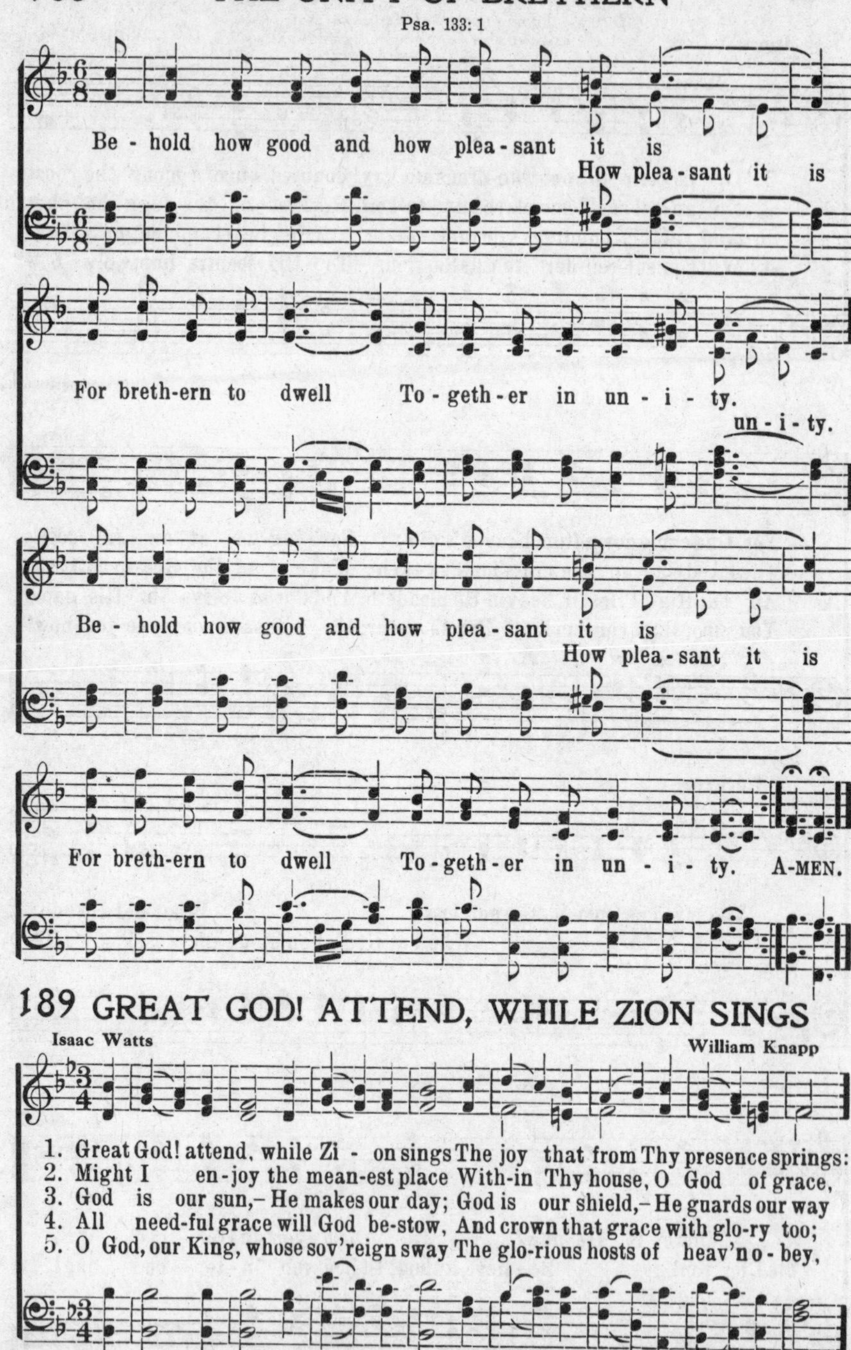
Be - hold how good and how plea - sant it is
How plea - sant it is
For breth-ern to dwell To - geth - er in un - i - ty.
un - i - ty.
Be - hold how good and how plea - sant it is
How plea - sant it is
For breth-ern to dwell To - geth - er in un - i - ty. A-MEN.

189 GREAT GOD! ATTEND, WHILE ZION SINGS

Isaac Watts

William Knapp

1. Great God! attend, while Zi - on sings The joy that from Thy presence springs:
2. Might I en-joy the mean-est place With-in Thy house, O God of grace,
3. God is our sun,– He makes our day; God is our shield,– He guards our way
4. All need-ful grace will God be-stow, And crown that grace with glo-ry too;
5. O God, our King, whose sov'reign sway The glo-rious hosts of heav'n o - bey,

GREAT GOD! ATTEND, WHILE ZION SINGS

To spend one day with Thee on earth Ex - ceeds a thou-sand days of mirth.
Not tents of ease, nor thrones of pow'r, Should tempt my feet to leave Thy door.
From all th' assaults of hell and sin, From foes with out and foes with-in.
He gives us all things, and withholds No re - al good from up - right souls.
Dis - play Thy grace, exert Thy pow'r, Till all on earth Thy name a - dore!
190 PRAYER AT EVENTIDE
Swiss Melody
1. The sun has set, the eve - ning shades Of night are draw - ing nigh.
2. Thou dost not slum - ber Lord nor sleep In day or dark - est night.
3. Re - mem - ber me, Oh gra - cious Lord, Through-out the dark'-ning night.
4. And should I die in this dark night O take me Lord to Thee.
5. It is my wish Lord God of Hosts, To live and die in Thee;
Now all the wear - y go to rest And those who weep and sigh.
There is no dark-ness Lord with Thee, For Thou thy - self art light.
May Guar-dian an - gels hov'-ring o'er Pro - tect me by their might.
And bring me to Thy heaven-ly home With thine e - lect to be.
In life and death, in grief or woe, Dear Lord, re - mem-ber me.
Now all the wear - y go to rest And those who weep and sigh.
There is no dark-ness Lord with Thee, For Thou thy self art light.
May Guard-ian an - gels hov-'ring o'er Pro - tect me by their might.
And bring me to Thy heavenly home With thine e - lect to be.
In life and death, in grief or woe, Dear Lord, re - mem-ber me.

191 BE STILL, MY SOUL

Katharina Von Schlegel
Tr. by Jane L. Borthwick
FINLANDIA
Jean Sibelius
1. Be still, my soul: the Lord is on thy side; . . . Bear pa - tient-
2. Be still, my soul: thy God doth un - der - take . . . To guide the
3. Be still, my soul: the hour is has - tening on . . . . When we shall
ly the cross of grief or pain; Leave to thy God to
fu - ture as He has the past. Thy hope, thy con - fi-
be for - ev - er with the Lord, When dis - ap - point - ment,
or - der and pro - vide; . . . In ev - ery change He faith - ful will re-
dence let noth - ing shake; . . All now mys - te - rious shall be bright at
grief, and fear are gone, . . . Sor - row for - got, love's pur - est joys re-
main. Be still, my soul: thy best, thy heaven - ly Friend, . .
last. Be still, my soul: the waves and winds still know. . . .
stored. Be still, my soul: when change and tears are past, . . .
Thro' thorn - y ways leads to a joy - ful end. . .
His voice who ruled them while He dwelt be - low. . .
All safe and bless - ed we shall meet at last. . . A - MEN.

192 O MY SOUL, BY PAIN SURROUNDED

1. O my soul, by pain-sur-round-ed, Firm-ly trust thy God in-deed;
2. O let not thy heart be vanquished By the Sa-tan's e-vil might.
3. Wouldst thou whol-ly live for Je-sus, Then all self must dis-ap-pear.
4. There-fore, let all doubt-ing van-ish; Cling to Christ with all thy might.
He would on-ly make thee wor-thy By this fear and dire.... need.
Lo, thy bless-ed Sav-iour's path-way Al-so led through darkest night.
Yield your-self to Him here ful-ly Walk with Him in God-ly fear.
For His child He hath in-tend-ed On-ly what is good and right.
Refrain
Fear thou not when days are drear-y, O de-spair not of God's Word;
What He saith will be ac-com-plished. Trust thou ev-er in the Lord!

193 HAVE YOU ANY ROOM FOR JESUS?

C. C. Williams

1. Have you an - y room for Je - sus, He who bore your load of sin?
2. Room for pleas-ure, room for busi - ness, But for Christ the Cru - ci - fied,
3. Have you an - y room for Je - sus, As in grace He calls a - gain?
4. Room and time now give to Je - sus, Soon will pass God's day of grace;

As He knocks and asks ad-mis - sion, Sin - ner, will you let Him in?
Not a place that He can en - ter, In the heart for which He died?
O to-day is time ac-cept - ed, To-mor - row you may call in vain.
Soon thy heart left cold and si - lent, And thy Sav-ior's pleading cease.

CHORUS

Room for Je - sus, King of glo - ry! Has - ten now His word o - bey;

Swing the heart's door wide-ly o - pen, Bid Him en - ter while you may.

194 FAREWELL, MY MORNING DAWNS

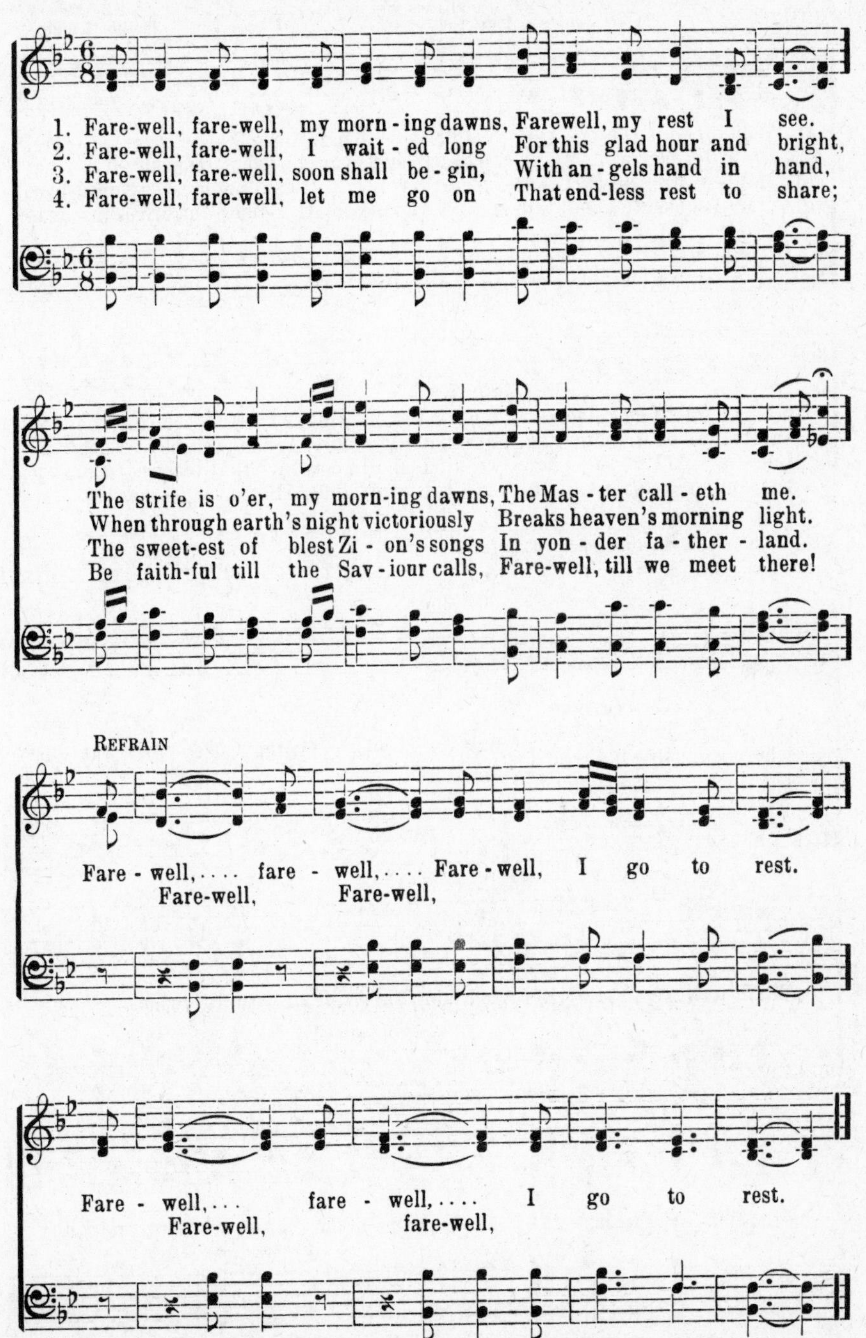
1. Fare-well, fare-well, my morn - ing dawns, Farewell, my rest I see.
2. Fare-well, fare-well, I wait - ed long For this glad hour and bright,
3. Fare-well, fare-well, soon shall be - gin, With an - gels hand in hand,
4. Fare-well, fare-well, let me go on That end-less rest to share;
The strife is o'er, my morn-ing dawns, The Mas - ter call - eth me.
When through earth's night victoriously Breaks heaven's morning light.
The sweet-est of blest Zi - on's songs In yon - der fa - ther - land.
Be faith-ful till the Sav - iour calls, Fare-well, till we meet there!
Refrain
Fare - well, ... fare - well, ... Fare - well, I go to rest.
Fare-well, Fare-well,
Fare - well, . . . fare - well, ... I go to rest.
Fare-well, fare-well,

195 MANY OF THEM THAT SLEEP

H. L. — Haldor Lillenas

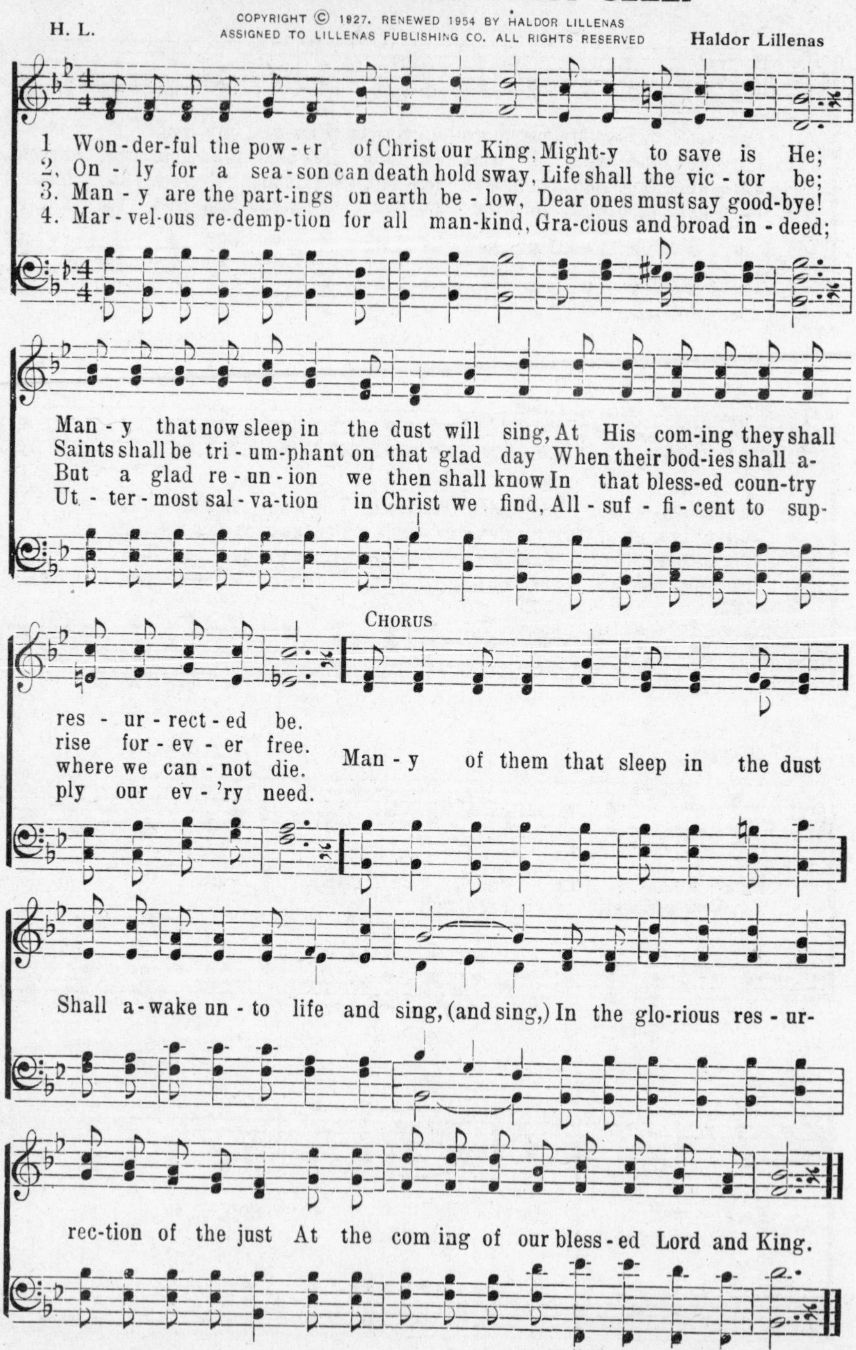
1 Won-der-ful the pow-er of Christ our King, Might-y to save is He;
2. On-ly for a sea-son can death hold sway, Life shall the vic-tor be;
3. Man-y are the part-ings on earth be-low, Dear ones must say good-bye!
4. Mar-vel-ous re-demp-tion for all man-kind, Gra-cious and broad in-deed;
Man-y that now sleep in the dust will sing, At His com-ing they shall res-ur-rect-ed be.
Saints shall be tri-um-phant on that glad day When their bod-ies shall a-rise for-ev-er free.
But a glad re-un-ion we then shall know In that bless-ed coun-try where we can-not die.
Ut-ter-most sal-va-tion in Christ we find, All-suf-fi-cent to sup-ply our ev-'ry need.
CHORUS
Man-y of them that sleep in the dust Shall a-wake un-to life and sing, (and sing,) In the glo-rious res-ur-rec-tion of the just At the com-ing of our bless-ed Lord and King.

196 THE VOICE THAT BREATHED O'ER EDEN
John Keble
Traditional Welsh Melody
1. The voice that breathed o'er E - den, That ear - liest wed - ding day,
2. Be pres - ent, gra - cious Fa - ther, To give a - way this bride,
3. Be pres - ent, ho - ly Spir - it, To bless them as they kneel,
The pri - mal mar - riage bless - ing, It hath not passed a - way:
As Eve thou gav'st to Ad - am Out of his own pierced side:
As thou, for Christ the Bride - groom, The heav'n - ly bride dost seal;
Still in the pure es - pous - al Of Chris - tian man and maid
Be pres - ent, bless - ed Je - sus, To join their lov - ing hands,
O spread thy pure wing o'er them; Let no ill pow'r find place,
The Ho - ly Three are with us, The three - fold grace is said.
As thou didst bind two na - tures In thine e - ter - nal bands:
While on - ward to thy pres - ence Their hal - lowed path they trace.

197 JUST OVER THE RIVER

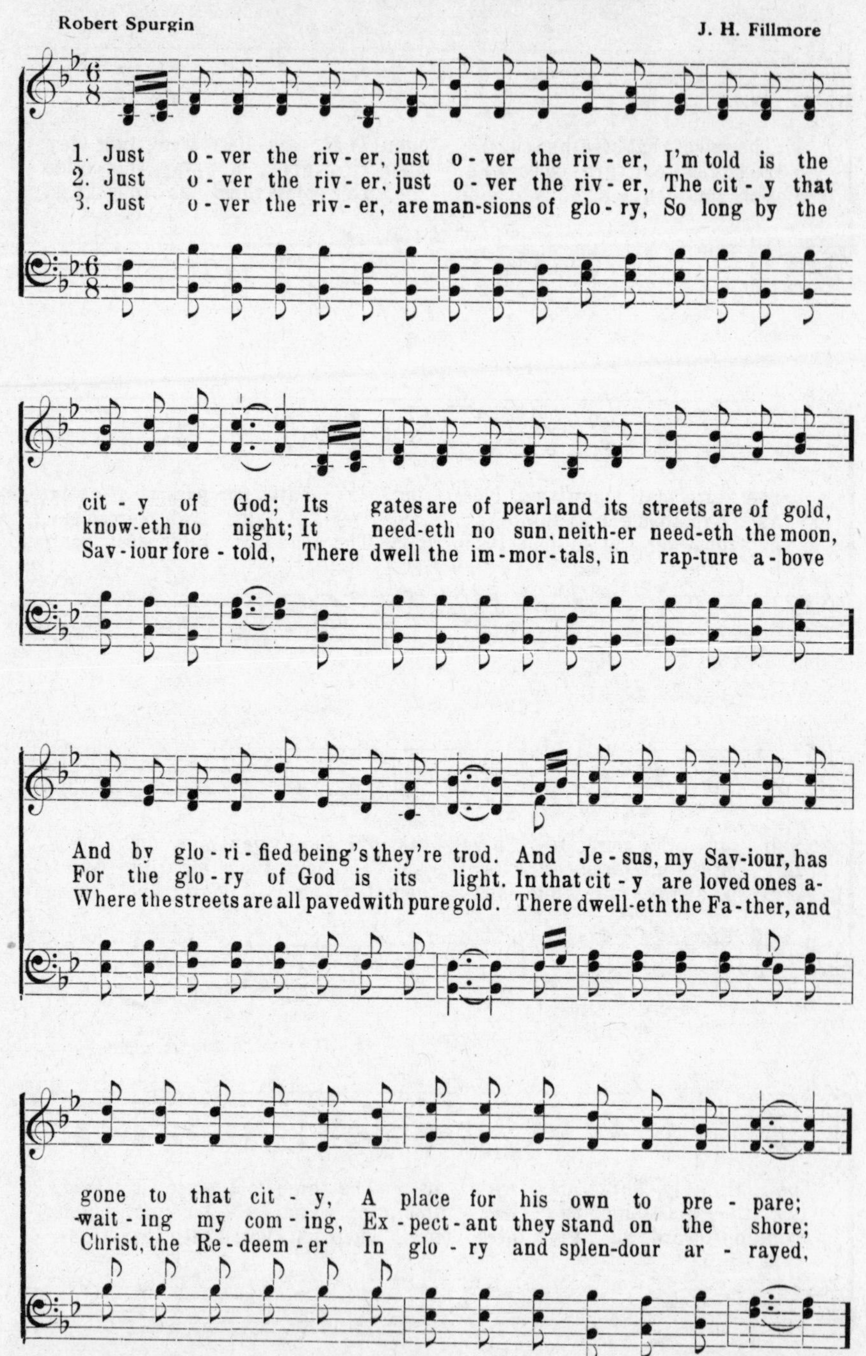

Robert Spurgin
J. H. Fillmore
1. Just o - ver the riv - er, just o - ver the riv - er, I'm told is the
2. Just o - ver the riv - er, just o - ver the riv - er, The cit - y that
3. Just o - ver the riv - er, are man-sions of glo - ry, So long by the
cit - y of God; Its gates are of pearl and its streets are of gold,
know-eth no night; It need-eth no sun, neith-er need-eth the moon,
Sav - iour fore - told, There dwell the im - mor - tals, in rap-ture a - bove
And by glo - ri - fied being's they're trod. And Je - sus, my Sav-iour, has
For the glo - ry of God is its light. In that cit - y are loved ones a-
Where the streets are all paved with pure gold. There dwell-eth the Fa - ther, and
gone to that cit - y, A place for his own to pre - pare;
-wait - ing my com - ing, Ex - pect - ant they stand on the shore;
Christ, the Re - deem - er In glo - ry and splen-dour ar - rayed,

JUST OVER THE RIVER

In the house of the Fa-ther the man-sions are ma - ny, And one is a-
O when shall I en-ter my man-sion in heav-en. A pil-grim to
Where praise shall resound from the lips of the ran-somed To Hfm who our
CHORUS
wait-ing me there. Just o - - - - ver the riv - - - er,
roam nev-er more. Just o-ver the riv-er, just o-ver the riv-er,
sin debt has paid!
That beau-ti-ful ci-ty I see; Just o - - - - ver the
That beau-ti-ful ci-ty I see; And Je-sus. my Sav-iour. has
riv - - - - - - - er, A place in that cit - y for me.
gone to make read - y, A place in that cit - y for me.

CHRISTIAN, WALK CAREFULLY

George C. Stebbins

1. Chris-tian, walk care-ful - ly, dan-ger is near; On in Thy jour-ney with
2. Chris-tian, walk cheer-ful - ly thro' the fierce storm, Dark tho' the sky with its
3. Chris-tian, walk pray'r-ful-ly, oft wilt thou fall If thou for - get on thy
4. Chris-tian, walk hope-ful - ly, sor-row and pain Cease when the ha - ven of

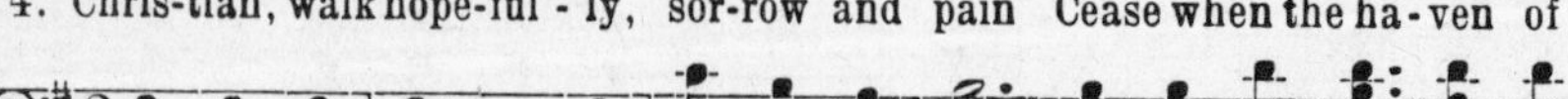

trembling and fear. Snares from with - out and temp - ta - tions with - in,
threat of a - larm. Soon will the clouds and the tem - pest be o'er,
Sav - iour to call; Safe thou shalt walk thro' each tri - al and care,
rest thou shalt gain; Then from the lips of the Judge, thy re - ward:

CHORUS

Seek to en - tice thee once more in - to sin. Chris-tian, walk care-ful - ly,
Then with thy Sav-iour thou'lt rest ev - er more. Chris-tian, walk cheer-ful - ly,
If thou art clad in the ar - mor of pray'r. Chris-tian, walk pray'r-ful-ly,
"En - ter thou in - to the joy of thy Lord." Chris-tian, walk hope-ful - ly,

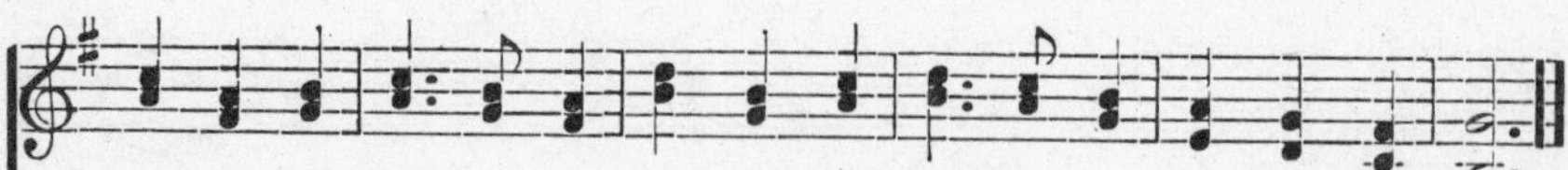

Chris-tian, walk care-ful - ly, Chris-tian, walk care-ful - ly, dan - ger is near.
Chris-tian, walk cheer-ful-ly, Chris-tian, walk cheer-ful-ly through the fierce storm.
Chris-tian, walk pray'r-ful-ly, Chris-tian, walk pray'r-ful-ly, fear lest thou fall.
Cbris-tian, walk hope-ful - ly, Chris-tian, walk hope-ful - ly, rest thou shalt gain.

199 KNOW YE THAT LAND?

From F. Cunningham's Selection of Psalm tunes 1834. Arr. W. E. Yoder

1. Know ye that land, on earth you'll find it not. To which in anx-ious
2. Know ye that land, where peace e-ter-nal dwells, The love of God each
3. Know ye that land, which yet no eye has seen? For which we long in

mo-ments turn our thoughts? Where sor-row fades and no more flows the tear;
faith-ful bos-om swells? Where earthly toil and care no more op-press,
faith and hope se-rene? Whose glo-ries draw us from the world a-part.

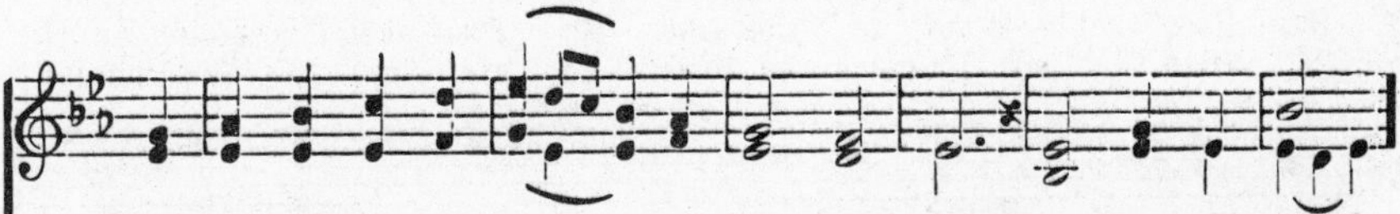

Where end-less bliss and last-ing joys ap-pear! Who knows that land?
Where rest and joy the bliss-ful heart ca-ress! Who knows that land?
But o-pen on-ly to the pure in heart! Who knows that land?

Its shores to find, Let us di-rect our heart and mind!
Its shores to find, Let us di-rect our heart and mind!
Its shores to find, Let us di-rect our heart and mind!

200 I KNOW THAT MY REDEEMER LIVES

Sam Medley | James McGranahan

1. I know that my Re-deem-er lives! What com - fort this sweet message gives!
2. He lives, to bless me with His love; He lives, to plead for me a - bove,
3. He lives, triumphant from the grave; He lives, e - ter - nal - ly to save;
4. He lives, my man-sion to pre - pare; He lives to bring me safe - ly there;

He lives, who once was dead; He lives, all glo-rious in the sky;
My hun - gry soul to feed; He lives, to grant me rich sup - ply;
And while He lives I'll sing: He lives, my ev - er faith - ful Friend;
My Je - sus still the same: What joy this blest as - sur - ance gives!

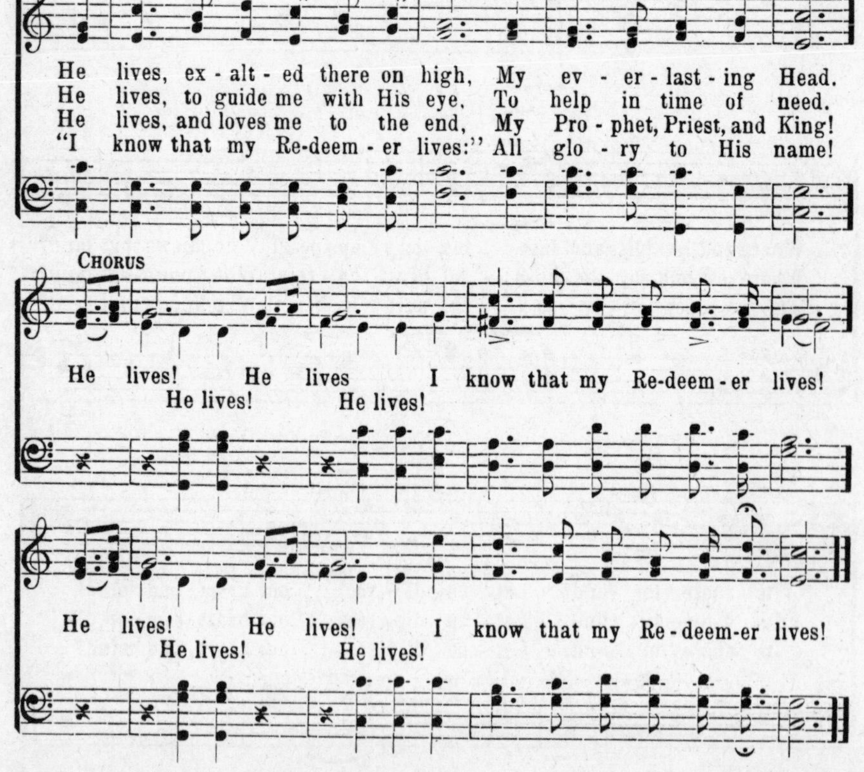
He lives, ex - alt - ed there on high, My ev - er - last - ing Head.
He lives, to guide me with His eye, To help in time of need.
He lives, and loves me to the end, My Pro - phet, Priest, and King!
"I know that my Re-deem - er lives:" All glo - ry to His name!
CHORUS
He lives! He lives! I know that my Re-deem - er lives!
He lives! He lives!
He lives! He lives! I know that my Re - deem-er lives!
He lives! He lives!

201 I NEED THE PRAYERS

J. D. V. James D. Vaughn

1. I need the prayers of those I love, While trav'ling o'er life's rug-ged way,
2. I need the prayers of those I love, To help me in each try-ing hour,
3. I want my friends to pray for me. To hold me up on wings of faith,

That I may true and faith-ful be, And live for Je-sus ev-ery day.
To bear my tempted soul to Him, That He may keep me by His power.
That I may walk the nar-row way, Kept by our Fa-ther's glo-rious grace.

CHORUS

I want my friends to pray for me, To bear my tempted soul a-bove,

And in-ter-cede with God for me. I need the prayers of those I love.

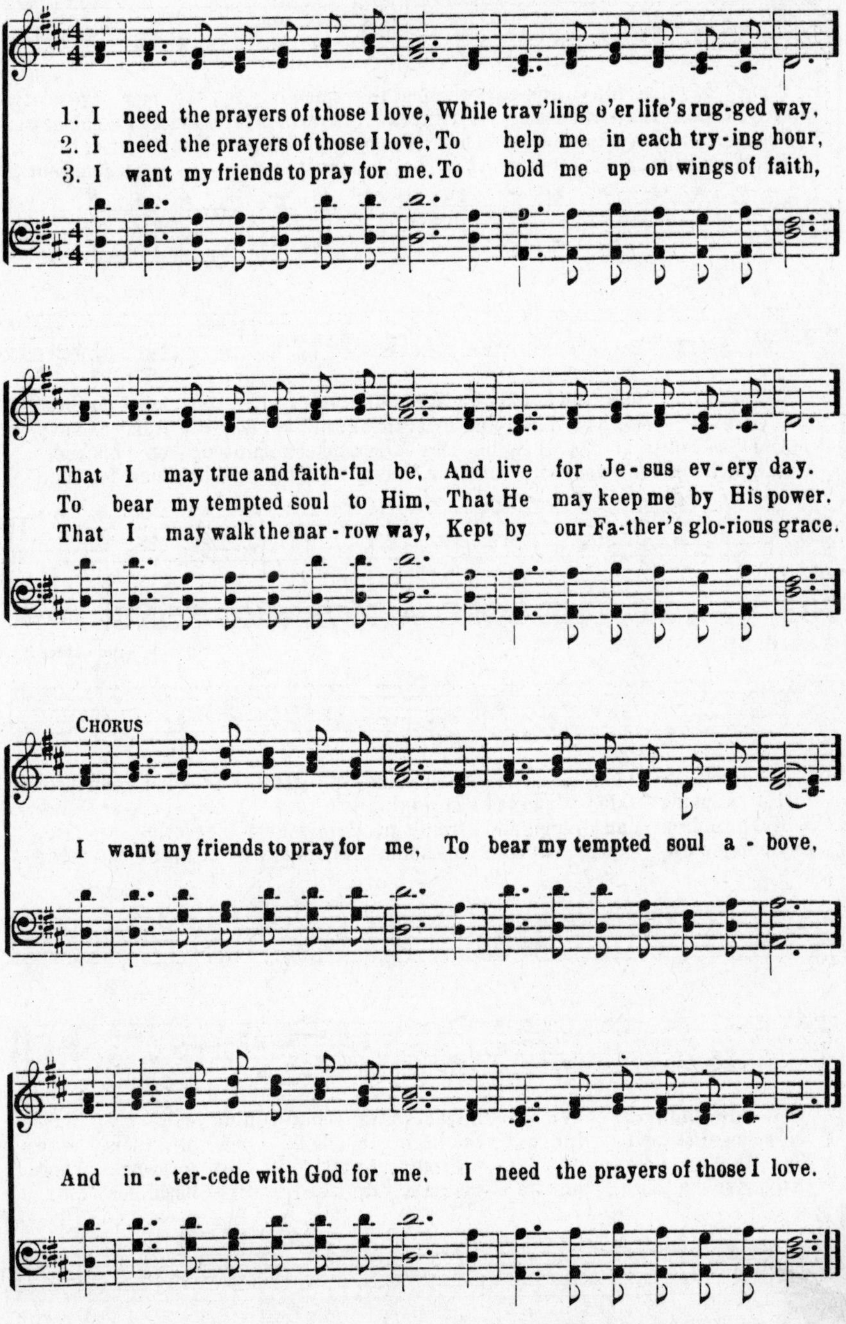

202 WHAT VARIOUS HINDRANCES WE MEET
William Cowper
G. J. Elvey
1. What va-rious hin-dranc-es we meet In com-ing to the mer-cy-seat;
2. Prayer makes the darkened clouds withdraw; Prayer climbs the ladder Ja-cob saw;
3. Re-strain-ing prayer, we cease to fight; Prayer makes the Christian's armor bright;
4. Were half the breath oft vain-ly spent, To heav'n in sup-pli-ca-tion sent,
Yet who that knows the worth of prayer But wish-es to be oft-en there?
Gives ex-er-cise to faith and love; Brings ev'-ry bless-ing from a-bove.
And Sa-tan trem-bles when he sees The weakest saint up-on his knees.
Our cheer-ful song would oft-'ner be, "Hear what the Lord has done for me."
203 I OWE THE LORD A MORNING SONG
A. H.
Amos Herr
1. I owe the Lord a morn-ing song Of grat-i-tude and praise,
2. He kept me safe an-oth-er night; I see an-oth-er day;
3. Keep me from dan-ger and from sin; Help me Thy will to do,
4. Keep me till Thou wilt call me hence, Where nev-er night can be;
For the kind mer-cy He has shown In length-'ning out my days.
Now may His Spir-it, as the light, Di-rect me in His way.
So that my heart be pure with-in; And I Thy good-ness know.
And save me, Lord, for Je-sus' sake, He shed His blood for me.

204 HEAVENLY FATHER, WE BESEECH THEE

Fanny J. Crosby
Robert Lowry
1. Heav'n-ly Fa - ther, we be-seech Thee, Grant Thy bless-ing ere we part;
2. Lov - ing Sav-iour, go Thou with us, Be our com - fort and our stay;
3. Ho - ly Spir - it, dwell with-in us, May our souls Thy tem-ple be;
4. Heav'n-ly Fa - ther, Lov-ing Sav - iour, Ho - ly Spir - it, Three in One,
Take us in Thy care and keep-ing, Guard from e - vil ev - 'ry heart.
Grateful praise to Thee we ren - der, For the joy we feel to - day.
May we tread the path to glo - ry, Led and guid - ed still by Thee.
As a-mong Thy saints and an - gels, So on earth, Thy will be done.
CHORUS
Bless the words we here have spo - ken, Of-fered prayer and cheer-ful strain;
If Thy will, O Lord, we pray Thee, Grant we all may meet a - gain.

205 PRAYER

H. B. M. Y. R.

1. How sweet the priv - i-lege of prayer, When we our cares and sor-rows share
2. 'Tis not com-mand nor mere de-cree That makes men come on bended knee
3. As friend to friend will oft con-fide, In prayer we seek the Sav-iour's side,
4. Wher'er we are is ho-ly ground, God lives wher-ev-er men are found,
5. Ashamed of Prayer? Oh, blush for shame If we should scorn that worthy name,
6. In life's deep sor-rows, e'en in death Let prayer sustain your fleeting breath

With Him who un-der-stands. With Him who un-der-stands. Our
To seek His ho - ly face. To seek His Ho - ly face. When-
And tell Him all our grief. And tell Him all our grief. If
And en - ters at their quest; And en - ters at their quest. Have
Whom heaven and saints a-dore! Whom heaven and saints adore! To
Un - til your Friend you meet; Un - til your Friend you meet. Lift

Fa-ther's house has large sup - plies He owns and rules the
'er the soul's deep needs a - rise, In fears and tri - als
we but ask He'll lend His aid; When on His al - tar
you not found some fa-vored place Where you can feel His
pen - i - tent and con-trite heart His heal - ing balm He
up your heart and kneel in prayer Your of - fer - ing is

earth and skies And bounteous are His hands, And bounteous are his hands.
it re - lies On His sus-tain-ing grace, On His sus-tain-ing grace.
prayers are laid, He'll send the soul re - lief, He'll send the soul re - lief.
kind em-brace, And feel su-premely blest, And feel su-premely blest.
will im-part And shield for-ev - er - more, And shield for-ev - er more,
ac-cepted there, As in-cense pure and sweet, As in-cense pure and sweet.

206 COME, FOR THE FEAST IS SPREAD

Henry Burton
P. P. Bliss
1. Come, for the feast is spread; Hark to the call!
2. Come where the foun - tain flows, Riv - er of life—
3. Come to the throne of grace, Bold - ly draw near;
4. Come to the Bet - ter Land, Pil - grim, make haste!
5. Je - sus, we come to Thee, O, take us in!
Come to the Liv - ing Bread, Bro - ken for all;
Heal - ing for all thy woes, Doubt - ing and strife;
He who would win the race Must tar - ry here;
Earth is a for - eign strand— Wil - der - ness waste!
Set Thou our spir - its free; Cleanse us from sin!
Come to His house of wine, Low on His breast re - cline,
Mil - lions have been sup - plied, No one was e'er de - nied;
What - e'er thy want may be, Here is the grace for thee,
Here are the harps of gold, Here are the joys un - told—
Then, in yon land of light, Clothed in our robes of white,
All that He hath is thine; Come, sin - ner, come.
Come to the crim - son tide, Come, sin - ner, come.
Je - sus thy on - ly plea, Come, Christ - ian come.
Crowns for the young and old; Come, pil - grim, come.
Rest - ing not day nor night, Thee will we sing.

207 CREATION

M. Y. R.

1. All things bright and beau-ti - ful, All crea-tures great and small,
2. Each lit - tle flow'r that o - pens, Each lit - tle bird that sings, He
3. The rich man in the cas - tle The poor man at the gate, God
4. The pur - ple head - ed moun - tain The riv - er flow - ing by, The
5. He gave us eyes to see them And lips that we might tell, How
All things wise and won-der - ful The Lord God made them all.
made their glow - ing col - ors, He made their ti - ny wings.
made them high or low - ly, And or-dered their es - tate.
sun - set and the morn - ing Which brighten up the sky.
great is God Al - might - y Who has made all things well.

208 LORD, SPEAK TO ME

M. Y. R.

1. Lord, speak to me that I may speak in liv - ing ech - oes
2. O, teach me, Lord, that I may teach the pre - cious things Thou
3. O lead me, Lord, that I may lead the wan-d'ring and the
of Thy tone; As Thou hast sought, so let me seek - -
dost im - part; And wing my words that they may reach - -
wav-'ring feet O feed me, Lord, that I may feed - -

LORD, SPEAK TO ME

Thy err - ing child - ren lost and lone. (lost and lone.)
The hid - den depths of many a heart. (many a heart.)
The hung' - ring ones with man - na sweet. (man - na sweet.)

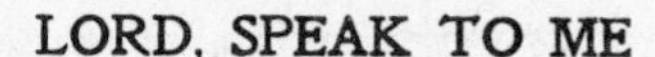

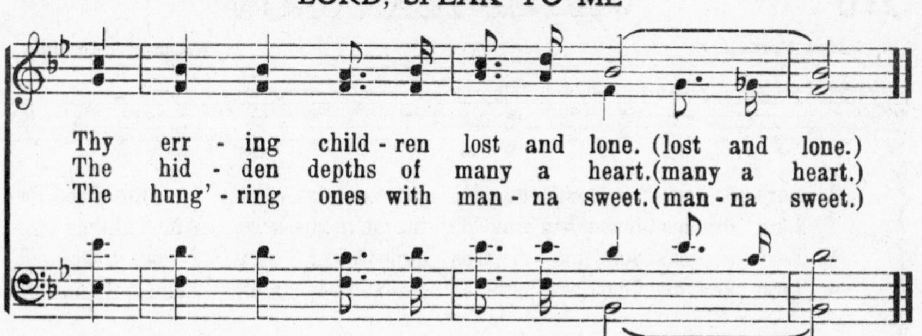

209. RISE, GLORIOUS CONQUEROR

Matthew Bridges — Lowell Mason

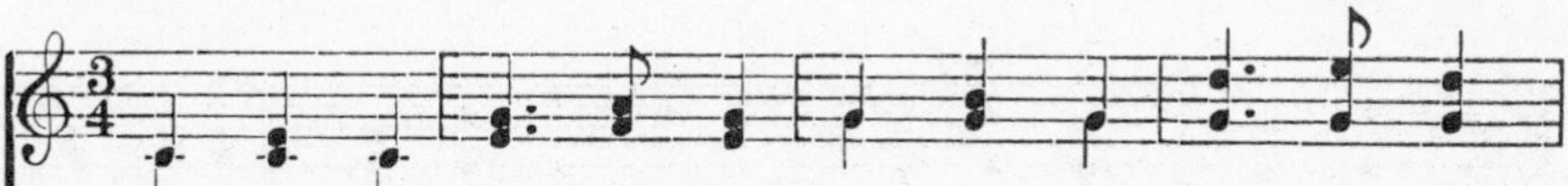

1. Rise, glo - rious Con - qu'ror, rise In - to Thy na - tive skies;
2. Vic - tor o'er death and hell, Cher - u - bic le - gions swell
3. En - ter, in - car - nate God! No feet but Thine have trod
4. Li - on of Ju - dah, hail! And let Thy name pre - vail

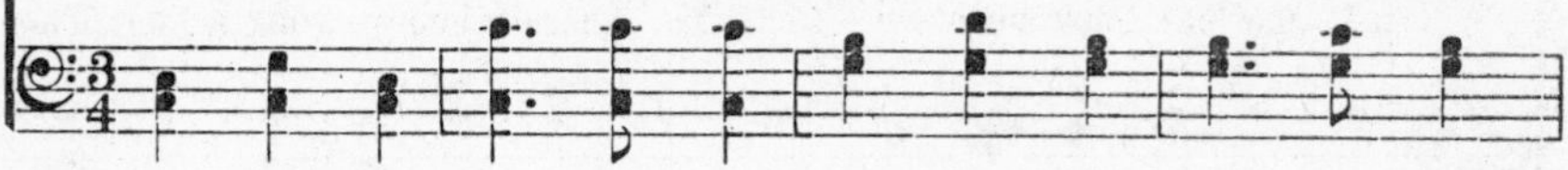

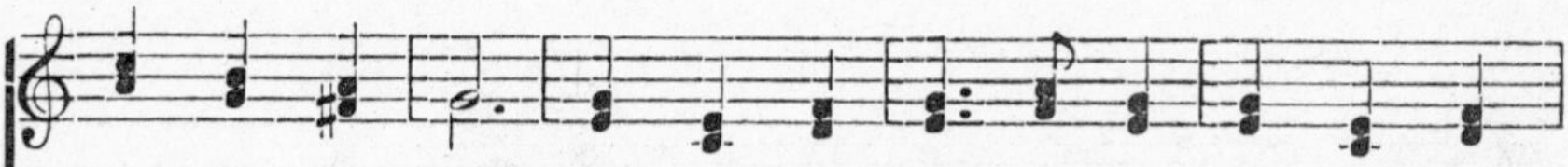

As - sume Thy right; And where in many a fold The clouds are
The ra - diant train: Prais - es all heav'n in - spire; Each an - gel
The ser - pent down: Blow the full trump - ets, blow, Wid - er yon
From age to age: Lord of the roll - ing years, Claim for Thine

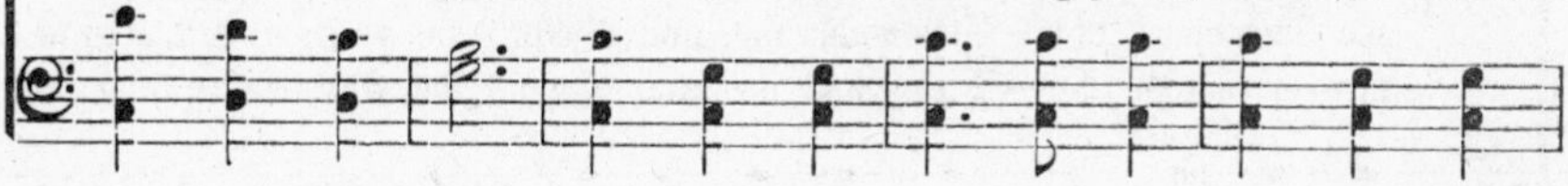

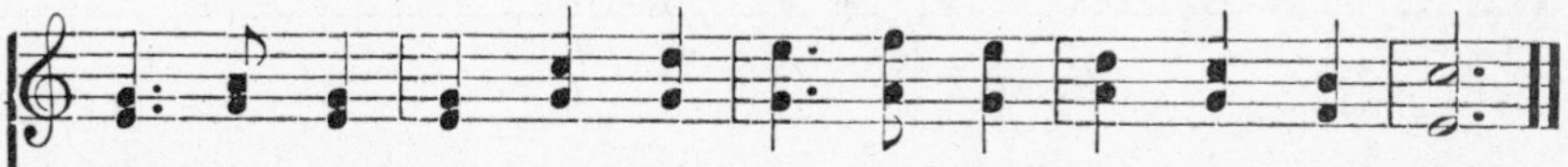

back - ward rolled, Pass thro' those gates of gold, And reign in light.
sweeps his lyre, And claps his wings of fire, Thou Lamb once slain!
por - tals throw, Sav - iour, tri - um - phant, go, And take Thy crown!
own the spheres Bought with Thy blood and tears, Thy her - it - age.

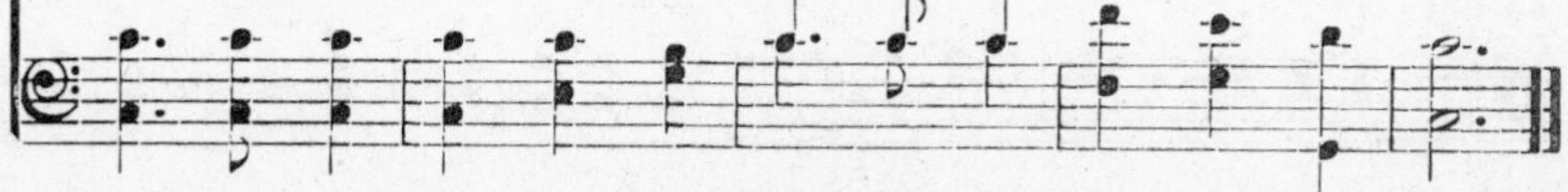

WHITER THAN SNOW

JAMES NICHOLSON
WILLIAM G. FISCHER
1. Lord Je - sus, I long to be per-fect-ly whole; I want Thee for-ev - er to live in my soul; Break down ev - ery i - dol, cast out ev - ery foe; Now wash me, and I shall be whit - er than snow.
2. Lord Je - sus, look down from Thy throne in the skies, And help me to make a com-plete sac - ri - fice; I give up my - self, and what-ev - er I know—Now wash me, and I shall be whit - er than snow.
3. Lord Je - sus, for this I most hum-bly en - treat, I wait, bless-ed Lord, at Thy cru - ci - fied feet; By faith, for my cleans-ing, I see Thy blood flow—Now wash me, and I shall be whit - er than snow.
4. Lord Je - sus, Thou see - est I pa - tient-ly wait, Come now, and with-in me a new heart cre - ate; To those who have sought Thee, Thou nev - er saidst No— Now wash me, and I shall be whit - er than snow.
CHORUS
Whiter than snow, yes, whiter than snow; Now wash me, and I shall be whiter than snow.

211 IS MY NAME WRITTEN THERE?

M. A. K. FRANK M. DAVIS

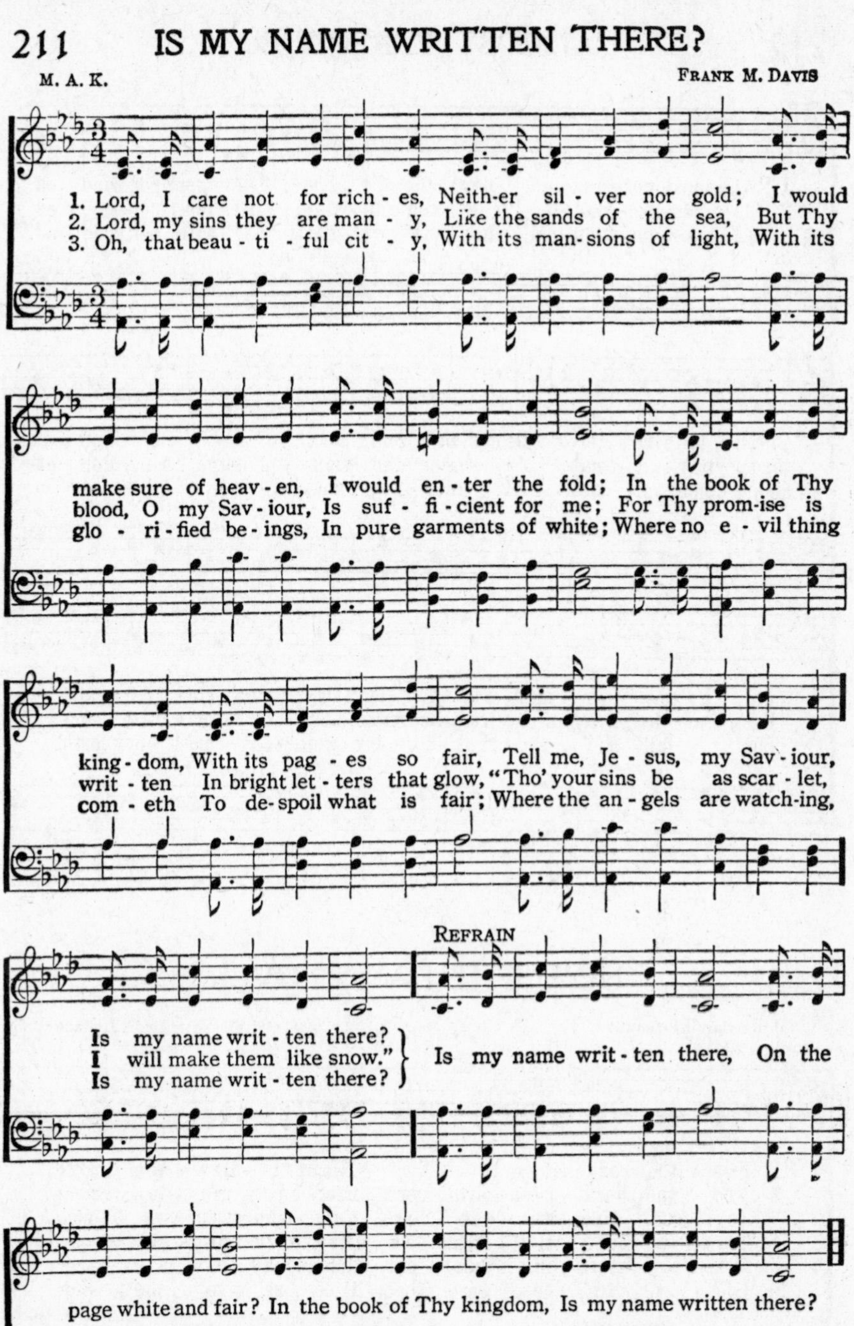
1. Lord, I care not for rich - es, Neith-er sil - ver nor gold; I would make sure of heav - en, I would en - ter the fold; In the book of Thy king - dom, With its pag - es so fair, Tell me, Je - sus, my Sav - iour, Is my name writ - ten there?
2. Lord, my sins they are man - y, Like the sands of the sea, But Thy blood, O my Sav - iour, Is suf - fi - cient for me; For Thy prom - ise is writ - ten In bright let - ters that glow, "Tho' your sins be as scar - let, I will make them like snow."
3. Oh, that beau - ti - ful cit - y, With its man - sions of light, With its glo - ri - fied be - ings, In pure garments of white; Where no e - vil thing com - eth To de - spoil what is fair; Where the an - gels are watch-ing, Is my name writ - ten there?
REFRAIN
Is my name writ - ten there, On the page white and fair? In the book of Thy kingdom, Is my name written there?

212 ALMOST PERSUADED

P. P. B. — P. P. Bliss

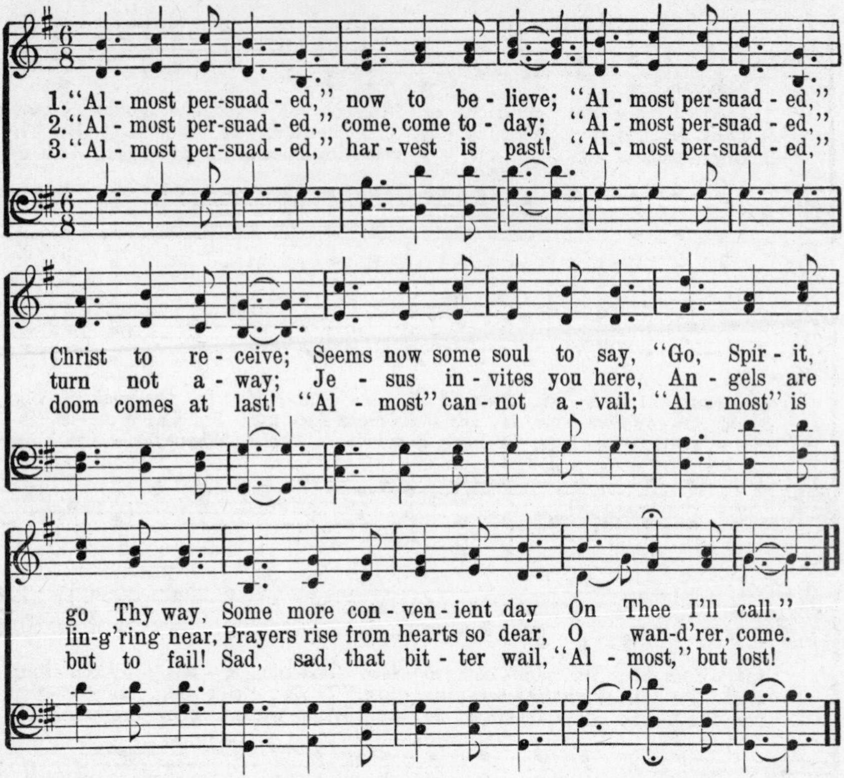

1. "Al - most per-suad - ed," now to be - lieve; "Al - most per-suad - ed," Christ to re - ceive; Seems now some soul to say, "Go, Spir - it, go Thy way, Some more con - ven - ient day On Thee I'll call."

2. "Al - most per-suad - ed," come, come to - day; "Al - most per-suad - ed," turn not a - way; Je - sus in - vites you here, An - gels are lin-g'ring near, Prayers rise from hearts so dear, O wan-d'rer, come.

3. "Al - most per-suad - ed," har - vest is past! "Al - most per-suad - ed," doom comes at last! "Al - most" can - not a - vail; "Al - most" is but to fail! Sad, sad, that bit - ter wail, "Al - most," but lost!

213 NOW THE DAY IS OVER

Sabine Barring-Gould — J. Barnby

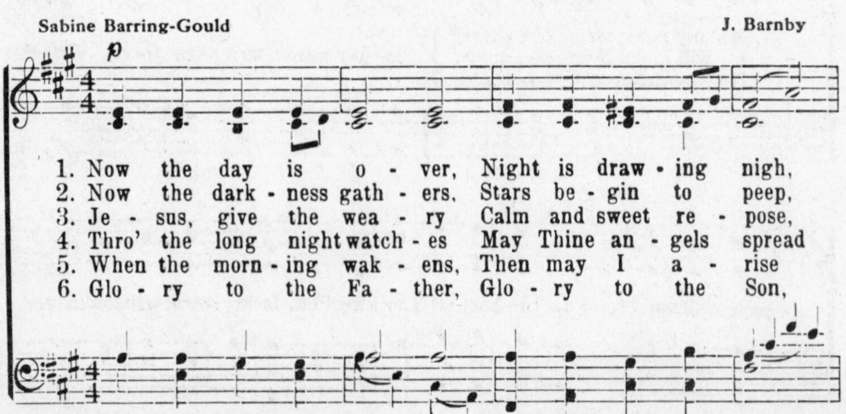

p
1. Now the day is o - ver, Night is draw - ing nigh,
2. Now the dark - ness gath - ers, Stars be - gin to peep,
3. Je - sus, give the wea - ry Calm and sweet re - pose,
4. Thro' the long night watch - es May Thine an - gels spread
5. When the morn - ing wak - ens, Then may I a - rise
6. Glo - ry to the Fa - ther, Glo - ry to the Son,

NOW THE DAY IS OVER

214 THE HEAVENLY HOME

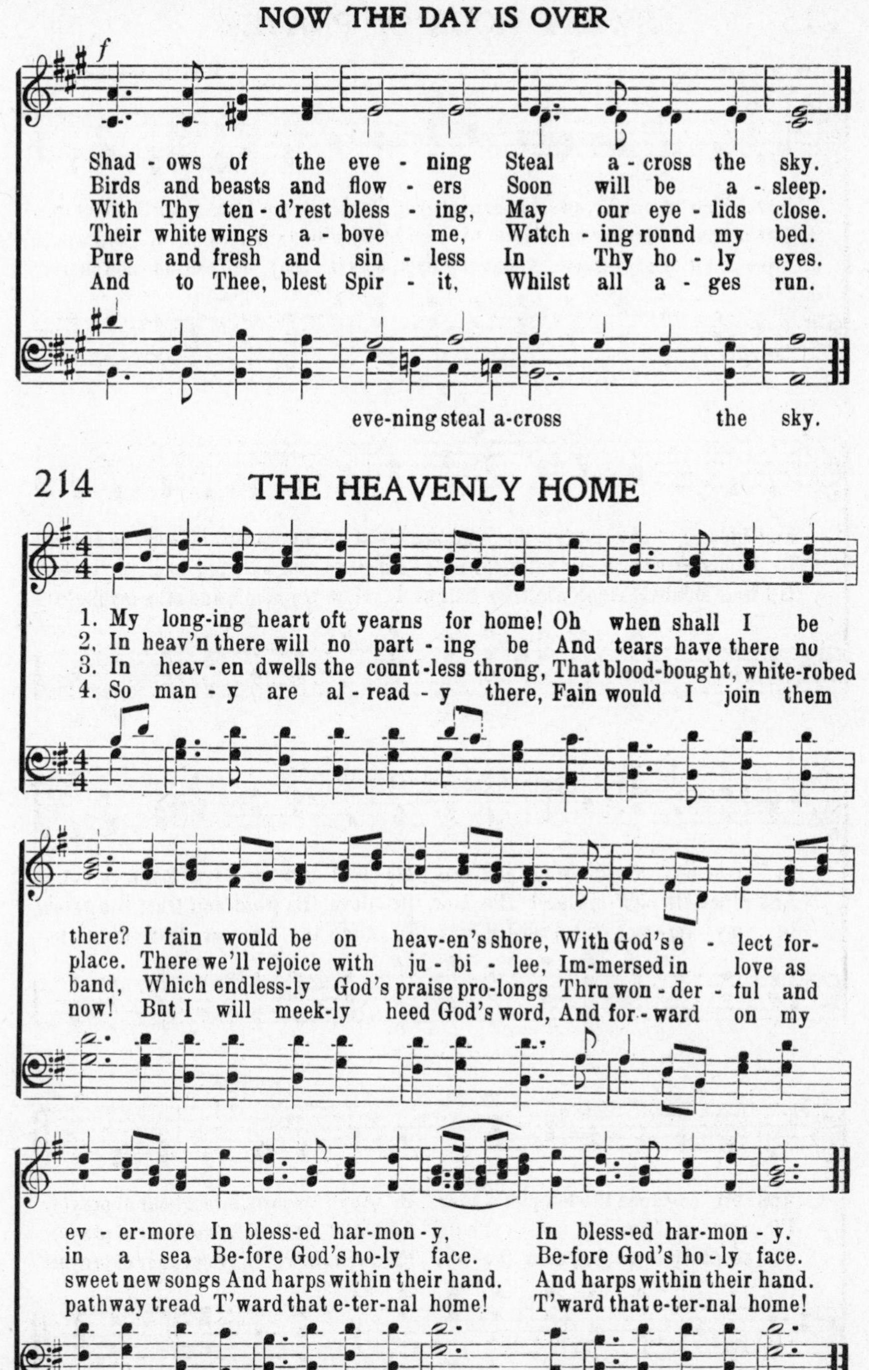

Shad - ows of the eve - ning Steal a - cross the sky.
Birds and beasts and flow - ers Soon will be a - sleep.
With Thy ten - d'rest bless - ing, May our eye - lids close.
Their white wings a - bove me, Watch - ing round my bed.
Pure and fresh and sin - less In Thy ho - ly eyes.
And to Thee, blest Spir - it, Whilst all a - ges run.
eve-ning steal a-cross the sky.
1. My long-ing heart oft yearns for home! Oh when shall I be there? I fain would be on heav-en's shore, With God's e - lect for ev - er-more In bless-ed har-mon - y, In bless-ed har-mon - y.
2. In heav'n there will no part - ing be And tears have there no place. There we'll rejoice with ju - bi - lee, Im-mersed in love as in a sea Be-fore God's ho-ly face. Be-fore God's ho - ly face.
3. In heav - en dwells the count - less throng, That blood-bought, white-robed band, Which endless-ly God's praise pro-longs Thru won - der - ful and sweet new songs And harps within their hand. And harps within their hand.
4. So man - y are al - read - y there, Fain would I join them now! But I will meek-ly heed God's word, And for - ward on my pathway tread T'ward that e-ter-nal home! T'ward that e-ter-nal home!

215 SWEET HOUR OF PRAYER

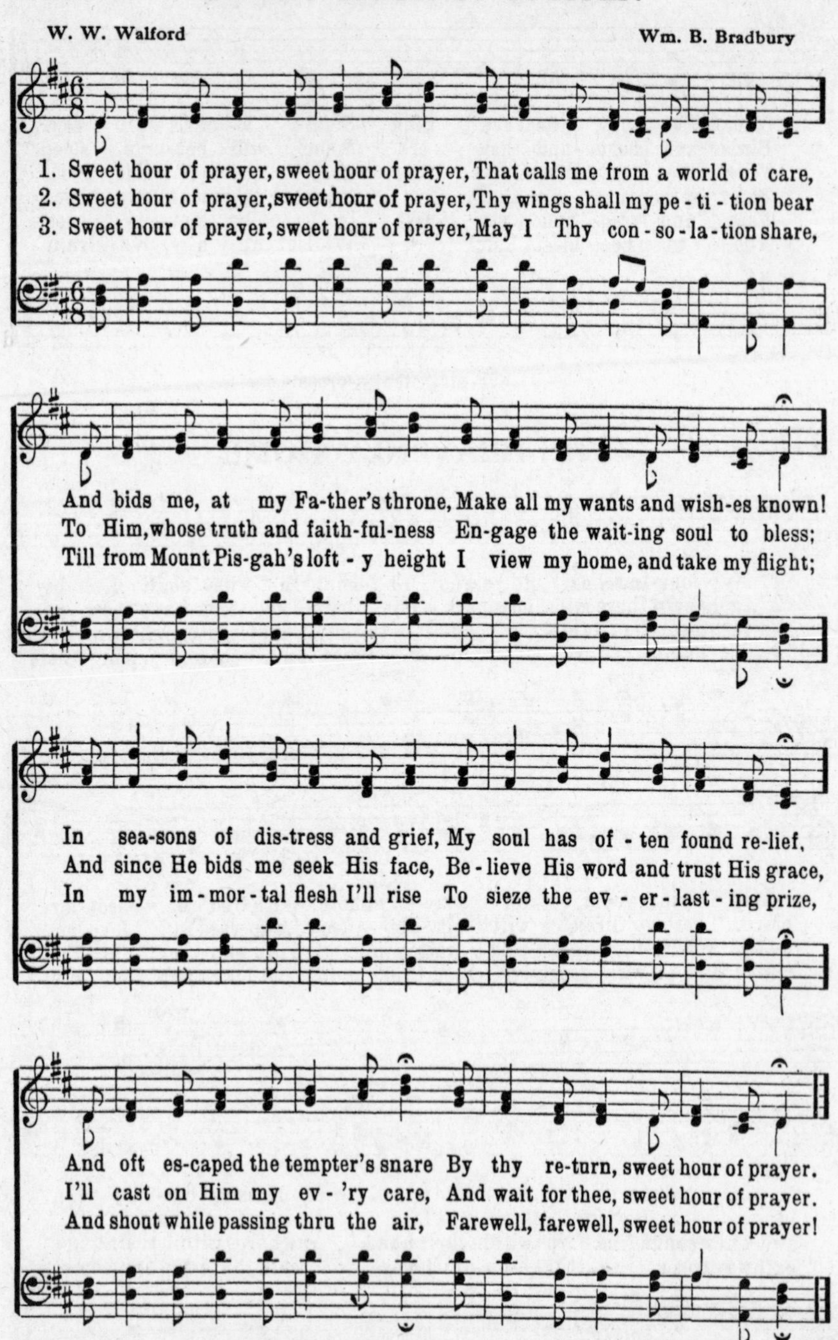
W. W. Walford
Wm. B. Bradbury
1. Sweet hour of prayer, sweet hour of prayer, That calls me from a world of care,
2. Sweet hour of prayer, sweet hour of prayer, Thy wings shall my pe - ti - tion bear
3. Sweet hour of prayer, sweet hour of prayer, May I Thy con - so - la - tion share,
And bids me, at my Fa-ther's throne, Make all my wants and wish-es known!
To Him, whose truth and faith-ful-ness En-gage the wait-ing soul to bless;
Till from Mount Pis-gah's loft - y height I view my home, and take my flight;
In sea-sons of dis-tress and grief, My soul has of - ten found re-lief,
And since He bids me seek His face, Be - lieve His word and trust His grace,
In my im - mor - tal flesh I'll rise To sieze the ev - er - last - ing prize,
And oft es-caped the tempter's snare By thy re-turn, sweet hour of prayer.
I'll cast on Him my ev - 'ry care, And wait for thee, sweet hour of prayer.
And shout while passing thru the air, Farewell, farewell, sweet hour of prayer!

216 GOD BE WITH YOU

J. E. Rankin
W. G. Tomer
1. God be with you till we meet a-gain; By His counsels guide, uphold you,
2. God be with you till we meet a-gain; 'Neath His wings protecting hide you,
3. God be with you till we meet a-gain; When life's perils thick confound you,
4. God be with you till we meet a-gain; Keep love's banner floating o'er you;
With His sheep se-cure-ly fold you; God be with you till we meet a-gain.
Dai-ly man-na still pro-vide you; God be with you till we meet a-gain.
Put His arms un-fail-ing round you; God be with you till we meet a-gain.
Smite death's threat'ning wave before you; God be with you till we meet a-gain.
Refrain
Till we meet, ... till we meet, Till we meet at Je-sus' feet;
Till we meet, till we meet, till we meet;
Till we meet, ... till we meet, God be with you till we meet a-gain.
Till we meet, till we meet,

217 SHALL WE MEET?

H. L. HASTINGS — ELIHU S. RICE

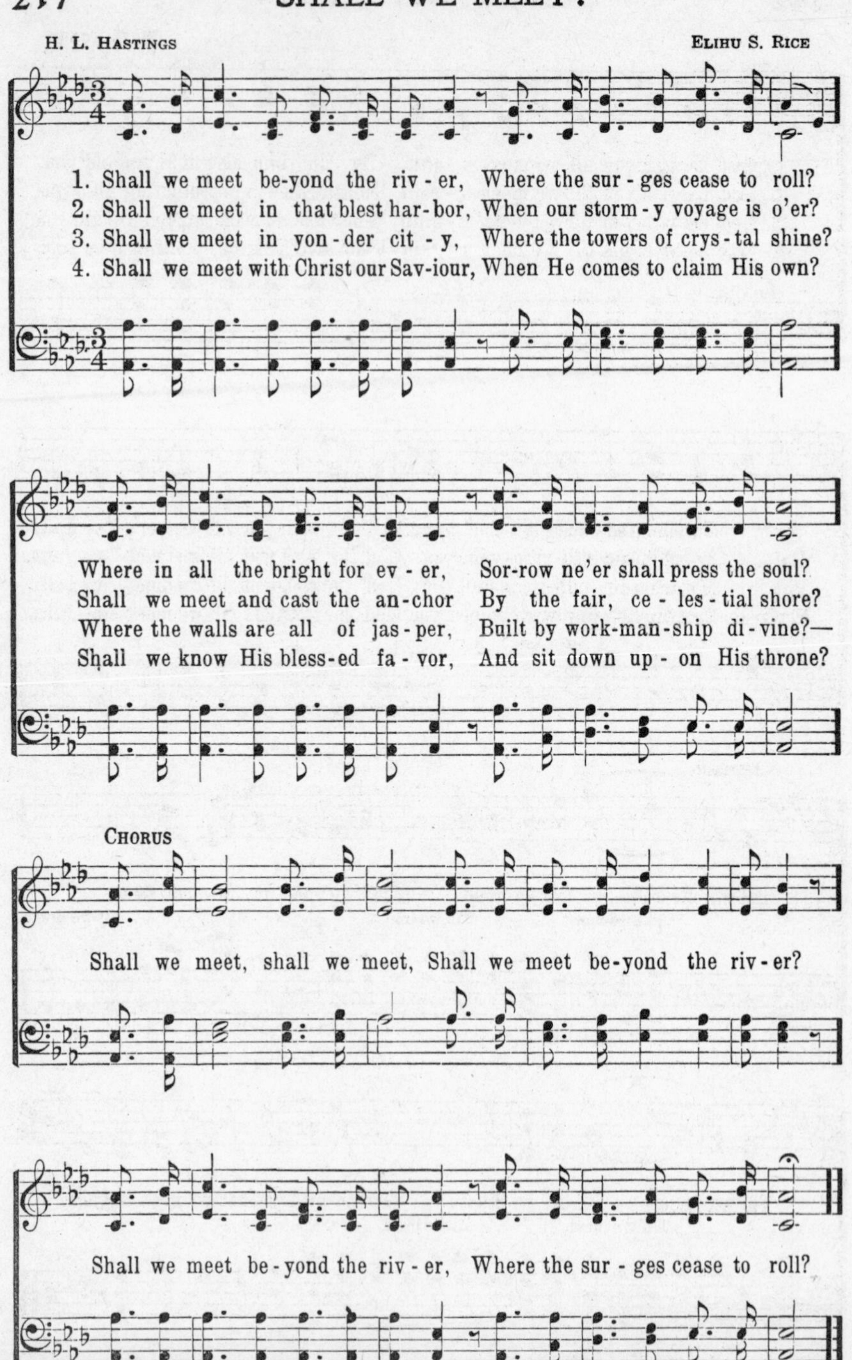
1. Shall we meet be-yond the riv - er, Where the sur - ges cease to roll?
2. Shall we meet in that blest har-bor, When our storm - y voyage is o'er?
3. Shall we meet in yon - der cit - y, Where the towers of crys - tal shine?
4. Shall we meet with Christ our Sav-iour, When He comes to claim His own?
Where in all the bright for ev - er, Sor-row ne'er shall press the soul?
Shall we meet and cast the an-chor By the fair, ce - les - tial shore?
Where the walls are all of jas - per, Built by work-man-ship di - vine?—
Shall we know His bless-ed fa - vor, And sit down up - on His throne?
CHORUS
Shall we meet, shall we meet, Shall we meet be-yond the riv - er?
Shall we meet be - yond the riv - er, Where the sur - ges cease to roll?

218 SAFE IN THE ARMS OF JESUS

FANNY J. CROSBY — W. H. DOANE

1. Safe in the arms of Je - sus, Safe on His gen - tle breast, There by His love o'er - shad - ed, Sweet-ly my soul shall rest. Hark! 'tis the voice of an - gels, Borne in a song to me, O - ver the fields of glo - ry, O - ver the jas - per sea.........
2. Safe in the arms of Je - sus, Safe from cor-rod - ing care, Safe from the world's temp-ta - tions, Sin can-not harm me there. Free from the blight of sor - row, Free from my doubts and fears; On - ly a few more tri - als, On - ly a few more tears!.....
3. Je - sus, my heart's dear ref - uge, Je - sus has died for me; Firm on the Rock of A - ges, Ev - er my trust shall be. Here let me wait with pa - tience, Wait till the night is o'er; Wait till I see the morn - ing Break on the gold-en shore......
CHORUS
Safe in the arms of Je - sus, Safe on His gen - tle breast, There by His love o'er - shad - ed, Sweetly my soul shall rest.

219 STAND UP FOR JESUS

G. DUFFIELD — G. J. WEBB

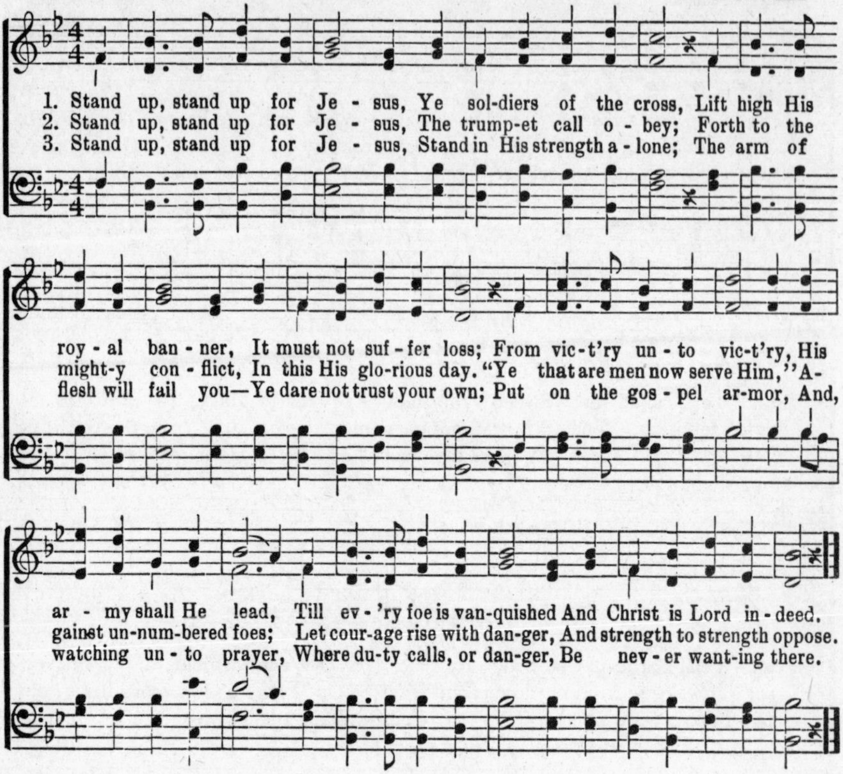

1. Stand up, stand up for Je - sus, Ye sol-diers of the cross, Lift high His roy - al ban - ner, It must not suf - fer loss; From vic-t'ry un - to vic-t'ry, His ar - my shall He lead, Till ev - 'ry foe is van-quished And Christ is Lord in - deed.
2. Stand up, stand up for Je - sus, The trump-et call o - bey; Forth to the might-y con - flict, In this His glo-rious day. "Ye that are men now serve Him," A-gainst un-num-bered foes; Let cour-age rise with dan-ger, And strength to strength oppose.
3. Stand up, stand up for Je - sus, Stand in His strength a - lone; The arm of flesh will fail you—Ye dare not trust your own; Put on the gos-pel ar-mor, And, watching un - to prayer, Where du-ty calls, or dan-ger, Be nev - er want-ing there.

220 HOLY SPIRIT, FAITHFUL GUIDE

M. M. W. — M. M. Wells

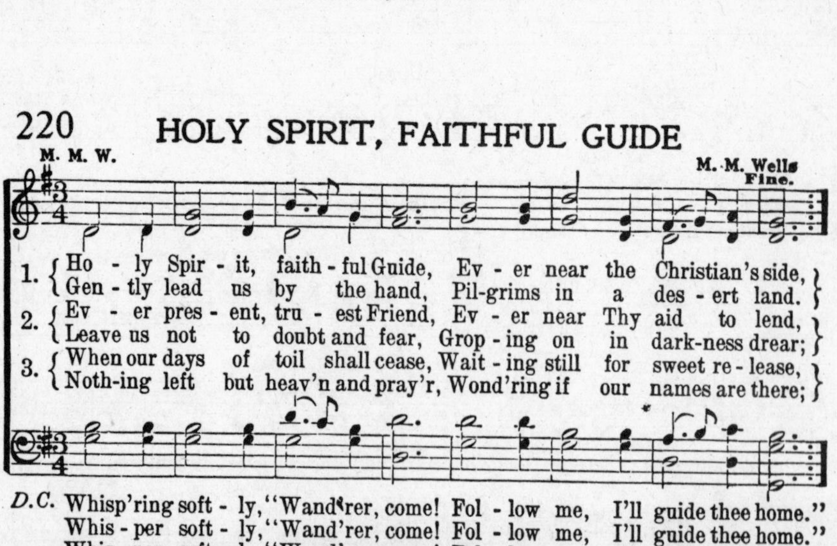

Fine.
1. { Ho - ly Spir - it, faith - ful Guide, Ev - er near the Christian's side, Gen - tly lead us by the hand, Pil-grims in a des - ert land. }
2. { Ev - er pres - ent, tru - est Friend, Ev - er near Thy aid to lend, Leave us not to doubt and fear, Grop - ing on in dark-ness drear; }
3. { When our days of toil shall cease, Wait - ing still for sweet re - lease, Noth-ing left but heav'n and pray'r, Wond'ring if our names are there; }
D.C. Whisp'ring soft - ly, "Wand'rer, come! Fol - low me, I'll guide thee home."
Whis - per soft - ly, "Wand'rer, come! Fol - low me, I'll guide thee home."
Whis - per soft - ly, "Wand'rer, come! Fol - low me, I'll guide thee home."

HOLY SPIRIT, FAITHFUL GUIDE

D. C.
Wea - ry souls for - e'er re - joice, While they hear the sweet - est voice,
When the storms are rag - ing sore, Hearts grow faint and hopes give o'er,
Wad - ing deep the dis - mal flood, Plead-ing naught but Je - sus' blood,

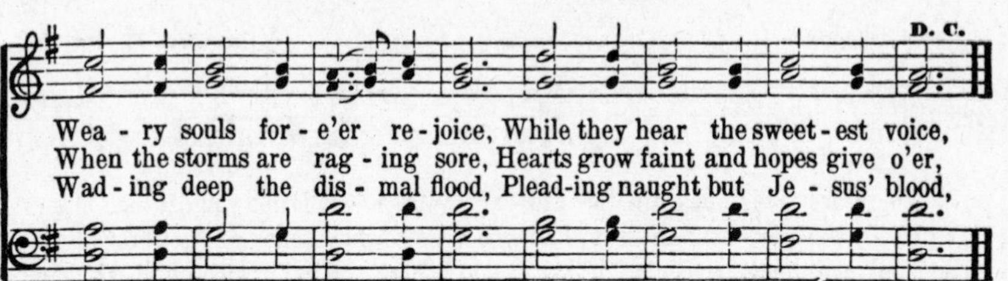

221 ONE SWEETLY SOLEMN THOUGHT

PHŒBE CARY PHILIP PHILLIPS

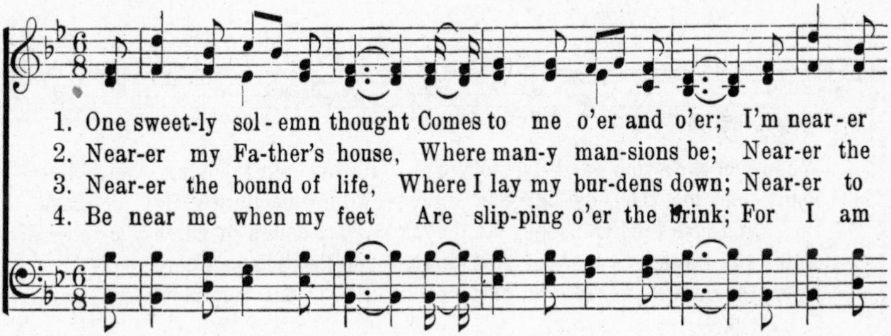

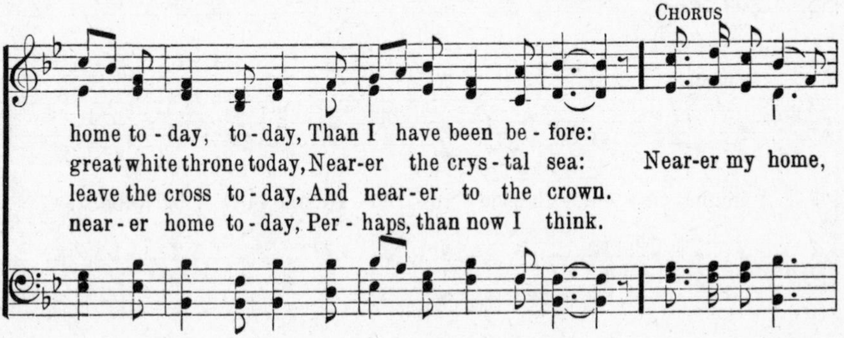

1. One sweet-ly sol - emn thought Comes to me o'er and o'er; I'm near - er
2. Near-er my Fa-ther's house, Where man-y man-sions be; Near-er the
3. Near-er the bound of life, Where I lay my bur-dens down; Near-er to
4. Be near me when my feet Are slip-ping o'er the brink; For I am

CHORUS
home to - day, to - day, Than I have been be - fore:
great white throne today, Near-er the crys - tal sea: Near-er my home,
leave the cross to - day, And near - er to the crown.
near - er home to - day, Per - haps, than now I think.

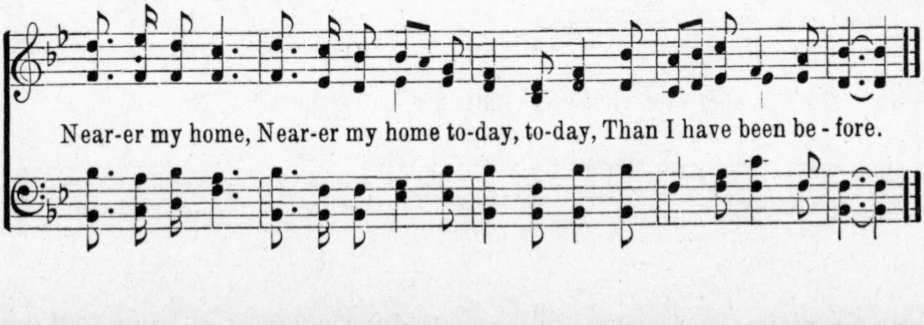

Near-er my home, Near-er my home to-day, to-day, Than I have been be - fore.

222 WILL THE CIRCLE BE UNBROKEN?

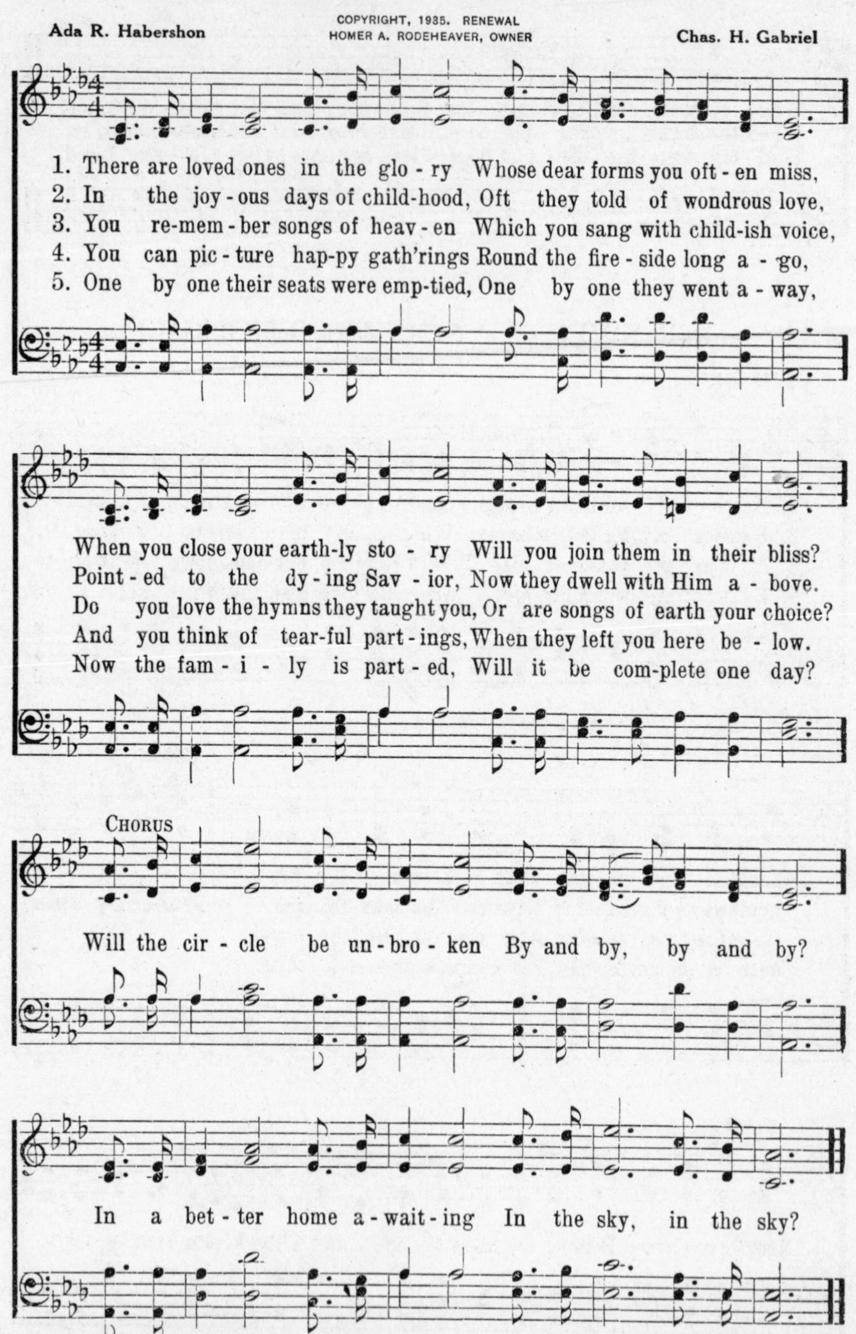

Ada R. Habershon
COPYRIGHT, 1935. RENEWAL
HOMER A. RODEHEAVER, OWNER
Chas. H. Gabriel
1. There are loved ones in the glo - ry Whose dear forms you oft - en miss,
2. In the joy - ous days of child-hood, Oft they told of wondrous love,
3. You re-mem - ber songs of heav - en Which you sang with child-ish voice,
4. You can pic - ture hap-py gath'rings Round the fire - side long a - go,
5. One by one their seats were emp-tied, One by one they went a - way,
When you close your earth-ly sto - ry Will you join them in their bliss?
Point - ed to the dy - ing Sav - ior, Now they dwell with Him a - bove.
Do you love the hymns they taught you, Or are songs of earth your choice?
And you think of tear-ful part - ings, When they left you here be - low.
Now the fam - i - ly is part - ed, Will it be com-plete one day?
CHORUS
Will the cir - cle be un - bro - ken By and by, by and by?
In a bet - ter home a - wait - ing In the sky, in the sky?

223 CLOSE TO THEE

Fanny J. Crosby — Silas J. Vail

1. Thou, my ev - er - last-ing por - tion, More than friend or life to me;
2. Not for ease or world-ly pleas - ure, Nor for fame my pray'r shall be;
3. Thou didst take the cup of suff'-ring, Pray-ing in Geth-sem - a - ne;
FINE
D. S. All a-long my pil-grim jour - ney, Sav-iour, let me walk with Thee.
D. S. Glad-ly will I toil and suf - fer, On - ly let me walk with Thee.
D. S. In the sor - row of Thine hou - 'r, Sav-iour, let me watch with Thee.
REFRAIN
D. S.
Close to Thee, close to Thee, Close to Thee, close to Thee;

4. Thou didst bear to Calv'ry's mountain,
Cross, and stripes, and thorns for me;
‖: Let me on that fateful journey,
Saviour, bear Thy cross with Thee. :‖

5. Tasting death for ev'ry mortal,
By God's grace on Calvary;
‖: Sharing there Thy crucifixion,
Saviour, let me die with Thee. :‖

6. Dead to sin, I am now buried,
From its curse forever free;
‖: Buried with Thee in baptism,
Saviour, let me rest with Thee. :‖

7. Planted with Thee in Thy dying,
Risen like Thee I shall be;
‖: By the Father's might and glory,
Saviour, let me rise with Thee. :‖

8. Dead to Law, and its dominion,
Under grace I am now free;
‖: In the new life of Thy Spirit,
Saviour, let me walk with Thee. :‖

9. Things above, I am now seeking,
Life is hid in God with Thee;
‖: In the heav'nlies with the blessed,
Saviour, let me sit with Thee. :‖

10. Blessed hope, I 'wait Thy coming,
In a moment changed I'll be;
‖: Should I sooner end my journey,
Saviour, let me sleep in Thee. :‖

11. Brought with Thee in resurrection,
Raised to meet Thee in the air;
‖: Immortality's perfection,
Saviour, let me with Thee share. :‖

12. Lead me through the vale of shadows,
Bear me o'er life's fitful sea;
‖: Then the gate of life eternal,
May I enter, Lord, with Thee. :‖

Stanzas 3 to 11, incl., by P. G., Jr.

THE HOLY LAND

Thomas Hastings

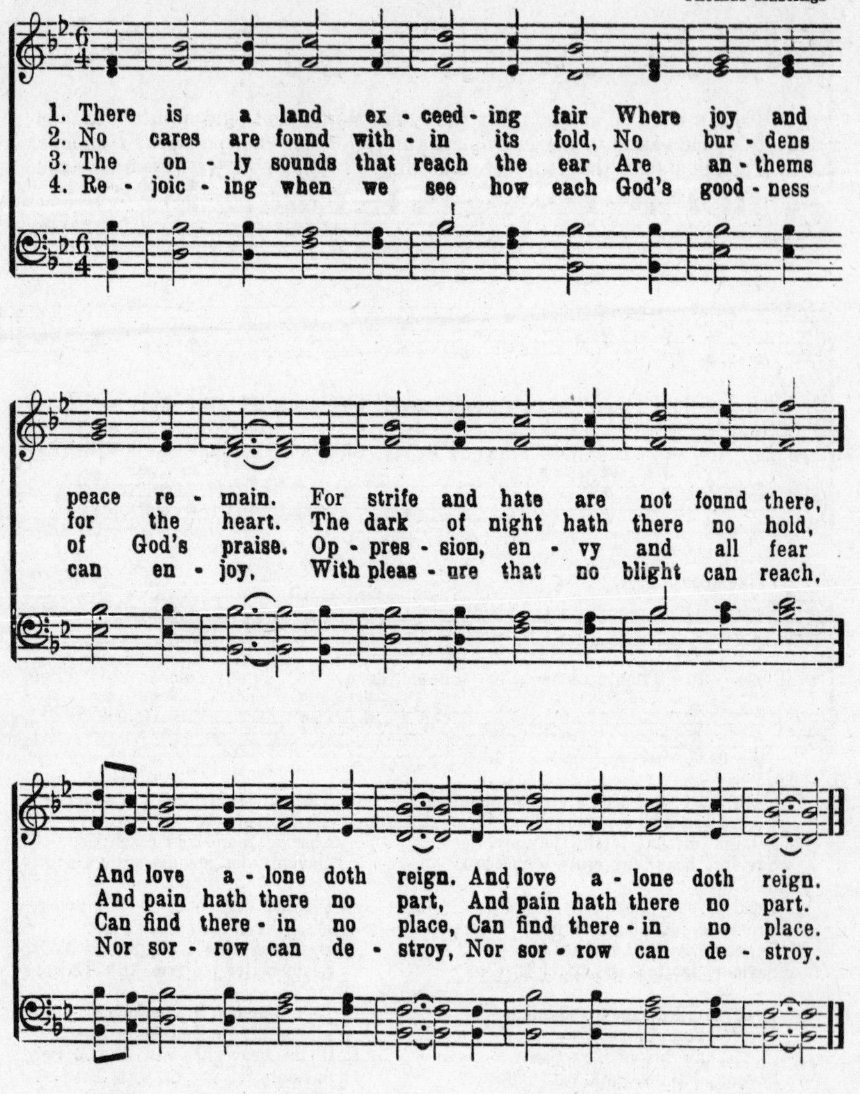
1. There is a land ex - ceed - ing fair Where joy and peace re - main. For strife and hate are not found there, And love a - lone doth reign. And love a - lone doth reign.
2. No cares are found with - in its fold, No bur - dens for the heart. The dark of night hath there no hold, And pain hath there no part, And pain hath there no part.
3. The on - ly sounds that reach the ear Are an - thems of God's praise. Op - pres - sion, en - vy and all fear Can find there - in no place, Can find there - in no place.
4. Re - joic - ing when we see how each God's good - ness can en - joy, With pleas - ure that no blight can reach, Nor sor - row can de - stroy, Nor sor - row can de - stroy.

5. The glory of the Lord will shine
Through-out this Holy land.
Eternal morn, without decline
:God's praises will expand,:.

6. And weary from this earthly strife
The pilgrim there finds rest,
Throughout that everlasting life
:God's holy name be blest,:.

7. O land of rest, thou sacred shrine!
When may I thee behold,
And enter through thy port divine
:To glory still untold,:.

8. How happy when relieved we'll be
From toils and cares of mind,
And in that holy land so free
.Eternal rest we'll find,:.

225 BE FAITHFUL

1. Faith - ful un - to death re - main, Faith - ful un - to
2. Faith - ful un - to death re - main, Faith - ful un - to
3. Faith - ful un - to death re - main, Faith - ful un - to
4. Faith - ful un - to death re - main, Faith - ful un - to
death re - main! Toil and care, O may they nev - er
death re - main! Those who strive have crowns a - wait - ing,
death re - main! With the shin - ing crown be - fore you
death re - main! Hope and trust in God con - fess - ing
From the cross of Christ thee sev - er! Glad - ly suf - fer
While the world with scorn is hat - ing, Though the tears thy
Rise un - to the re - gions o'er you In the Lamb thy
Dai - ly on my heart im - press-ing Thy Word, Lord, so
grief and pain. Faith - ful un - to death re - main!
food may stain, Faith - ful un - to death re - main!
trust re - tain, Faith - ful un - to death re - main!
clear and plain, Faith - ful un - to death re - main!

ALL THAT FILLS MY HEART

1. My life's best de - light and pleas - ure Is yon heav - en,
2. Oth - ers may find sat - is - fac - tion In the greed for
3. No-where are there great - er treas - ures Than in Je - sus
4. Though I lived a thou - sand sea - sons, World - ly joys would
5. When the Word of Christ the Faith - ful Fi - nal - ly shall
6. Share then, Lord, to me the rap - ture That with Thee I
God's own throne! And my great - est prize and treas - ure
world - ly gain; Heav'n a - lone is my at - trac - tion
Christ I find. All the earth - ly joys and pleas - ures
not en - dure; But to live one day for Je - sus
be ful - filled, Then His own will come re - joic - ing,
may a - bide! Be my guide, my sun of splen - dor
Is my Sav - iour, God's own Son. All that fills my
Close to Je - sus I'll re - main! Earth-ly rich - es
On - ly bur - den heart and mind. Just to call the
Would more hap - pi - ness se - cure. In the high - est
Tears and cry - ing shall be stilled. Then His glo - ry
That will nev - er lose its light! Draw me whol - ly
heart with joy Waits in glo - ry there on high,
pass and fail, Je - sus and His realm pre - vail,
Lord my own, Sat - is - fies my soul a - lone.
ranks they stand Who at - tain to God's right hand,
will ap - pear, Un - to all, both far and near,
un - to Thee, Ev - er - more with Thee to be,

ALL THAT FILLS MY HEART

Waits in glo - ry there on high! All that fills my heart with joy Waits in glo - ry there on high, Waits in glo - ry there on high, Waits in glo - ry there on high
Je - sus and His realm pre - vail! Earth - ly rich - es pass and fail, Je - sus and His realm pre - vail. Je - sus and His realm pre - vail, Je - sus and His realm pre - vail.
Sat - is - fies my soul a - lone. Just to call the Lord my own, Sat - is- fies my soul a - lone, Sat - is - fies my soul a - lone, Sat - is - fies my soul a - lone.
Who at - tain to God's right hand. In the high - est ranks they stand Who at- tain to God's right hand, Who at - tain to God's right hand, Who at - tain to God's right hand.
Un - to all, both far and near! Then His glo - ry will ap - pear Un - to all both far and near, Un - to all both far and near, Un - to all both far and near.
Ev - er - more with Thee to be, Draw me whol - ly un - to Thee, Ev - er more with Thee to be, Ev - er - more with Thee to be, Ev - er - more with Thee to be.

227 PSALM 117

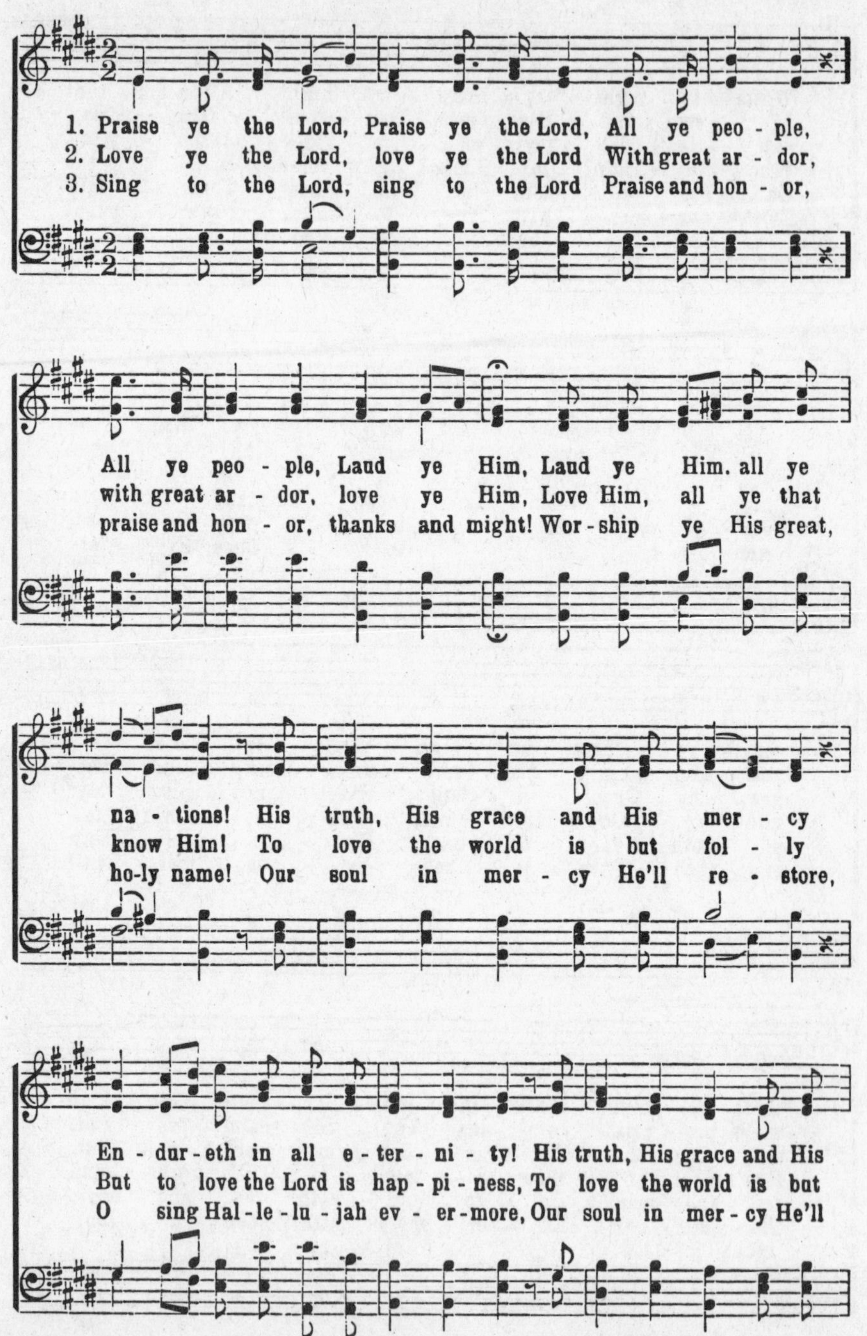
1. Praise ye the Lord, Praise ye the Lord, All ye peo - ple,
2. Love ye the Lord, love ye the Lord With great ar - dor,
3. Sing to the Lord, sing to the Lord Praise and hon - or,
All ye peo - ple, Laud ye Him, Laud ye Him. all ye
with great ar - dor, love ye Him, Love Him, all ye that
praise and hon - or, thanks and might! Wor - ship ye His great,
na - tions! His truth, His grace and His mer - cy
know Him! To love the world is but fol - ly
ho-ly name! Our soul in mer - cy He'll re - store,
En - dur - eth in all e - ter - ni - ty! His truth, His grace and His
But to love the Lord is hap - pi - ness, To love the world is but
O sing Hal - le - lu - jah ev - er - more, Our soul in mer - cy He'll

PSALM 117

mer - cy En - dur-eth in all e - ter - ni - ty! Hal - le - lu - jah!
fol - ly, But to love the Lord is hap - pi - ness! Hal - le - lu - jah!
re - store, O sing Hal - le - lu - jah ev - er - more! Hal - le - lu - jah!
Hal - le - lu - jah Hal - le - lu - jah Hal - le - lu - jah
228 THE UNION IN JESUS' DEATH
ZION'S HARP. 11
We, who in God's name are here as-sem-bled, Sol-emn-ly do clasp our hands;
That Christ's death and suff'ring be remembered, Faithful-ly for Him to stand.
Thus in un - i - son our hearts have spoken. Lord to show Thy fav-or give the
rit.
tok - en, Speak thy blessing ev - er true, "A - men", Peace be un - to you.

229 THE HOME OF THE SOUL

1. O where is the home of the soul to be found? Who knows
2. How bliss - ful the rest in that cit - y so fair, Where, dwell-
3. So leave this poor earth if that home thou wouldst see, The home
its true shel - ter where com - forts a - bound? What cit - y of
ing with Je - sus, the soul has no care! The sound - ing of
of the saint - ed from sor - row made free, Je - ru - sa - lem,
ref - uge will of - fer a place That sin can - not en-
harps in those man - sions a - bove Do bid the soul wel-
cit - y re - splend - ent in gold, Wilt Thou to the soul
ter the soul to dis - grace? No - where, no - where do we be-
come in heav - en - ly love. Rest, rest, rest, rest, heav - en - ly
all thy beau - ties un - fold? Tru - ly, tru - ly, Thou art the
hold On earth such a cit - y of bless - ings un - told.
rest, I long to em - brace thee, to be with the blest.
goal, Where rest is the por - tion of ev - 'ry pure soul!
f
f

230 FAREWELL

1. Be - lov - ed breth - ren, fare ye well! As
2. How oft did Je - sus come so near That
3. How oft did God our spir - its raise When
4. Should we be sev - ered far a - part We
5. There re - u - nit - ed we will be, Where
we must part, in love we tell, Fare - well; un - til we
we were moved with god - ly fear, And when our hearts, in-
we in prayer did seek His grace; And there be - fore His
know the Lord leads ev - 'ry heart He, as the Shep-herd,
part - ing tears no more we'll see. With count-less hosts we
meet a - gain Per - haps be - fore God's throne to stand.
flamed with love, Re - ceived the bless - ing from a - bove.
throne did plead The Son of God to in - ter - cede!
full of love Will gath - er us in heav'n a - bove.
shall a - dore And praise our God for - ev - er - more.
CHORUS
p
pp
p
Fare - well, fare - well, fare - well, fare-
p
pp
p
well! Our dear, cher - ished breth - ren, fare ye well!
f

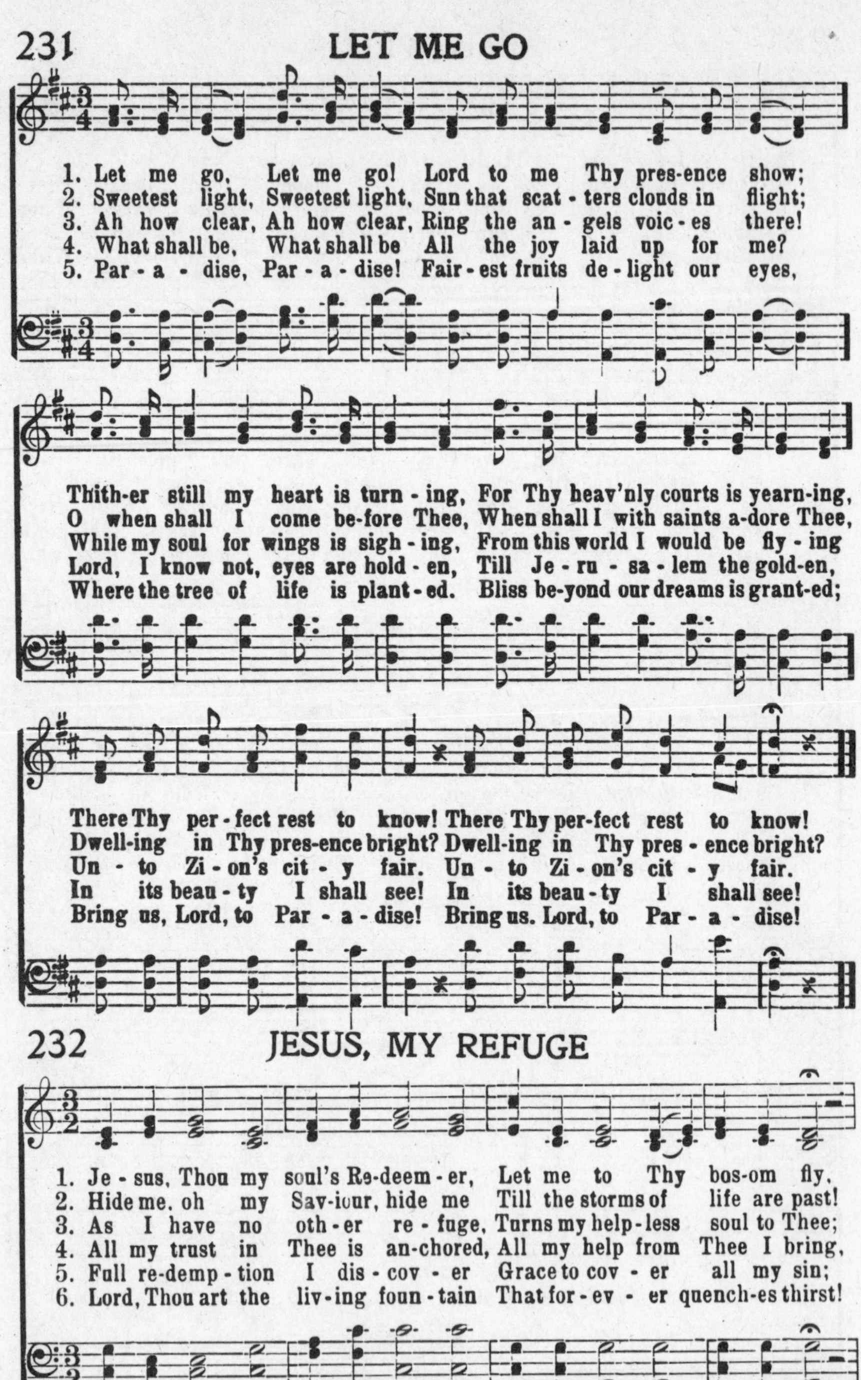
231 LET ME GO
1. Let me go, Let me go! Lord to me Thy pres-ence show;
2. Sweetest light, Sweetest light, Sun that scat - ters clouds in flight;
3. Ah how clear, Ah how clear, Ring the an - gels voic - es there!
4. What shall be, What shall be All the joy laid up for me?
5. Par - a - dise, Par - a - dise! Fair - est fruits de - light our eyes,
Thith-er still my heart is turn - ing, For Thy heav'nly courts is yearn-ing,
O when shall I come be-fore Thee, When shall I with saints a-dore Thee,
While my soul for wings is sigh - ing, From this world I would be fly - ing
Lord, I know not, eyes are hold - en, Till Je - ru - sa - lem the gold-en,
Where the tree of life is plant - ed. Bliss be-yond our dreams is grant-ed;
There Thy per - fect rest to know! There Thy per-fect rest to know!
Dwell-ing in Thy pres-ence bright? Dwell-ing in Thy pres - ence bright?
Un - to Zi - on's cit - y fair. Un - to Zi - on's cit - y fair.
In its beau - ty I shall see! In its beau - ty I shall see!
Bring us, Lord, to Par - a - dise! Bring us. Lord, to Par - a - dise!
232 JESUS, MY REFUGE
1. Je - sus, Thou my soul's Re-deem - er, Let me to Thy bos-om fly,
2. Hide me, oh my Sav-iour, hide me Till the storms of life are past!
3. As I have no oth - er re - fuge, Turns my help - less soul to Thee;
4. All my trust in Thee is an-chored, All my help from Thee I bring,
5. Full re-demp - tion I dis - cov - er Grace to cov - er all my sin;
6. Lord, Thou art the liv - ing foun - tain That for - ev - er quench-es thirst!

JESUS, MY REFUGE

233 WHEN HEAVEN'S WAYS A SOUL FORSAKES

While the floods are roll - ing near - er, While the temp-est still is high!
Safe in - to the ha - ven guide me, O receive my soul at last!
Leave me not, nor yet for-sake me, Still sup - port and com - fort me!
Cov - er my de - fense-less should-ers With the shad-ow of Thy wing!
Let the heal - ing stream o'erflow me, Make me, keep me pure with - in!
May the source of life e - ter - nal In - to my heart free - ly burst!
1. When heav-en's ways a soul for - sakes, A - las! As man-y do,
2. What does the world of sin af - ford Of hap-pi-ness for thee?
3. If in My house thou dost a - bide, Rich for-tune thou shalt see;
4. There threat-ens thee e - ter - nal death In Sa-tan's realm of night;
5. Lord strength-en Thou me from a - bove That I may stand thro' grace;
It seems I hear the Mas - ter say: Wilt thou for-sake me too?
A for-tune of dur - a - tion short, So do not turn from me!
Since once thou didst in me con - fide, Now do not turn from Me!
So strive un - til the Vic-t'ry's won, The crown in end-less light.
And af - ter that dread night of death, May see Thee face to face!
Wilt thou for-sake me too? Wilt thou for-sake me too?
So do not turn from me! So do not turn from me!
Now do not turn from Me! Now do not turn from Me!
The crown in end-less light, The crown in end-less light.
May see Thee face to face! May see Thee face to face!

234 SUNDAY MORNING

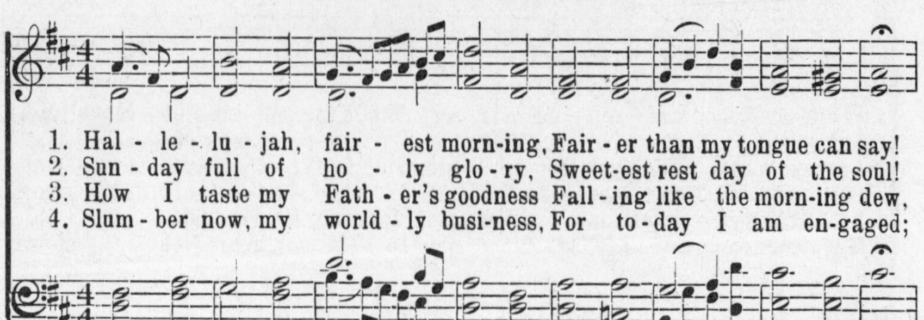
1. Hal - le - lu - jah, fair - est morn-ing, Fair - er than my tongue can say!
2. Sun - day full of ho - ly glo - ry, Sweet-est rest day of the soul!
3. How I taste my Fath - er's goodness Fall - ing like the morn-ing dew,
4. Slum - ber now, my world - ly busi-ness, For to-day I am en-gaged;

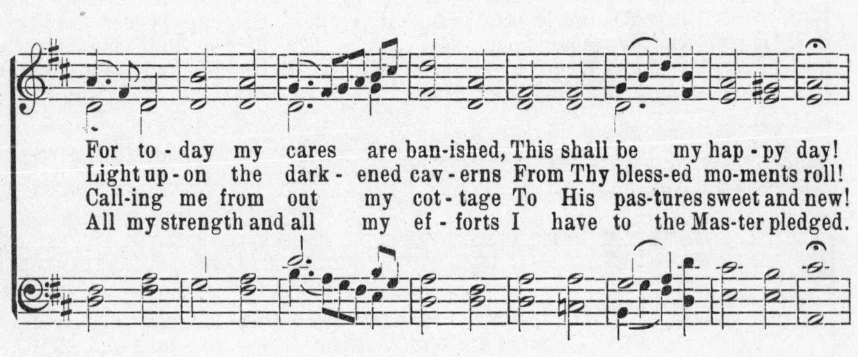
For to-day my cares are ban-ished, This shall be my hap - py day!
Light up-on the dark - ened cav - erns From Thy bless-ed mo-ments roll!
Call-ing me from out my cot - tage To His pas-tures sweet and new!
All my strength and all my ef - forts I have to the Mas-ter pledged.

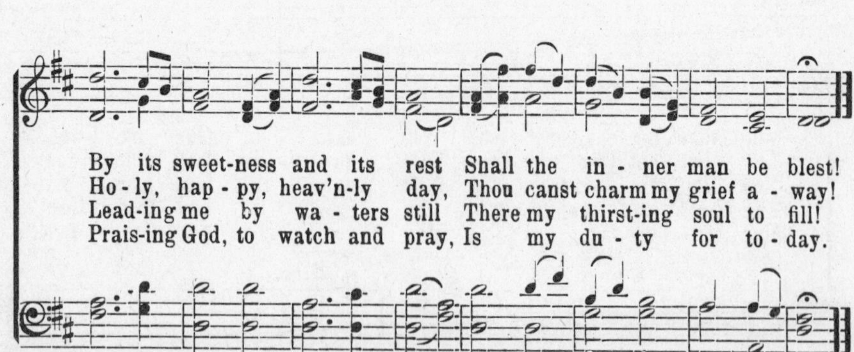
By its sweet-ness and its rest Shall the in - ner man be blest!
Ho - ly, hap - py, heav'n-ly day, Thou canst charm my grief a - way!
Lead-ing me by wa - ters still There my thirst-ing soul to fill!
Prais-ing God, to watch and pray, Is my du - ty for to - day.

235 SONG OF PRAISE

mf
1. Praise ye in His sanc-tu - a - ry Him who does such won-drous deeds!
2. Laud ye Him with tears of glad-ness, Praise Him now with harp and song!
3. Then re-joice ye in His glo - ry Who from death to life a - rose!
mf
Who to His e - ter - nal glo - ry All His ran-somed chil-dren leads!
Let us crown Him high-est rul - er, Sound the cho - rus loud and long!
Who a white and glo-rious gar-ment And rich gifts on you be - stows!
f p f
Hal - le - lu - jah, hal - le - lu - jah, hal - le - lu - jah, A - men!
f f
Hal - le - lu - jah, hal - le - lu - jah, hal - le - lu - jah.
p
A - men! A - men! A - men! A - men!
p
Hal - le - lu - jah, hal - le - lu - jah, hal - le - lu - jah,
f p f
Hal - le - lu - jah, hal - le - lu - jah, hal - le - lu - jah, A - men!
f f

236 JESUS, THE CRUCIFIED

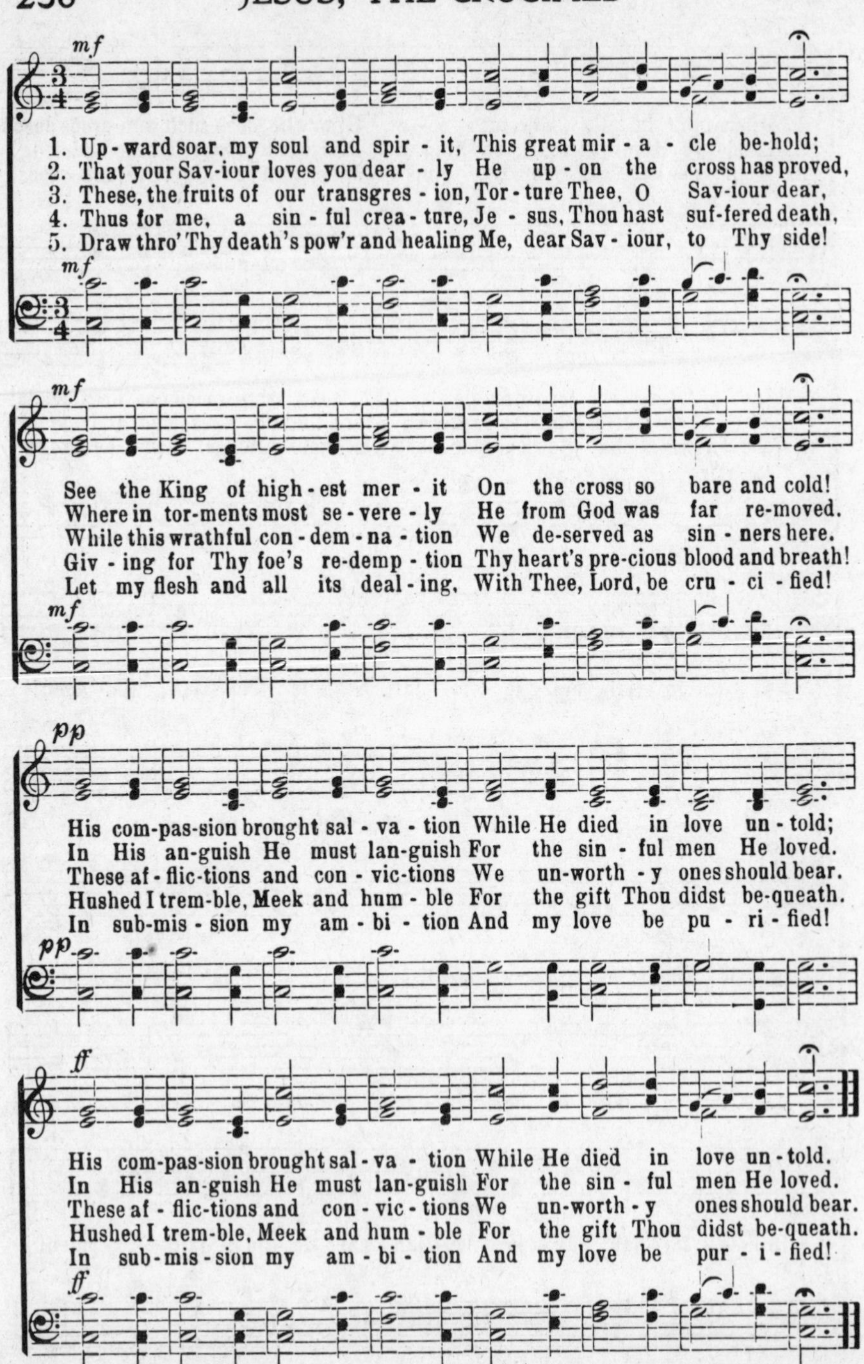
mf
1. Up-ward soar, my soul and spir - it, This great mir - a - cle be-hold;
2. That your Sav-iour loves you dear - ly He up - on the cross has proved,
3. These, the fruits of our transgres - ion, Tor - ture Thee, O Sav-iour dear,
4. Thus for me, a sin - ful crea - ture, Je - sus, Thou hast suf-fered death,
5. Draw thro' Thy death's pow'r and healing Me, dear Sav - iour, to Thy side!
mf
mf
See the King of high - est mer - it On the cross so bare and cold!
Where in tor-ments most se - vere - ly He from God was far re-moved.
While this wrathful con - dem - na - tion We de-served as sin - ners here.
Giv - ing for Thy foe's re-demp - tion Thy heart's pre-cious blood and breath!
Let my flesh and all its deal - ing, With Thee, Lord, be cru - ci - fied!
mf
pp
His com-pas-sion brought sal - va - tion While He died in love un - told;
In His an-guish He must lan-guish For the sin - ful men He loved.
These af - flic-tions and con - vic-tions We un-worth - y ones should bear.
Hushed I trem-ble, Meek and hum - ble For the gift Thou didst be-queath.
In sub-mis - sion my am - bi - tion And my love be pu - ri - fied!
pp
ff
His com-pas-sion brought sal - va - tion While He died in love un - told.
In His an-guish He must lan-guish For the sin - ful men He loved.
These af - flic-tions and con - vic - tions We un-worth - y ones should bear.
Hushed I trem-ble, Meek and hum - ble For the gift Thou didst be-queath.
In sub-mis - sion my am - bi - tion And my love be pur - i - fied!
ff

237 THE HOLY BIBLE

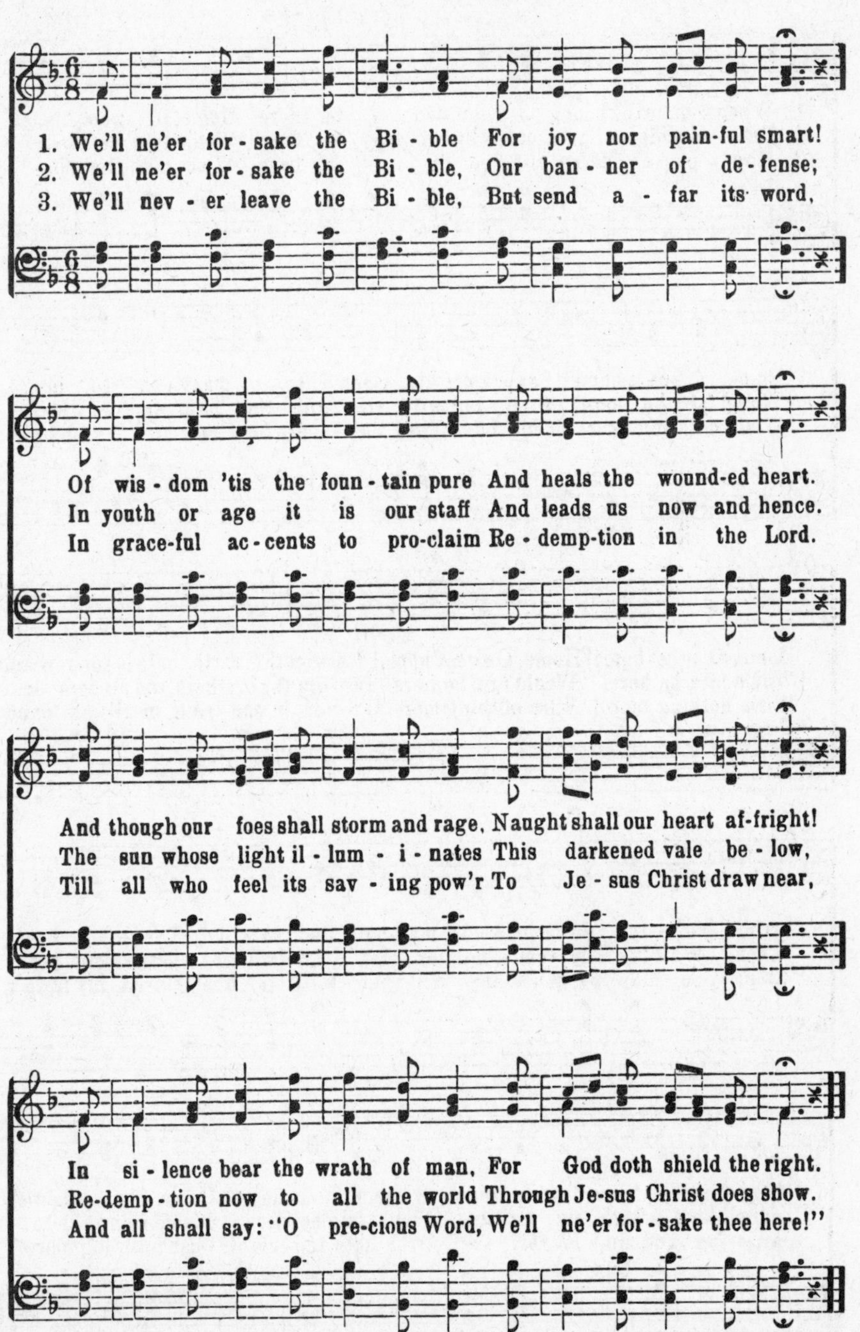
1. We'll ne'er for - sake the Bi - ble For joy nor pain-ful smart!
2. We'll ne'er for - sake the Bi - ble, Our ban - ner of de - fense;
3. We'll nev - er leave the Bi - ble, But send a - far its word,
Of wis - dom 'tis the foun - tain pure And heals the wound-ed heart.
In youth or age it is our staff And leads us now and hence.
In grace-ful ac - cents to pro-claim Re - demp-tion in the Lord.
And though our foes shall storm and rage, Naught shall our heart af-fright!
The sun whose light il - lum - i - nates This darkened vale be - low,
Till all who feel its sav - ing pow'r To Je - sus Christ draw near,
In si - lence bear the wrath of man, For God doth shield the right.
Re-demp - tion now to all the world Through Je-sus Christ does show.
And all shall say: "O pre-cious Word, We'll ne'er for - sake thee here!"

LONGING FOR THE HOMELAND

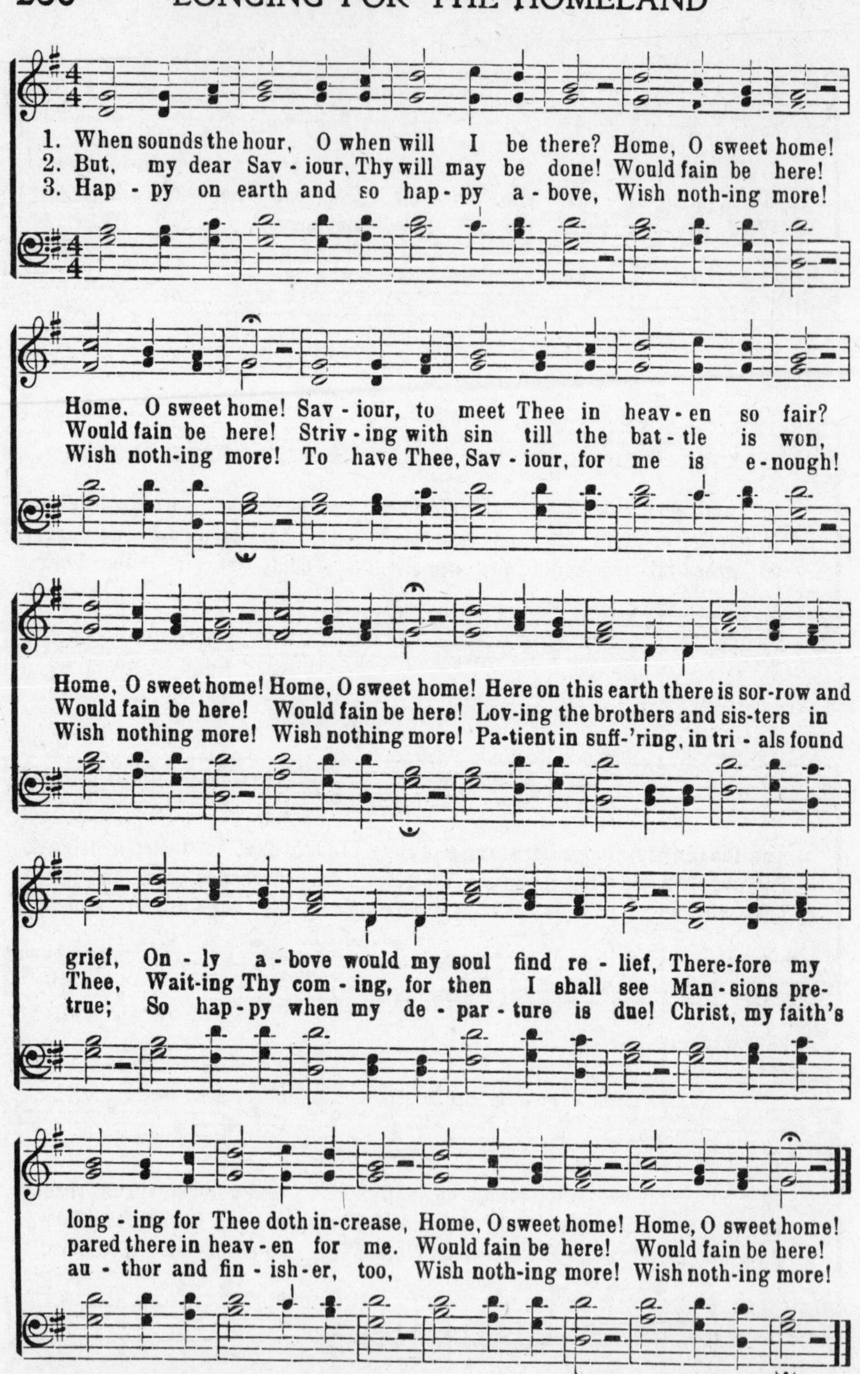
1. When sounds the hour, O when will I be there? Home, O sweet home!
2. But, my dear Sav - iour, Thy will may be done! Would fain be here!
3. Hap - py on earth and so hap - py a - bove, Wish noth-ing more!
Home, O sweet home! Sav - iour, to meet Thee in heav - en so fair?
Would fain be here! Striv - ing with sin till the bat - tle is won,
Wish noth-ing more! To have Thee, Sav - iour, for me is e - nough!
Home, O sweet home! Home, O sweet home! Here on this earth there is sor-row and
Would fain be here! Would fain be here! Lov-ing the brothers and sis-ters in
Wish nothing more! Wish nothing more! Pa-tient in suff-'ring, in tri - als found
grief, On - ly a - bove would my soul find re - lief, There-fore my
Thee, Wait-ing Thy com - ing, for then I shall see Man - sions pre-
true; So hap - py when my de - par - ture is due! Christ, my faith's
long - ing for Thee doth in-crease, Home, O sweet home! Home, O sweet home!
pared there in heav - en for me. Would fain be here! Would fain be here!
au - thor and fin - ish - er, too, Wish noth-ing more! Wish noth-ing more!

239

GOING HOME

1. Joy - ful - ly, joy - ful - ly on - ward I move, Bound for the land of bright
2. Friends, fondly cher-ished, have passed on be-fore, Wait - ing they watch me ap-
3. Death with thy weap-ons of war lay me low, Strike, King of ter - rors, I
spir - its a - bove! An - gel - ic chor-is - ters sing as I come; Meet me with
proach-ing the shore; Sing-ing to cheer me thru death's chilling gloom; "Joy - ful - ly,
fear not thy blow! Je - sus, the he - ro, hath vic-t'ry a-chieved, Bless-ed is
glad-ness and wel-come me home; Soon with my pil-grim-age end - ed be - low,
joy - ful - ly haste to thy home!" Sounds of sweet mel-o - dy fall on the ear;
he who on Him hath be-lieved! Bright will the morn of e - ter - ni - ty dawn,
Home to the land of de-light will I go; Pil - grim and stran-ger no
Harps of the bless-ed, your voic - es I hear; Ring with the har - mo - ny
Bright is my vi - sion, be - hold-ing the crown; Fold - ed in Je - sus' arms,
more shall I roam, Joy - ful - ly, joy - ful - ly rest - ing at home!
heav-en's high dome: Joy - ful - ly, joy - ful - ly haste to thy home!
no more I'll roam Joy - ful - ly, joy - ful - ly, safe - ly at home!

THAT HEAVENLY LAND

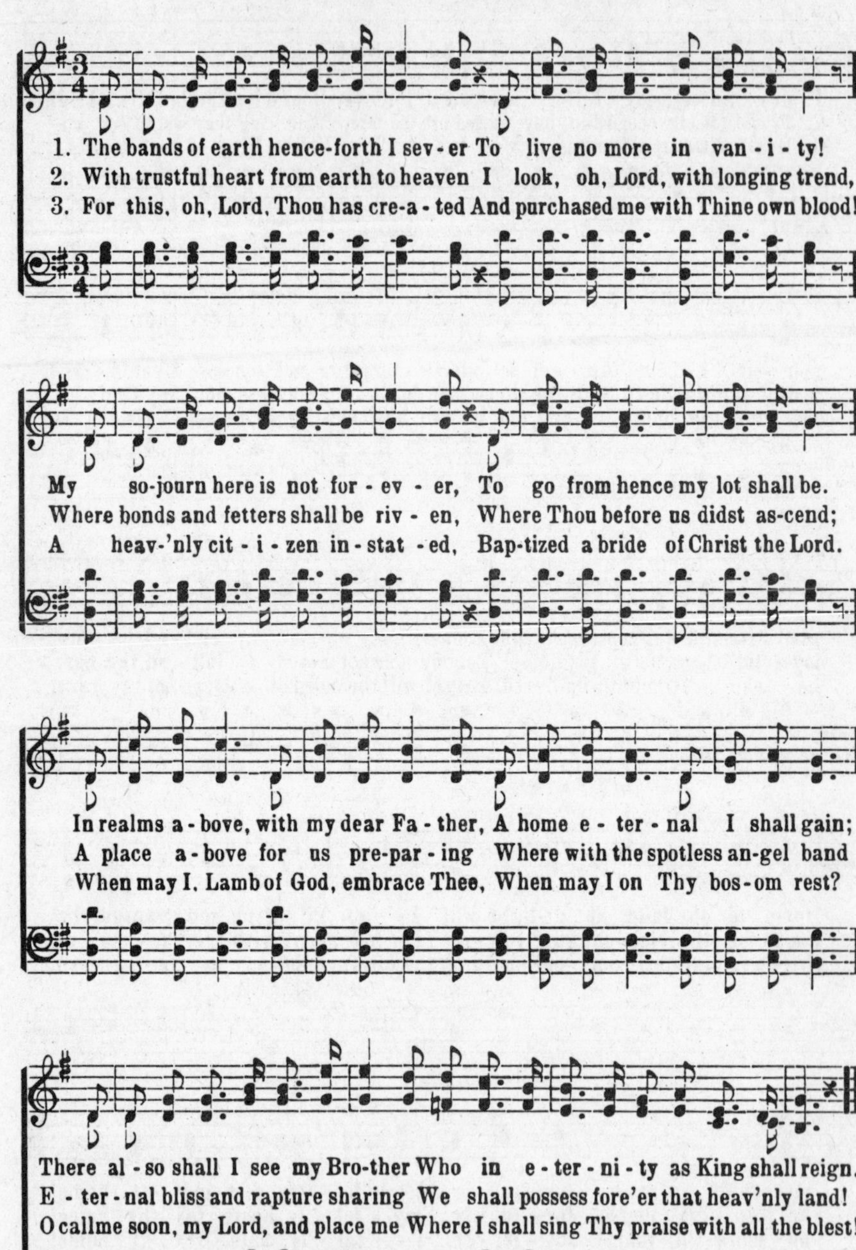
1. The bands of earth hence-forth I sev-er To live no more in van-i-ty!
2. With trustful heart from earth to heaven I look, oh, Lord, with longing trend,
3. For this, oh, Lord, Thou has cre-a-ted And purchased me with Thine own blood!
My so-journ here is not for-ev-er, To go from hence my lot shall be.
Where bonds and fetters shall be riv-en, Where Thou before us didst as-cend;
A heav-'nly cit-i-zen in-stat-ed, Bap-tized a bride of Christ the Lord.
In realms a-bove, with my dear Fa-ther, A home e-ter-nal I shall gain;
A place a-bove for us pre-par-ing Where with the spotless an-gel band
When may I, Lamb of God, embrace Thee, When may I on Thy bos-om rest?
There al-so shall I see my Bro-ther Who in e-ter-ni-ty as King shall reign.
E-ter-nal bliss and rapture sharing We shall possess fore'er that heav'nly land!
O callme soon, my Lord, and place me Where I shall sing Thy praise with all the blest!

241 ELIJAH AND ELISHA'S FAREWELL

1. Wrapped in thoughts of heav'nly na-ture Si - lent - ly E - li - jah stands; At his
2. "Tar - ry with me and the peo-ple!" Thus he speaks with aching heart. "Darkness
3. And his mas - ter's eye is shin-ing With sub-lime and no-ble light; Asks, "What
4. "Great is thy de-mand!" he an-swers As the oth-er's thought he reads; En-vies
5. Thus he speaks, when lo! a-round him All is bright and glo-rious light; Fier-y
6. Trem - bling, quak-ing stands E - lish - a, Sees with-out a veil the flight, And with
side the true dis - ci - ple, Pain and grief his heart ex-pands. Feel - ing
all the earth en - vel - ops, Fa - ther, do not thou depart!" "Soon by
is thy last pe - ti - tion Ere from earth I take my flight?" And E-
not the loved dis - ci - ple From whose heart this wish pro-ceeds. "If thou
steeds and fier - y char - iot Sent by great Je - ho - vah's might. He who
tear - filled eye is gaz - ing In - to that ce - les - tial light. Calls with
that to heav-en's glo - ry Soon his Mas - ter shall at - tain. Oh, what
flam - ing heights and mountains Sep - a - rat - ed we shall be!" "To the
lish - a cries with fer-vor: "Grant that I may work like thee! Let, I
see me when I van - ish, Thy de - sire shall be sup - plied. But if
once the fire of heav-en Kin - dled in a thou - sand hearts, Now as-
yearn-ing: "Fa - ther, fa - ther, Dost thou en - ter heav - en's gate? Woe to
loss the earth must suf-fer By the ho - ly Prophet's gain! By the ho - ly Prophet's gain!
end, oh let me tar - ry, Nev-er will I part from thee! Nev-er will I part from thee!"
pray, a dou-ble por-tion Of thy spir - it rest on me! Of thy spir - it rest on me!"
thou shalt not be-hold me, Then thy plea shall be de-nied! Then thy plea shall be de-nied!"
cends in flaming tri-umph And from earthly night departs! And from earthly night departs!
this un-hap - py peo-ple Whom thou leavest to its fate Whom thou leavest to its fate!"

242 REST, MY SOUL, IN COMFORT

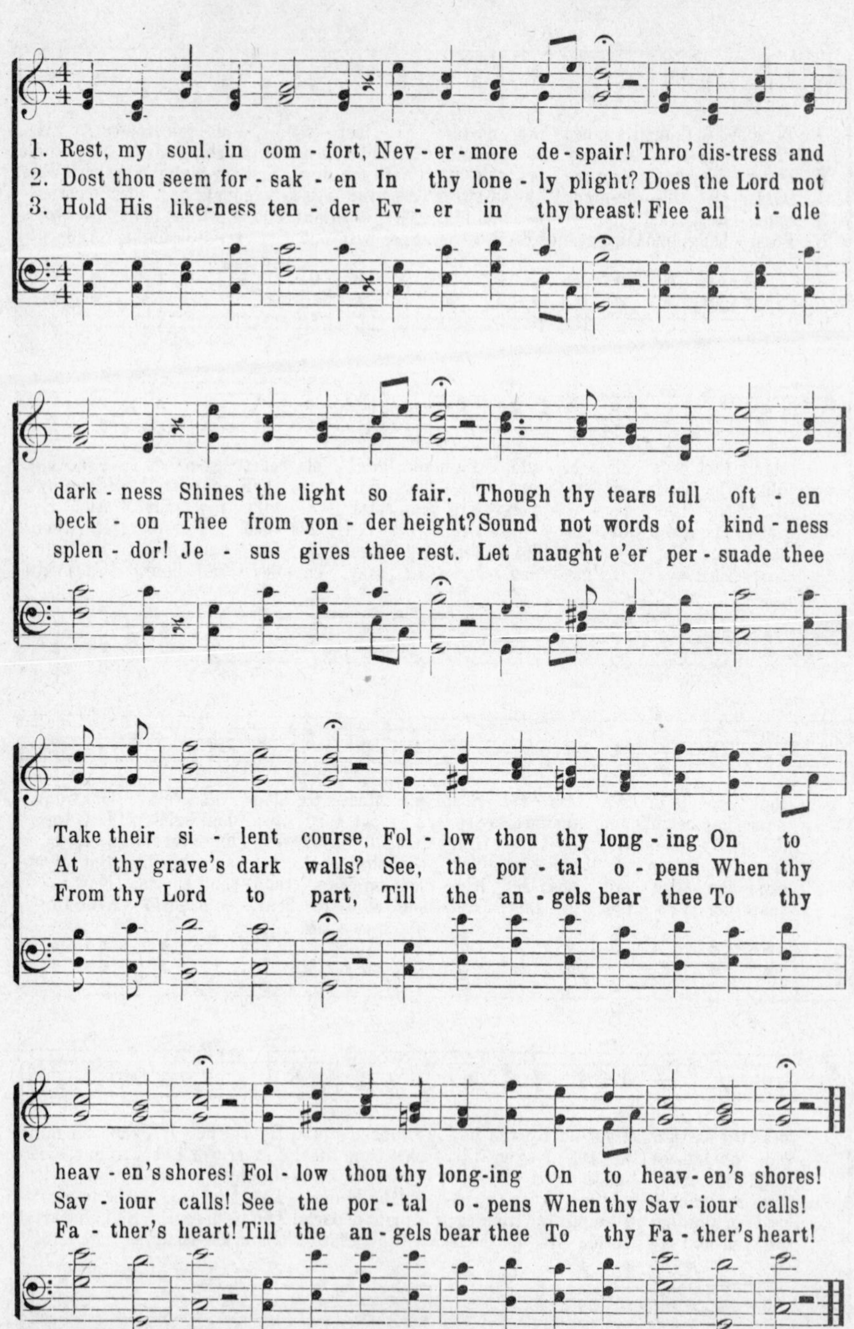
1. Rest, my soul, in com - fort, Nev - er - more de - spair! Thro' dis-tress and
2. Dost thou seem for - sak - en In thy lone - ly plight? Does the Lord not
3. Hold His like-ness ten - der Ev - er in thy breast! Flee all i - dle
dark - ness Shines the light so fair. Though thy tears full oft - en
beck - on Thee from yon - der height? Sound not words of kind - ness
splen - dor! Je - sus gives thee rest. Let naught e'er per - suade thee
Take their si - lent course, Fol - low thou thy long - ing On to
At thy grave's dark walls? See, the por - tal o - pens When thy
From thy Lord to part, Till the an - gels bear thee To thy
heav - en's shores! Fol - low thou thy long-ing On to heav - en's shores!
Sav - iour calls! See the por - tal o - pens When thy Sav - iour calls!
Fa - ther's heart! Till the an - gels bear thee To thy Fa - ther's heart!

243 CHRISTMAS CAROL

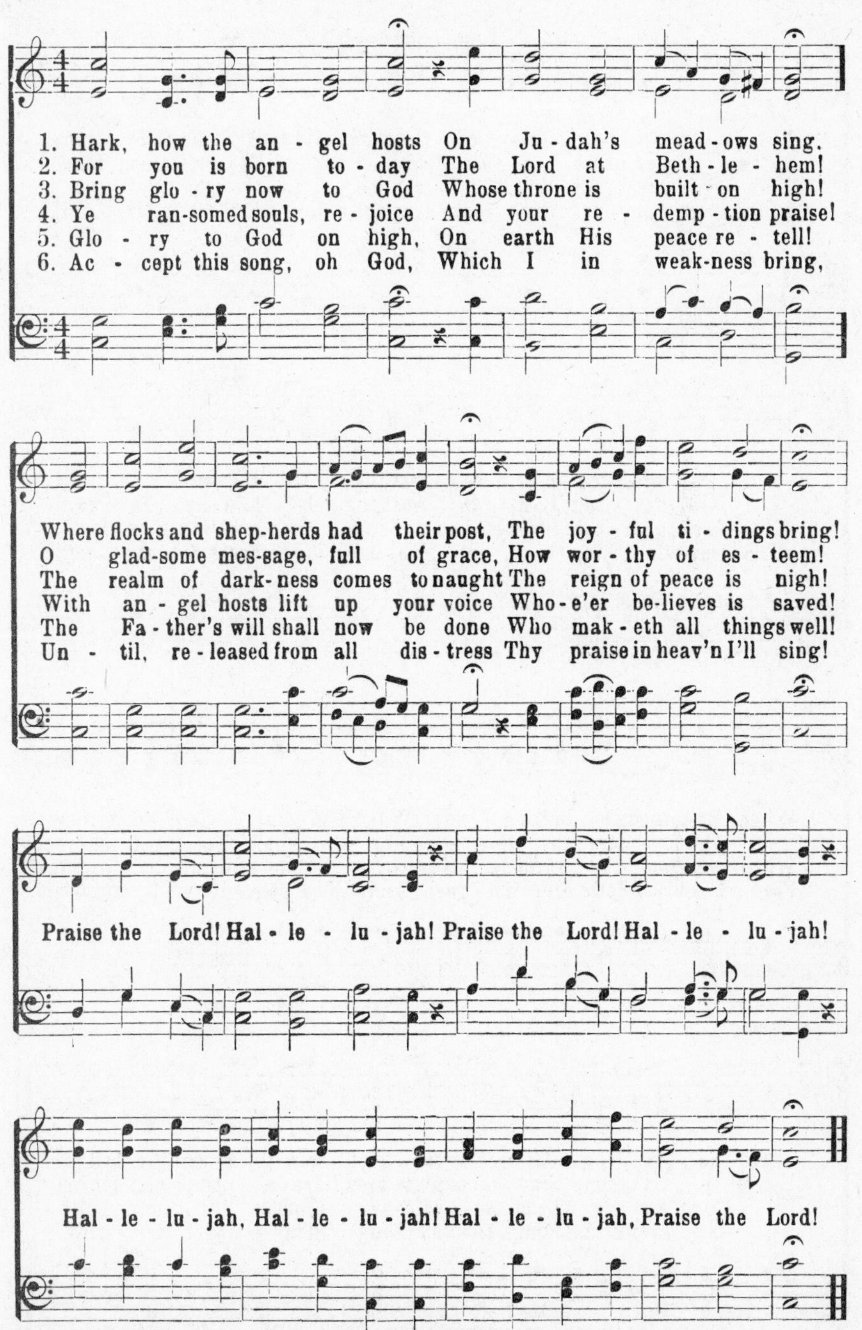
1. Hark, how the an - gel hosts On Ju - dah's mead - ows sing.
2. For you is born to - day The Lord at Beth - le - hem!
3. Bring glo - ry now to God Whose throne is built on high!
4. Ye ran-somed souls, re - joice And your re - demp - tion praise!
5. Glo - ry to God on high, On earth His peace re - tell!
6. Ac - cept this song, oh God, Which I in weak-ness bring,
Where flocks and shep-herds had their post, The joy - ful ti - dings bring!
O glad-some mes-sage, full of grace, How wor - thy of es - teem!
The realm of dark-ness comes to naught The reign of peace is nigh!
With an - gel hosts lift up your voice Who - e'er be-lieves is saved!
The Fa - ther's will shall now be done Who mak - eth all things well!
Un - til, re - leased from all dis - tress Thy praise in heav'n I'll sing!
Praise the Lord! Hal - le - lu - jah! Praise the Lord! Hal - le - lu - jah!
Hal - le - lu - jah, Hal - le - lu - jah! Hal - le - lu - jah, Praise the Lord!

I WILL STRIVE

1. I am striv-ing, Life re-viv-ing Where I find de-light.
2. As a-noint-ed And ap-point-ed To Thy pres-ence, Lord,
3. O pro-tect me And di-rect me, Lord, to yon-der goal!
4. Draw me ev-er, My en-deav-or Is but fee-ble, Lord!
I am wrest-ing, E'er con-test-ing, Till I win the fight.
I will has-ten, Lest in wast-ing I lose my re-ward.
Ev-er guid-ing, Strength pro-vid-ing For my wea-ry soul.
Tho' my fail-ing Is pre-vail-ing Thou dost strength af-ford.
When de-tained, I break a-way; When I'm faint, God's Word doth say:
He who loi-ters in this race Nev-er shall the crown em-brace!
Warn me from the world-ly lure, Help its mock-ings to en-dure!
For Thy blood doth life im-part And Thy spir-it fills my heart.
Keep en-dur-ing, Per-se-ver-ing, Win the treas-ure bright!
World-ly treas-ures, Sin-ful pleas-ures Are a-like ab-horred.
In Thy mer-cy Lead me safe-ly From its lur-ing call!
At the crown-ing Songs re-sound-ing Blend in sweet ac-cord.

245 PSALM OF PRAISE

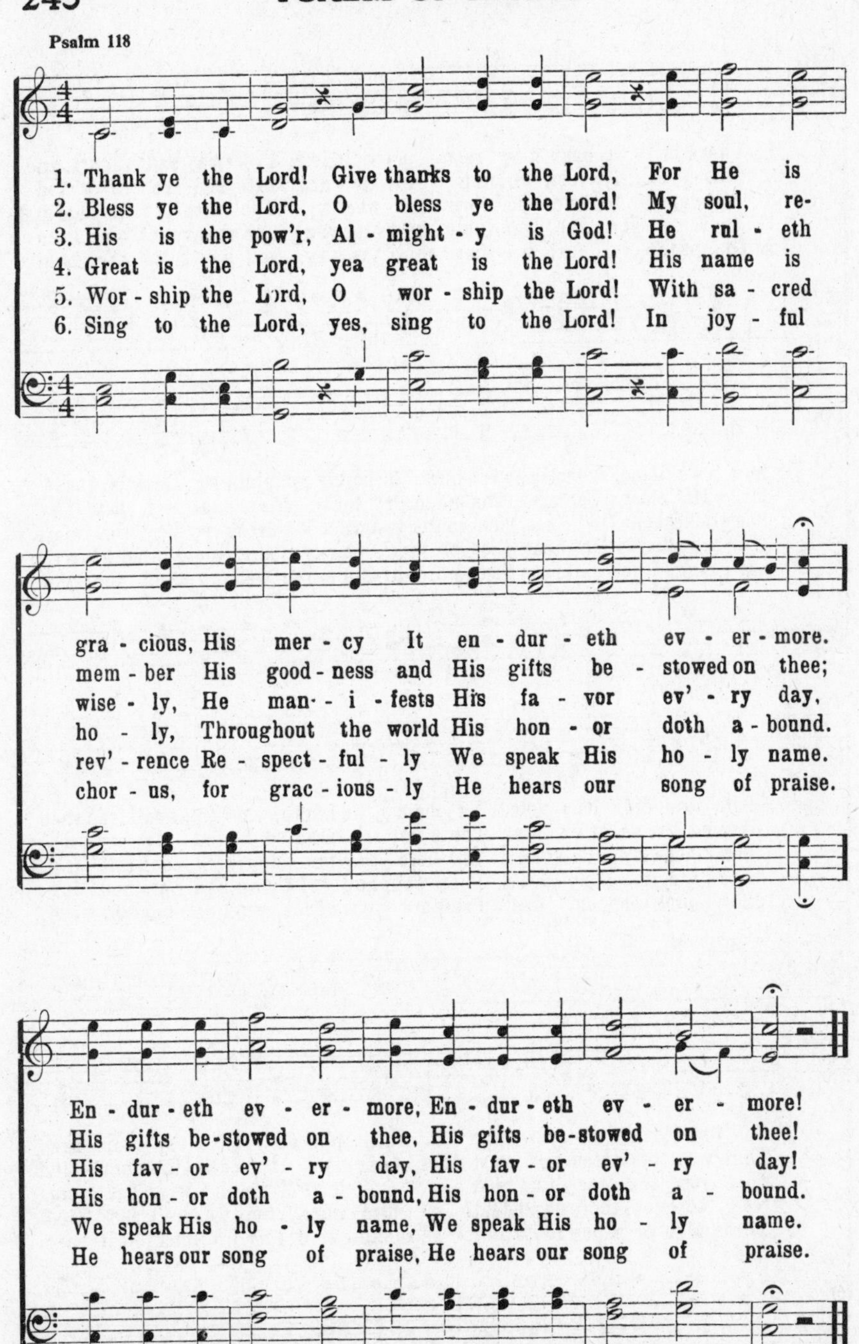
Psalm 118
1. Thank ye the Lord! Give thanks to the Lord, For He is
2. Bless ye the Lord, O bless ye the Lord! My soul, re-
3. His is the pow'r, Al - might - y is God! He rul - eth
4. Great is the Lord, yea great is the Lord! His name is
5. Wor - ship the Lord, O wor - ship the Lord! With sa - cred
6. Sing to the Lord, yes, sing to the Lord! In joy - ful
gra - cious, His mer - cy It en - dur - eth ev - er - more.
mem - ber His good - ness and His gifts be - stowed on thee;
wise - ly, He man - i - fests His fa - vor ev' - ry day,
ho - ly, Throughout the world His hon - or doth a - bound.
rev' - rence Re - spect - ful - ly We speak His ho - ly name.
chor - us, for grac - ious - ly He hears our song of praise.
En - dur - eth ev - er - more, En - dur - eth ev - er - more!
His gifts be - stowed on thee, His gifts be - stowed on thee!
His fav - or ev' - ry day, His fav - or ev' - ry day!
His hon - or doth a - bound, His hon - or doth a - bound.
We speak His ho - ly name, We speak His ho - ly name.
He hears our song of praise, He hears our song of praise.

246

THE ETERNAL REST

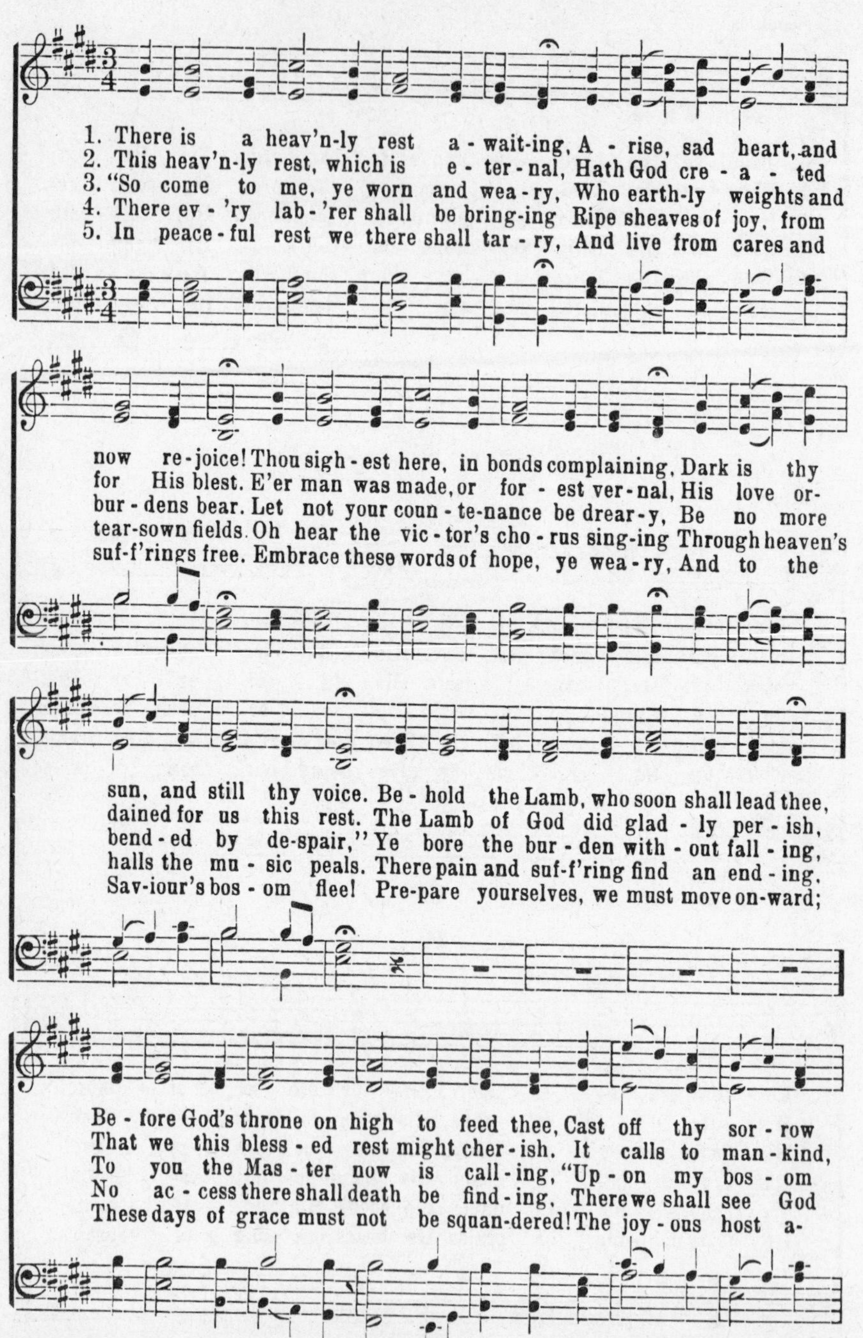
1. There is a heav'n-ly rest a-wait-ing, A-rise, sad heart, and
2. This heav'n-ly rest, which is e-ter-nal, Hath God cre-a-ted
3. "So come to me, ye worn and wea-ry, Who earth-ly weights and
4. There ev-'ry lab-'rer shall be bring-ing Ripe sheaves of joy, from
5. In peace-ful rest we there shall tar-ry, And live from cares and
now re-joice! Thou sigh-est here, in bonds complaining, Dark is thy
for His blest. E'er man was made, or for-est ver-nal, His love or-
bur-dens bear. Let not your coun-te-nance be drear-y, Be no more
tear-sown fields. Oh hear the vic-tor's cho-rus sing-ing Through heaven's
suf-f'rings free. Embrace these words of hope, ye wea-ry, And to the
sun, and still thy voice. Be-hold the Lamb, who soon shall lead thee,
dained for us this rest. The Lamb of God did glad-ly per-ish,
bend-ed by de-spair," Ye bore the bur-den with-out fall-ing,
halls the mu-sic peals. There pain and suf-f'ring find an end-ing.
Sav-iour's bos-om flee! Pre-pare yourselves, we must move on-ward;
Be-fore God's throne on high to feed thee, Cast off thy sor-row
That we this bless-ed rest might cher-ish. It calls to man-kind,
To you the Mas-ter now is call-ing, "Up-on my bos-om
No ac-cess there shall death be find-ing. There we shall see God
These days of grace must not be squan-dered! The joy-ous host a-

THE ETERNAL REST
and thy woe. Soon Sa - tan's host shall be de - feat-ed, Soon thy sad
far and near, "Ye ho - ly men, and wea - ry mor-tals, Make haste to
ye shall rest. For you, my flock, I'm bat - tle wag-ing, Tho' sin and
face to face. He'll dry our tears with hand ca - ress-ing; The stream of
waits us there. My soul, 'tis time for ju - bi - la - tion, Join now in
jour - ney be com-plet - ed. To rest in com - fort thou shalt go.
en - ter at the por-tals Where rest e - ter - nal shall ap - pear."
world, and hell be rag-ing, So en - ter in with all the blest."
life shall be re - fresh-ing Be - yond all hopes we now em - brace.
tri - umph's ex - ul - ta - tion! Now comes the year of rest so fair!
247
I'M GOING HOME
Wm. Hunter
Wm. Miller
1. My heav'n-ly home is bright and fair, Nor pain nor death can en - ter there:
2. My Fa-ther's house is built on high, Far, far a - bove the star-ry sky;
3. Let oth - ers seek a home be - low, Which flames devour, or waves o'erflow,
CHO. I'm go - ing home, I'm go - ing home, I'm go - ing home to die no more!
Its glit-t'ring tow'rs the sun out-shine; That heav'n-ly man-sion shall be mine.
When from this earth-ly pris-on free, That heav'n-ly man-sion mine shall be.
Be mine a hap-pier lot to own A heav'n-ly man-sion near the throne.
D. C.
To die no more, to die no more, I'm go - ing home to die no more.

1. When a Chris - tian dies Pre - cious is the
2. When a Chris - tian dies His grief bur - ied
3. When a Chris - tian dies In re - pose he
4. A Chris - tian's de - mise Leads to Par - a-
5. A Chris - tian's de - mise Breaks all earth - ly
prize! Last - ing joys for days of sor - row,
lies. All dis - tress and trib - u - la - tion
lies. As in slum - ber, worn and wea - ry,
dise. Af - ter days of trib - u - la - tion
ties. When the night of death is o - ver
Rest from con - flict on the mor - row Fol - lows
In death's slum - ber find ces - sa - tion. When a
He in si - lent grave will tar - ry Un - til
He will find his full sal - va - tion, Death the
Spring e - ter - nal he'll dis - cov - er. When a
when he dies, Fol - lows when he dies.
Chris - tian dies His grief bur - ied lies.
called to rise By our God all wise.
way sup - plies Un - to Par - a - dise.
Chris - tian dies Glo - rious dawn will rise.

249 THE SON OF GOD

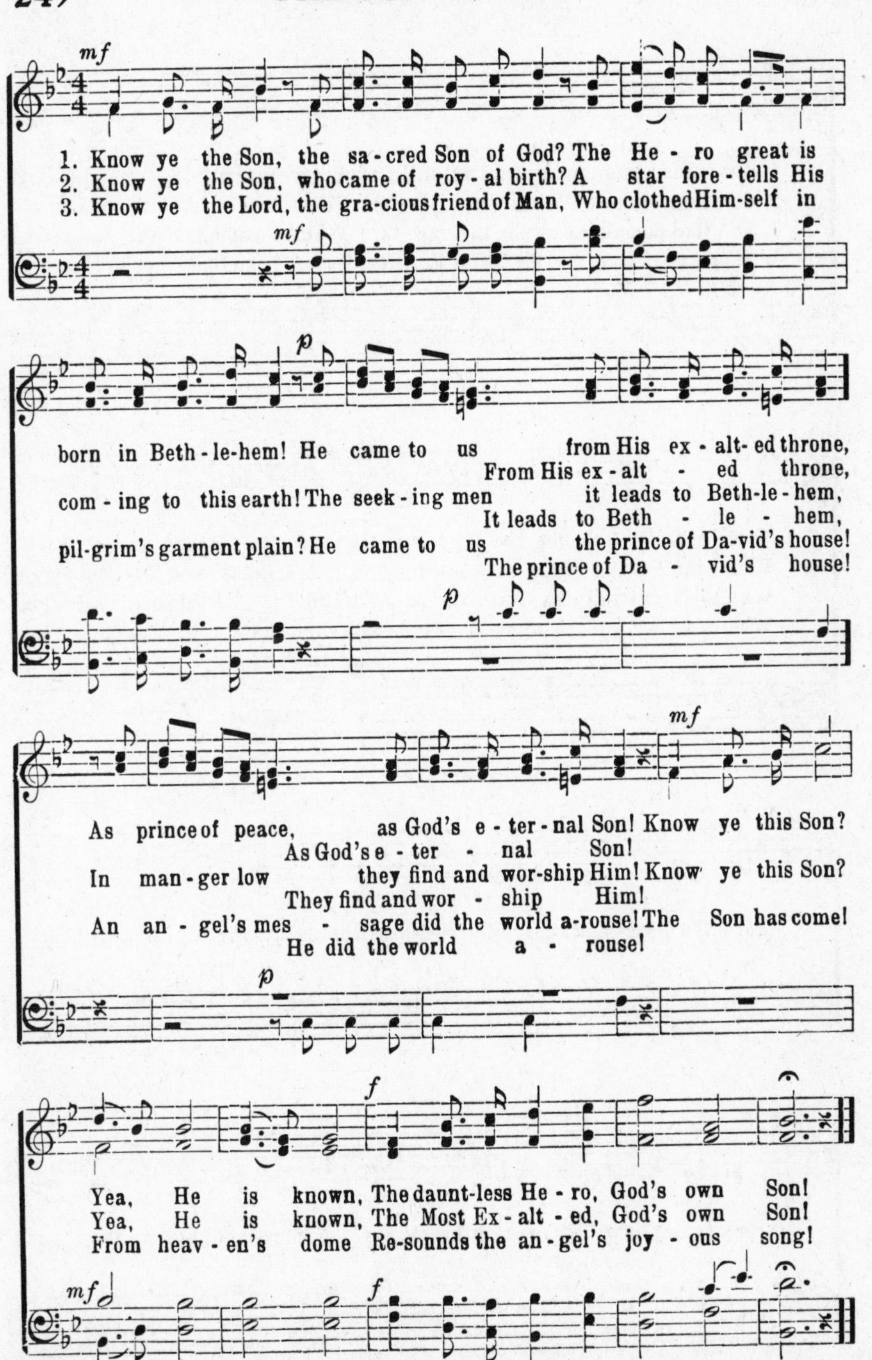
mf
1. Know ye the Son, the sa-cred Son of God? The He-ro great is
2. Know ye the Son, who came of roy-al birth? A star fore-tells His
3. Know ye the Lord, the gra-cious friend of Man, Who clothed Him-self in
mf
p
born in Beth-le-hem! He came to us from His ex-alt-ed throne,
From His ex-alt - ed throne,
com-ing to this earth! The seek-ing men it leads to Beth-le-hem,
It leads to Beth - le - hem,
pil-grim's garment plain? He came to us the prince of Da-vid's house!
The prince of Da - vid's house!
p
mf
As prince of peace, as God's e-ter-nal Son! Know ye this Son?
As God's e-ter - nal Son!
In man-ger low they find and wor-ship Him! Know ye this Son?
They find and wor - ship Him!
An an-gel's mes - sage did the world a-rouse! The Son has come!
He did the world a - rouse!
p
f
Yea, He is known, The daunt-less He-ro, God's own Son!
Yea, He is known, The Most Ex-alt-ed, God's own Son!
From heav-en's dome Re-sounds the an-gel's joy-ous song!
mf
f

250 YEARNING FOR THE HOMELAND

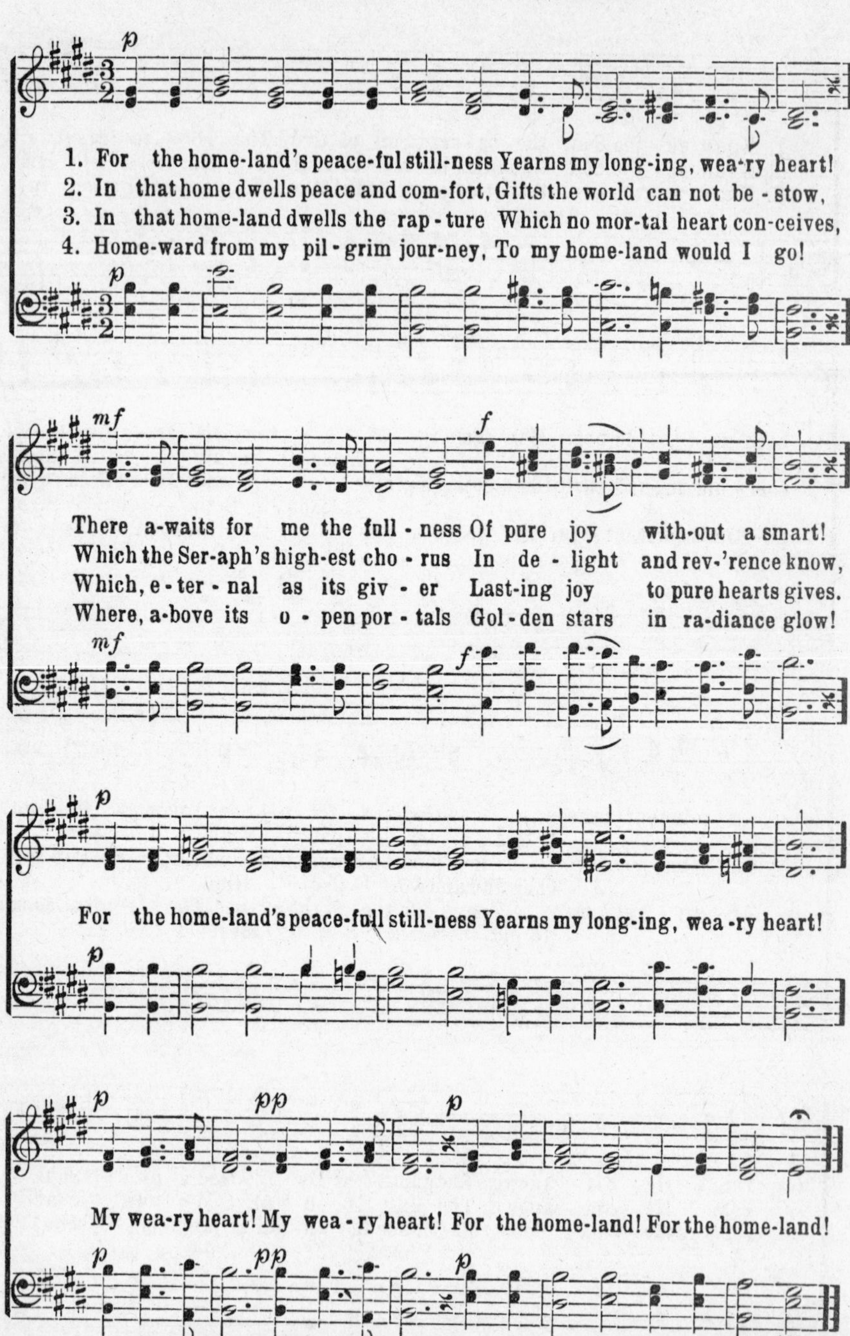
p
1. For the home-land's peace-ful still-ness Yearns my long-ing, wea-ry heart!
2. In that home dwells peace and com-fort, Gifts the world can not be - stow,
3. In that home-land dwells the rap - ture Which no mor-tal heart con-ceives,
4. Home-ward from my pil - grim jour-ney, To my home-land would I go!
mf
f
There a-waits for me the full - ness Of pure joy with-out a smart!
Which the Ser-aph's high-est cho - rus In de - light and rev-'rence know,
Which, e - ter - nal as its giv - er Last-ing joy to pure hearts gives.
Where, a-bove its o - pen por - tals Gol - den stars in ra-diance glow!
For the home-land's peace-full still-ness Yearns my long-ing, wea -ry heart!
pp
My wea-ry heart! My wea - ry heart! For the home-land! For the home-land!

251 CHRIST'S KINGDOM DRAWETH NEAR

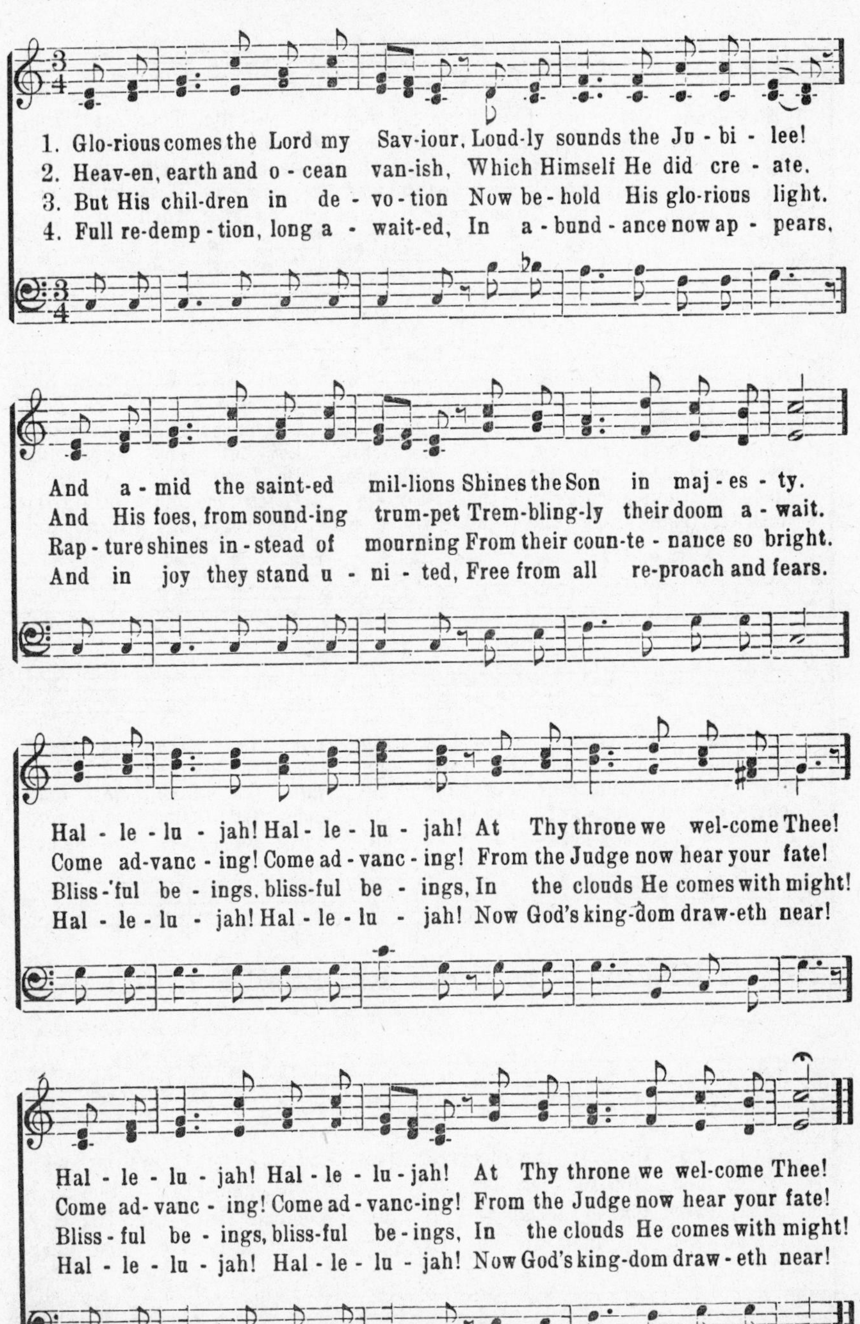
3
4
1. Glo-rious comes the Lord my Sav-iour, Loud-ly sounds the Ju - bi - lee!
2. Heav-en, earth and o - cean van-ish, Which Himself He did cre - ate.
3. But His chil-dren in de - vo - tion Now be - hold His glo-rious light.
4. Full re-demp - tion, long a - wait-ed, In a - bund - ance now ap - pears,
3
4
And a - mid the saint-ed mil-lions Shines the Son in maj - es - ty.
And His foes, from sound-ing trum-pet Trem-bling-ly their doom a - wait.
Rap - ture shines in - stead of mourning From their coun-te - nance so bright.
And in joy they stand u - ni - ted, Free from all re-proach and fears.
Hal - le - lu - jah! Hal - le - lu - jah! At Thy throne we wel-come Thee!
Come ad-vanc - ing! Come ad - vanc - ing! From the Judge now hear your fate!
Bliss-ful be - ings, bliss-ful be - ings, In the clouds He comes with might!
Hal - le - lu - jah! Hal - le - lu - jah! Now God's king-dom draw-eth near!
Hal - le - lu - jah! Hal - le - lu - jah! At Thy throne we wel-come Thee!
Come ad- vanc - ing! Come ad - vanc-ing! From the Judge now hear your fate!
Bliss - ful be - ings, bliss-ful be - ings, In the clouds He comes with might!
Hal - le - lu - jah! Hal - le - lu - jah! Now God's king-dom draw - eth near!

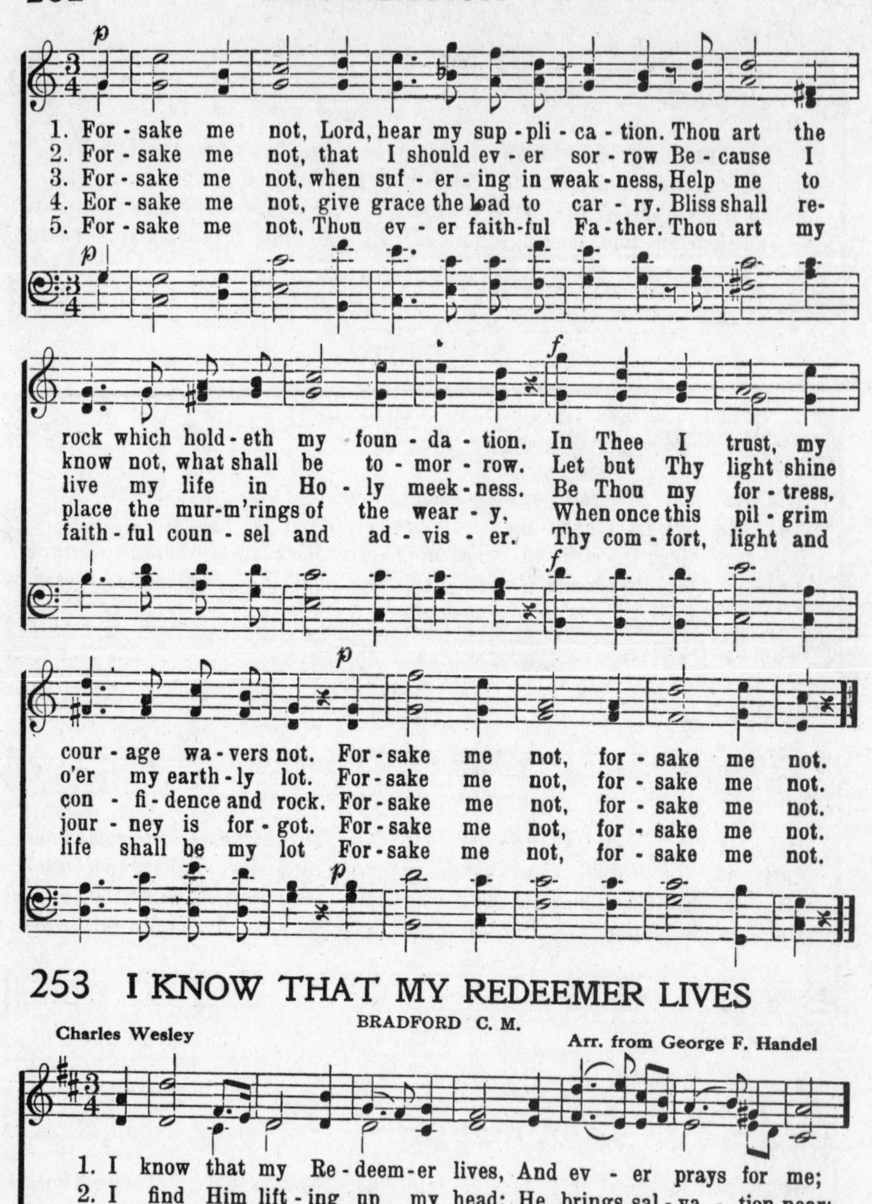
p
1. For - sake me not, Lord, hear my sup - pli - ca - tion. Thou art the rock which hold - eth my foun - da - tion. In Thee I trust, my cour - age wa - vers not. For - sake me not, for - sake me not.
2. For - sake me not, that I should ev - er sor - row Be - cause I know not, what shall be to - mor - row. Let but Thy light shine o'er my earth - ly lot. For - sake me not, for - sake me not.
3. For - sake me not, when suf - er - ing in weak - ness, Help me to live my life in Ho - ly meek - ness. Be Thou my for - tress, con - fi - dence and rock. For - sake me not, for - sake me not.
4. Eor - sake me not, give grace the load to car - ry. Bliss shall re- place the mur - m'rings of the wear - y, When once this pil - grim jour - ney is for - got. For - sake me not, for - sake me not.
5. For - sake me not, Thou ev - er faith - ful Fa - ther. Thou art my faith - ful coun - sel and ad - vis - er. Thy com - fort, light and life shall be my lot For - sake me not, for - sake me not.
f

253 I KNOW THAT MY REDEEMER LIVES

BRADFORD C. M.

Charles Wesley

Arr. from George F. Handel

1. I know that my Re - deem - er lives, And ev - er prays for me;
2. I find Him lift - ing up my head; He brings sal - va - tion near;
3. He wills that I should ho - ly be; Who can with - stand His will?
4. Je - sus, I hang up - on Thy word; I stead - fast - ly be - lieve

I KNOW MY REDEEMER LIVES

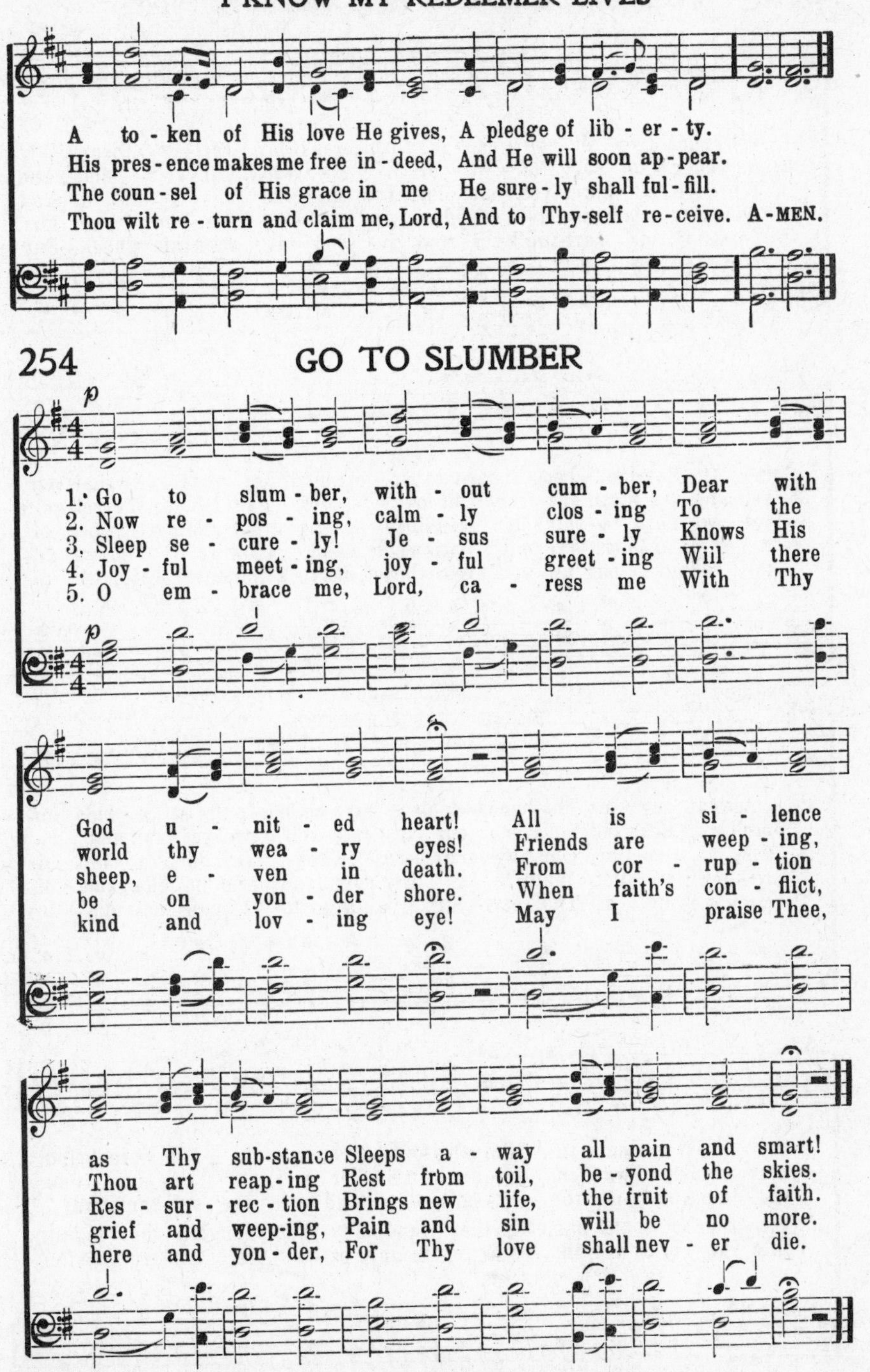
A to - ken of His love He gives, A pledge of lib - er - ty.
His pres - ence makes me free in - deed, And He will soon ap - pear.
The coun - sel of His grace in me He sure - ly shall ful - fill.
Thou wilt re - turn and claim me, Lord, And to Thy - self re - ceive. A - MEN.
254 GO TO SLUMBER
p
1. Go to slum - ber, with - out cum - ber, Dear with God u - nit - ed heart! All is si - lence as Thy sub - stance Sleeps a - way all pain and smart!
2. Now re - pos - ing, calm - ly clos - ing To the world thy wea - ry eyes! Friends are weep - ing, Thou art reap - ing Rest from toil, be - yond the skies.
3. Sleep se - cure - ly! Je - sus sure - ly Knows His sheep, e - ven in death. From cor - rup - tion Res - sur - rec - tion Brings new life, the fruit of faith.
4. Joy - ful meet - ing, joy - ful greet - ing Will there be on yon - der shore. When faith's con - flict, grief and weep - ing, Pain and sin will be no more.
5. O em - brace me, Lord, ca - ress me With Thy kind and lov - ing eye! May I praise Thee, here and yon - der, For Thy love shall nev - er die.

255 WHY SHOULD YE ALL BE WEEPING

p

1. Why should ye all be weep-ing And break my ver - y heart? We're
2. As though to part for - ev - er We press each oth - er's hands, And
3. We say: "I here, you yon - der, You go and I re - main, And
4. Then let us cease from weep-ing, And mod - er - ate our woe; For
5. Then not to part-ing's sor - rows We ded - i - cate this hour, But

in the Sav-iour's keep-ing, And there-fore shall not part. No time nor
yet no pow'r can sev - er Our love's e - ter - nal bands. We look quite
yet are not a - sun - der, But links of one great chain. In tones of
we are in Christ's keeping, With whom we al - ways go. Thus un - der
to re-new our un - ion With Christ, our rock and tow'r. If faith in

mf

place can sev - er The bonds which us have bound; In Christ a - bide for-
bro - ken - heart - ed And sob our last fare-well, And yet can not be
deep af - fec - tion "Our ways part here," we say, Yet go in one di-
His pro - tec - tion We're led by His sure hand, And in the same di-
Him u - nite us, Tho' part - ing give us pain, It can not dis - u-

ev - er Who once in Him were found, Who once in Him were found.
part - ed, For we in Je - sus dwell, For we in Je - sus dwell.
rec - tion And in the self-same way, And in the self-same way.
rec - tion To the same Fa - ther - land, To the same Fa - ther - land.
nite us For we in Him re - main, For we in Him re - main.

256 EVENING HYMN

p
mf
1. Stay Thou with me, faith-ful Friend, Christ, the hope I cher - ish!
2. Let me ev - er, bless ed Light, In my heart en - fold Thee,
3. Lord, a - noint us with the oil Of sin - cere de - vo - tion!
4. Then we'll en - ter, Lord with Thee In - to joys un - end - ing,
Now the day has reached its end, And the sun has van - ished.
And for - ev - er day and night In Thy love be - hold Thee!
Fill our spir - it, life and soul With its an - i - ma - tion!
Where no pow - er us from Thee Ev - er can be rend - ing.
Let Thy grace, O Lord, a - new My dark path be light - ing.
Dark-ness reign-eth far and near; Yet in Thy blest near - ness,
That in bright-est, pur - est light Our lamps may be burn - ing,
With the ho - ly an - gels there We shall be pro - claim - ing
And with flames of love so true Me with Thee u - nit - ing.
I am free from pain and fear, See - ing all in clear-ness.
That we may in dark - est night All things be dis - cern-ing.
Thy great might, Thy love so fair. Hal - le - lu - jah, A - MEN!

257 CHRIST AROSE

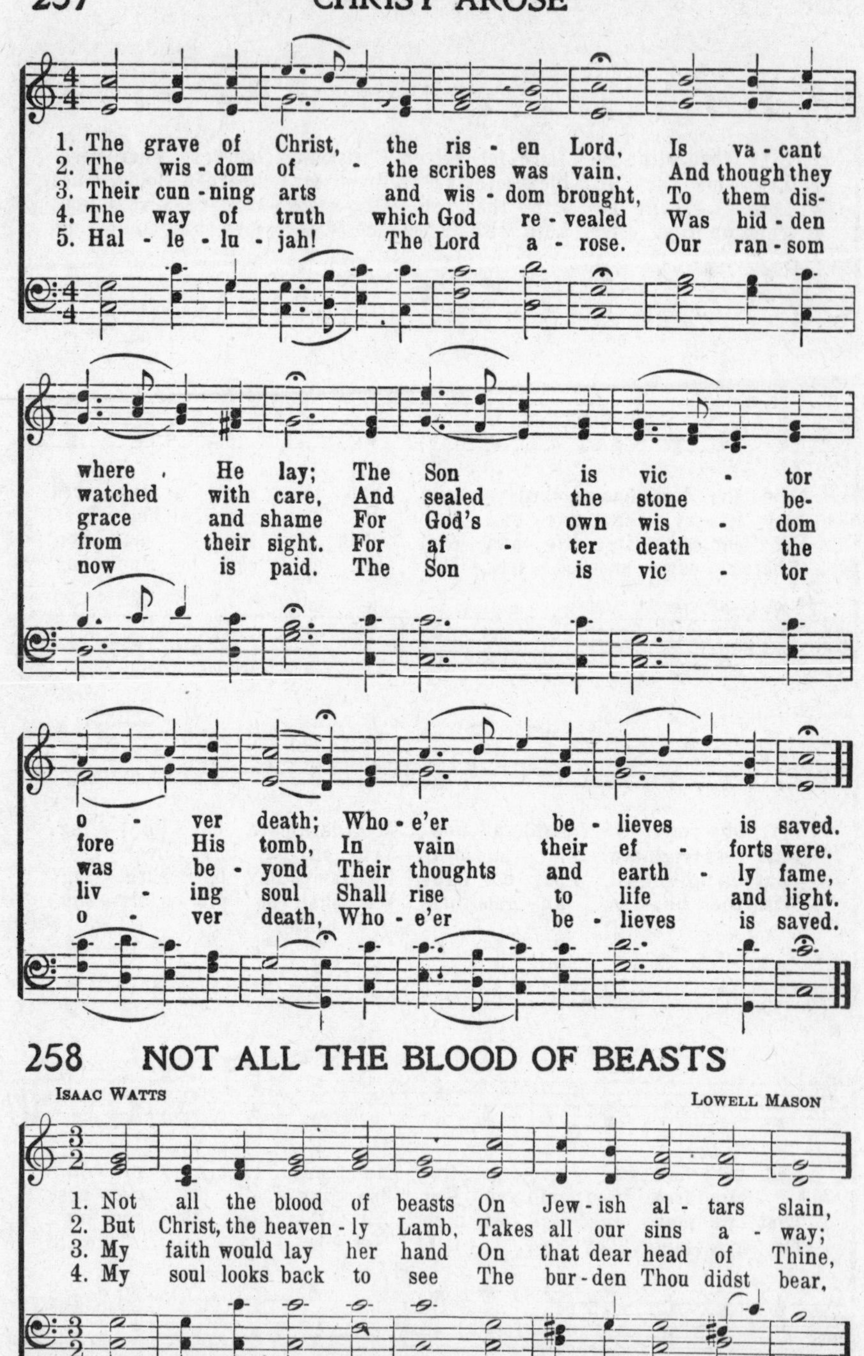
1. The grave of Christ, the ris - en Lord, Is va - cant
2. The wis - dom of - the scribes was vain. And though they
3. Their cun - ning arts and wis - dom brought, To them dis-
4. The way of truth which God re - vealed Was hid - den
5. Hal - le - lu - jah! The Lord a - rose. Our ran - som
where He lay; The Son is vic - tor
watched with care, And sealed the stone be-
grace and shame For God's own wis - dom
from their sight. For af - ter death the
now is paid. The Son is vic - tor
o - ver death; Who - e'er be - lieves is saved.
fore His tomb, In vain their ef - forts were.
was be - yond Their thoughts and earth - ly fame,
liv - ing soul Shall rise to life and light.
o - ver death, Who - e'er be - lieves is saved.
258 NOT ALL THE BLOOD OF BEASTS
ISAAC WATTS
LOWELL MASON
1. Not all the blood of beasts On Jew - ish al - tars slain,
2. But Christ, the heaven - ly Lamb, Takes all our sins a - way;
3. My faith would lay her hand On that dear head of Thine,
4. My soul looks back to see The bur - den Thou didst bear,

NOT ALL THE BLOOD OF BEASTS

259 TRUST AND CONFIDENCE

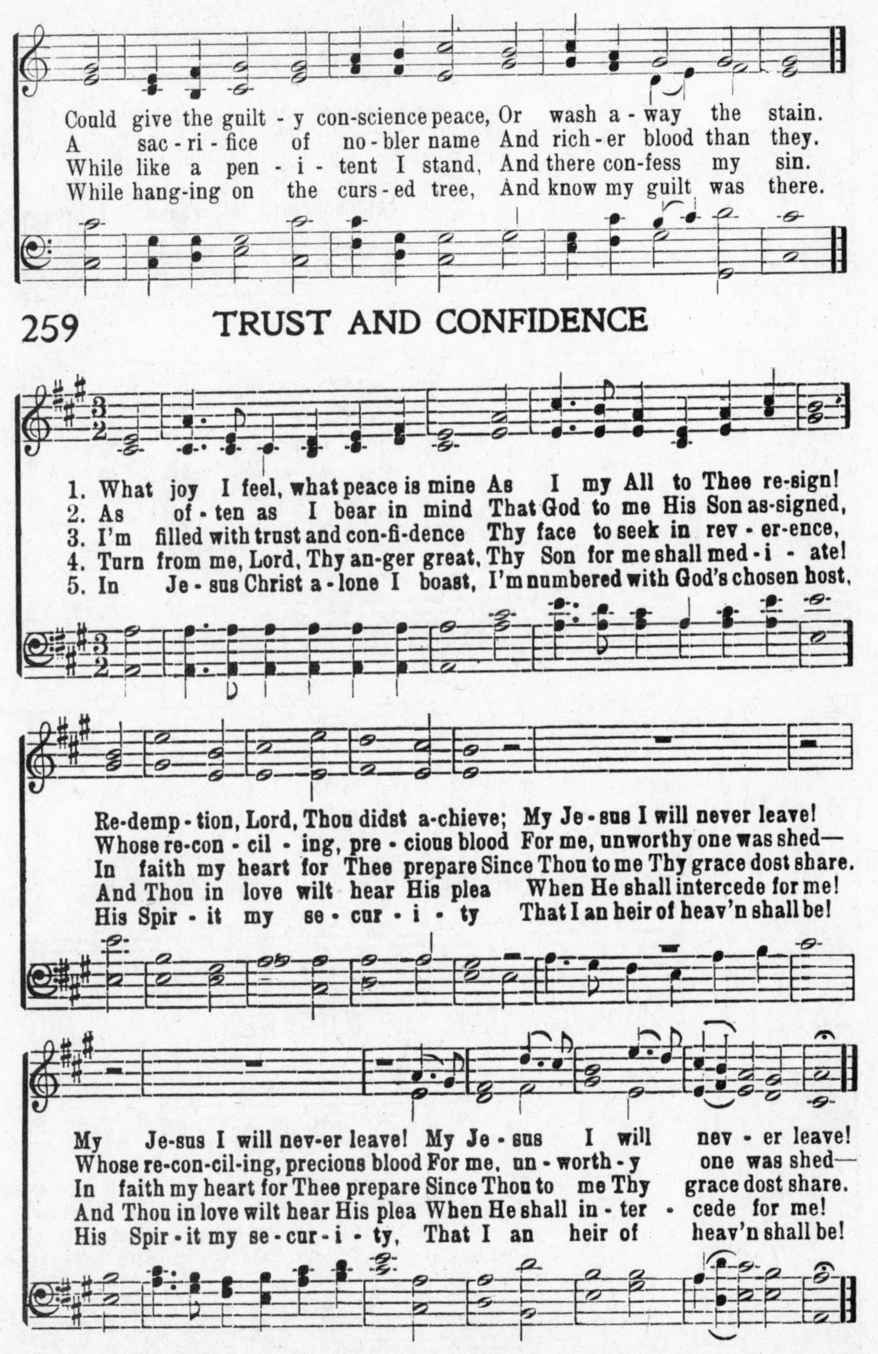
Could give the guilt - y con-science peace, Or wash a - way the stain.
A sac - ri - fice of no - bler name And rich - er blood than they.
While like a pen - i - tent I stand, And there con-fess my sin.
While hang-ing on the curs - ed tree, And know my guilt was there.
1. What joy I feel, what peace is mine As I my All to Thee re-sign!
2. As of - ten as I bear in mind That God to me His Son as-signed,
3. I'm filled with trust and con-fi-dence Thy face to seek in rev - er-ence,
4. Turn from me, Lord, Thy an-ger great, Thy Son for me shall med - i - ate!
5. In Je - sus Christ a - lone I boast, I'm numbered with God's chosen host,
Re-demp - tion, Lord, Thou didst a-chieve; My Je - sus I will never leave!
Whose re-con - cil - ing, pre - cious blood For me, unworthy one was shed—
In faith my heart for Thee prepare Since Thou to me Thy grace dost share.
And Thou in love wilt hear His plea When He shall intercede for me!
His Spir - it my se - cur - i - ty That I an heir of heav'n shall be!
My Je-sus I will nev-er leave! My Je - sus I will nev - er leave!
Whose re-con-cil-ing, precious blood For me, un - worth - y one was shed—
In faith my heart for Thee prepare Since Thou to me Thy grace dost share.
And Thou in love wilt hear His plea When He shall in - ter - cede for me!
His Spir - it my se - cur - i - ty, That I an heir of heav'n shall be!

260 FOLLOWING JESUS

261 THE YEAR OF JUBILEE

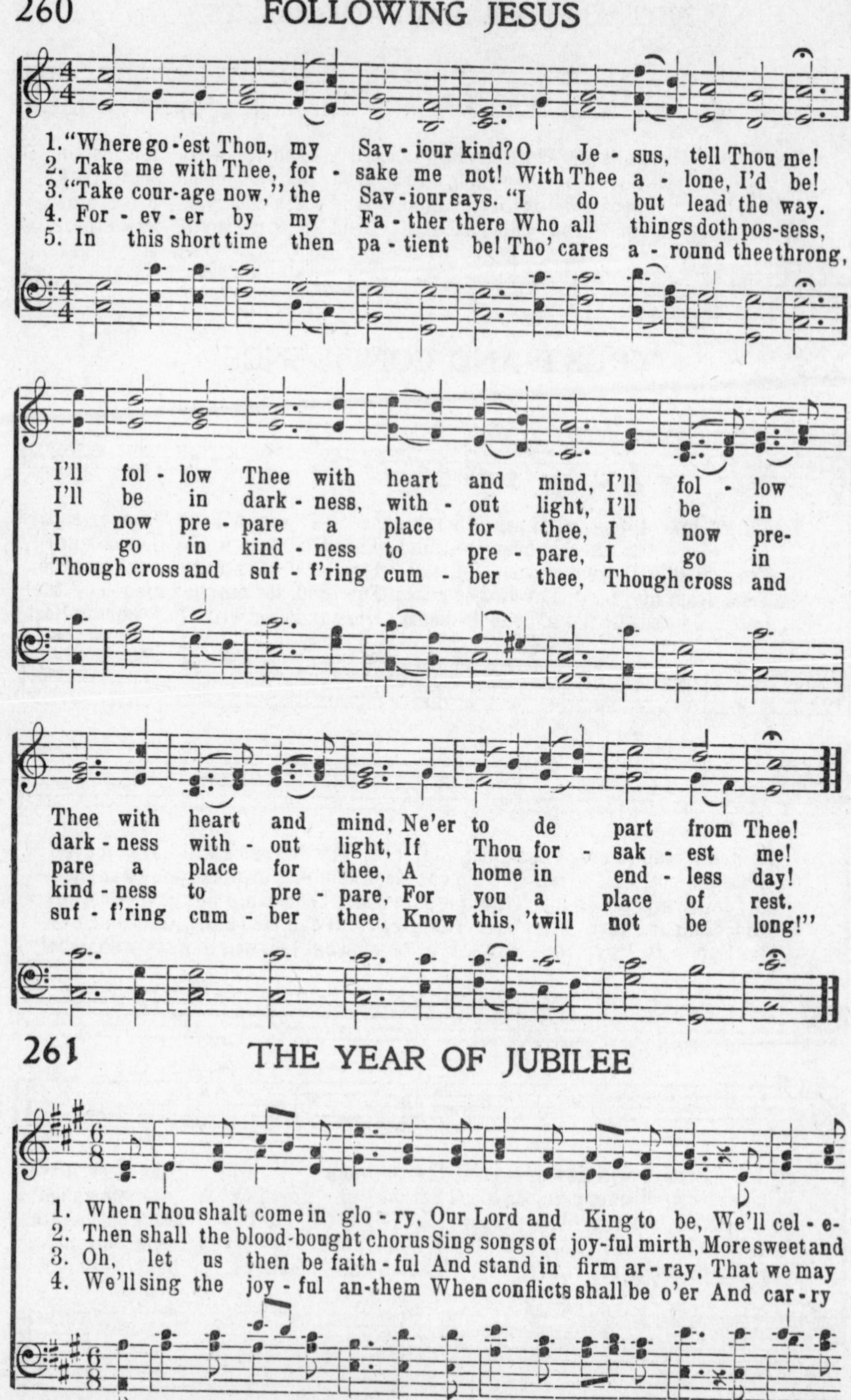
1. "Where go-'est Thou, my Sav - iour kind? O Je - sus, tell Thou me!
2. Take me with Thee, for - sake me not! With Thee a - lone, I'd be!
3. "Take cour-age now," the Sav - iour says. "I do but lead the way.
4. For - ev - er by my Fa - ther there Who all things doth pos-sess,
5. In this short time then pa - tient be! Tho' cares a - round thee throng,
I'll fol - low Thee with heart and mind, I'll fol - low
I'll be in dark - ness, with - out light, I'll be in
I now pre - pare a place for thee, I now pre-
I go in kind - ness to pre - pare, I go in
Though cross and suf - f'ring cum - ber thee, Though cross and
Thee with heart and mind, Ne'er to de part from Thee!
dark - ness with - out light, If Thou for - sak - est me!
pare a place for thee, A home in end - less day!
kind - ness to pre - pare, For you a place of rest.
suf - f'ring cum - ber thee, Know this, 'twill not be long!"
1. When Thou shalt come in glo - ry, Our Lord and King to be, We'll cel - e-
2. Then shall the blood-bought chorus Sing songs of joy-ful mirth, More sweet and
3. Oh, let us then be faith - ful And stand in firm ar - ray, That we may
4. We'll sing the joy - ful an-them When conflicts shall be o'er And car - ry

THE YEAR OF JUBILEE
brate be-fore Thee The year of ju - bi - lee! The year of ju - bi - lee!
more me - lo - dious Than ev-er here on earth, Than ev - er here on earth!
share Thy glo - ry On Res - ur - rec-tion Day, On Res-ur - rec-tion Day!
vic-t'ry's em-blems In peace for - ev - er - more, In peace for - ev - er - more!
262
THE BLESSED RESURRECTION
mf
1. Rise a - gain shalt thou, O man of clay, On that great
2. Sown in weak - ness, I shall bloom a - gain! The Lord of
3. Shout for joy, all who the Lord o - bey! Soon comes the
4. Then 'twill seem as wak-ing from a dream! A - long the
5. To His sanc - tu - a - ry He will lead, On bread of
glo - rious day! In life un - end - ing, With God the
Har - vest then As sheaves will gath - er The ran-somed
bless - ed day, When from death's cham-ber, Where I have
liv - ing stream All trib - u - la - tion At last will
life to feed. I'll see His glo - ry And sing the
f
a - ges spend-ing. Hal - le - lu - jah! Hal - le - lu - jah!
to the Fa - ther. Praise to His name, praise to His name!
lain in slum-ber, The Lord shall call, the Lord shall call!
find ces - sa - tion At Je - sus' side, at Je - sus' side.
won - drous sto - ry. Hal - le - lu - jah! Hal - le - lu - jah!

263 SHALL WE MEET UP YONDER

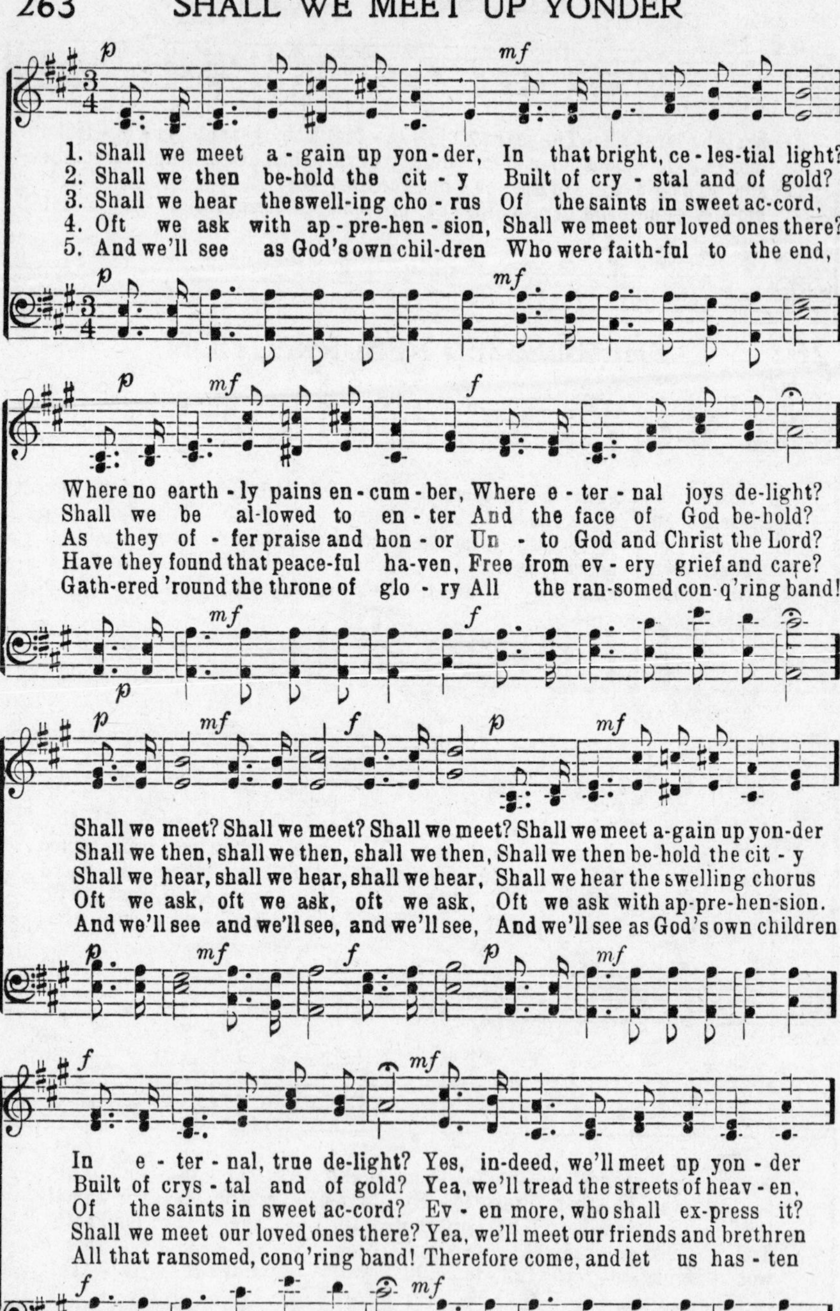
p
mf
1. Shall we meet a-gain up yon-der, In that bright, ce-les-tial light?
2. Shall we then be-hold the cit-y Built of cry-stal and of gold?
3. Shall we hear the swell-ing cho-rus Of the saints in sweet ac-cord,
4. Oft we ask with ap-pre-hen-sion, Shall we meet our loved ones there?
5. And we'll see as God's own chil-dren Who were faith-ful to the end,
f
Where no earth-ly pains en-cum-ber, Where e-ter-nal joys de-light?
Shall we be al-lowed to en-ter And the face of God be-hold?
As they of-fer praise and hon-or Un-to God and Christ the Lord?
Have they found that peace-ful ha-ven, Free from ev-ery grief and care?
Gath-ered 'round the throne of glo-ry All the ran-somed con-q'ring band!
Shall we meet? Shall we meet? Shall we meet? Shall we meet a-gain up yon-der
Shall we then, shall we then, shall we then, Shall we then be-hold the cit-y
Shall we hear, shall we hear, shall we hear, Shall we hear the swelling chorus
Oft we ask, oft we ask, oft we ask, Oft we ask with ap-pre-hen-sion.
And we'll see and we'll see, and we'll see, And we'll see as God's own children
In e-ter-nal, true de-light? Yes, in-deed, we'll meet up yon-der
Built of crys-tal and of gold? Yea, we'll tread the streets of heav-en,
Of the saints in sweet ac-cord? Ev-en more, who shall ex-press it?
Shall we meet our loved ones there? Yea, we'll meet our friends and brethren
All that ransomed, conq'ring band! Therefore come, and let us has-ten

SHALL WE MEET UP YONDER

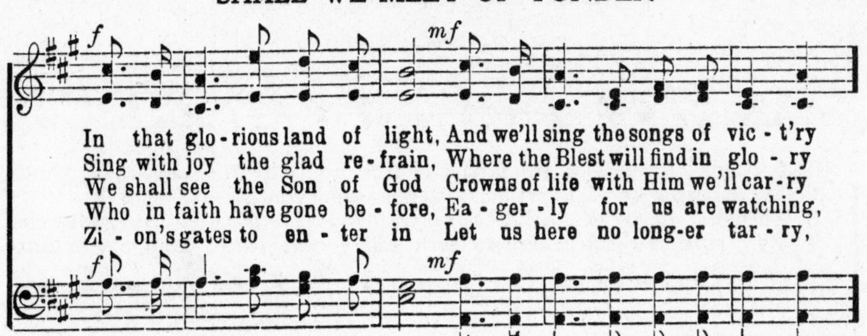
f
mf
In that glo-rious land of light, And we'll sing the songs of vic - t'ry
Sing with joy the glad re - frain, Where the Blest will find in glo - ry
We shall see the Son of God Crowns of life with Him we'll car - ry
Who in faith have gone be - fore, Ea - ger - ly for us are watching,
Zi - on's gates to en - ter in Let us here no long-er tar - ry,
f
mf

f
p
mf
f

If found faith-ful in the fight. Yes. in-deed, yes, in-deed, yes, in-deed!
What no eye has ev - er seen Yes we'll tread. yes we'll tread, yes we'll tread,
Who for us re-demp-tion brought. E - ven more e - ven more, e - ven more,
Waiting on the oth - er shore Yes we'll meet, yes we'll meet, yes we'll meet,
Striv-ing brave-ly brings us gain Therefore come, therefore come, therefore come,

f
p
mf
f

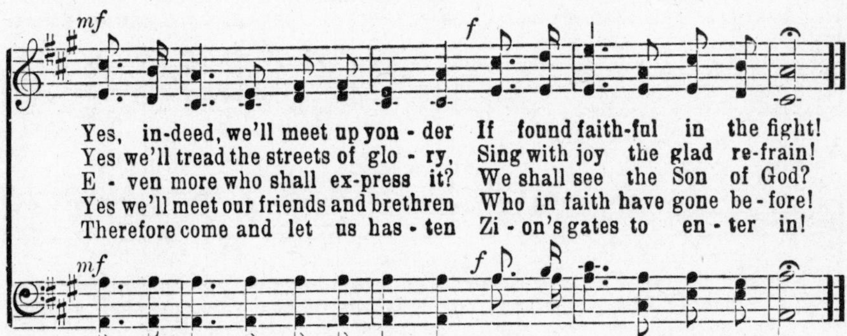
mf
f
Yes, in-deed, we'll meet up yon - der If found faith-ful in the fight!
Yes we'll tread the streets of glo - ry, Sing with joy the glad re-frain!
E - ven more who shall ex-press it? We shall see the Son of God?
Yes we'll meet our friends and brethren Who in faith have gone be - fore!
Therefore come and let us has - ten Zi - on's gates to en - ter in!
mf
f

264 LONGING FOR HOME

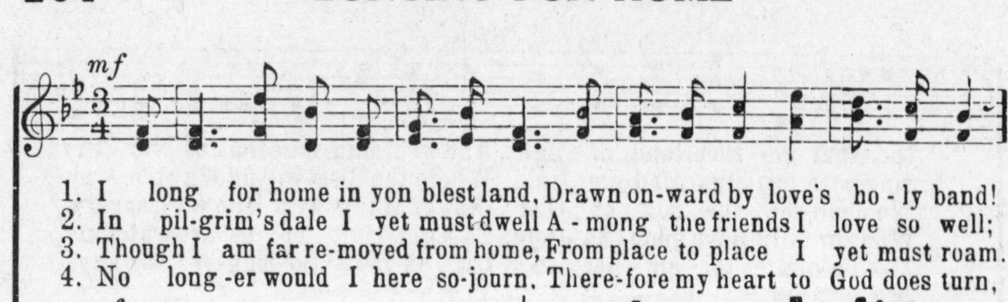

1. I long for home in yon blest land, Drawn on-ward by love's ho - ly band!
2. In pil-grim's dale I yet must dwell A - mong the friends I love so well;
3. Though I am far re-moved from home, From place to place I yet must roam.
4. No long - er would I here so-journ, There-fore my heart to God does turn,

At home! O what a pleas-ant place! T'ward home I now have set my face.
Yet ev - er sighs my wea - ry heart That peace at home might be my part.
Yet ev - er turns my long - ing mind To my dear Fa - ther, good and kind.
Who leads me from this tear - ful vale Home, where de-light and joy pre - vail.

Home-ward! O what a thrill-ing word! Home to my Fa - ther and my Lord!
At home, there longs my soul to be! At home, from pain and sor - row free!
Home-ward! I'm not con-tent - ed here On this dark world and e - vil sphere!
Learn pa-tience then, my wea - ry heart, Lest yearn-ing cause you pain and smart!

Home to my Fa - ther's house I'd go, And leave be-hind this world-ly woe!
At home, where I shall find de-light, And bliss e - ter - nal shall a-bide,
The scorn-ful host now grieves me sore; For home I'm long-ing more and more,
Hold still, for you can not go home Un - til the Fa-ther bids you come,

LONGING FOR HOME

Home to my Fa - ther's house I'd go, And leave be-hind this world - ly woe!
At home, where I shall find de-light, And bliss e - ter - nal shall a - bide.
The scorn-ful host here grieves me sore; For home I'm long-ing more and more.
Hold still, for you can not go home Un - til the Fa - ther bids you come!

265 LORD JESUS, OUR LIGHT

1. Lord Je - sus, Thou our light now be, And sen - ti - nel this night!
2. Thou didst for us this day cre - ate Which now has passed a - way;
3. Therefore we praise Thy ho - ly love, Un - speak - a - ble and great,
4. In this dark night of un - be - lief, When loud its bil - lows roar,
5. O hold us fast while we are here Up - on our pil - grim way,
6. Yea, lead us where Thy rest is shared In Fa - ther's house se-cure,

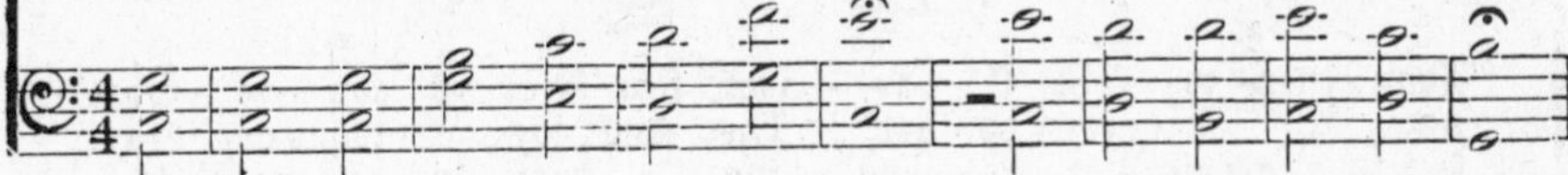

We place our faith and hope in Thee, Thy mer - cy, grace and might.
With life, sal - va - tion and Thy grace Hast filled our hearts each day!
That ev - er flow - eth from a - bove And free for all to take!
Af - ford pro - tec - tion and re - lief, Grant courage ev - er - more!
Un - til our jour - ney we com-plete With Thee for - e'er to stay!
And where a man - sion is pre-pared To Him who shall en - dure!

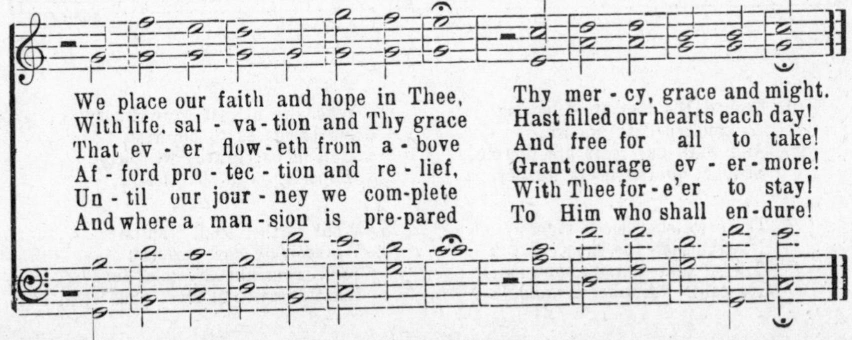

266 LIVING IN FAITH

1. What could be more de - light - ful, More joy and peace cre - ate,
2. We live in bless - ed near - ness, To Thee, Lord day by day.
3. Our lips may be in si - lence, Yet prays our heart to Thee;
4. With mer - cy and with good - ness Our hearts are oft re - freshed.
Than when to Thee, O Sav - iour, Our lives we con - se - crate?
As if our eyes be - held Thee And joy at - tends our way,
Our thoughts are e'er as - cend - ing To heav - en con - stant - ly.
And when we need His pres - ence He an - swers our re - quest,
Than when to Thee, O Sav - iour, Our lives we con - se - crate?
As if our eyes be - held Thee And joy at - tends our way.
Our thoughts are e'er as - cend - ing To heav - en con - stant - ly.
And when we need His pres - ence He an - swers our re - quest.

5. Around His foot stool bowing
   As children dear are we,
   :And when our tears are flowing,
   Straight to His heart we flee.:

6. When we at last grow weary,
   He brings us to our rest,
   :And in our graves we tarry,
   Reposing with the blest.:

7. There we shall sleep securely,
   Naught shall the silence break,
   :Till on that glorious morning,
   He calls; "Awake, Awake,"

8. What further shall transpire,
   We scarcely now surmise;
   :'Twill seem like dreamful fancy,:
   What there shall meet your eyes.:

267 THE BLESSED REST

p
1. Bless-ed rest, when earth-ly toil is end-ed, Shall be mine in
2. Yea, there is a heav'n-ly rest a-wait-ing All the faith-ful
3. Heav'n-ly bliss, con-sol-ing, sooth-ing rap-ture From a-bove a-
4. In that ev-er-last-ing, peace-ful man-sion We in blest and
5. Heaven's dwell-ing, peace-ful hab-i-ta-tion. Which for me the
p
p
all e-ter-ni-ty, From the Fa-ther, who His call ex-tend-ed
serv-ants of the Lord! To the faith-ful, o-ver sin pre-vail-ing
noints the ho-ly heart, Where we've o-ver-come all pain and tor-ture
tran-quil joy shall rest. Ev-er near the Son who paid the ran-som
Fa-ther hath pre-pared! When I reach my jour-ney's des-ti-na-tion
p
mf
To me, that I serve Him faith-ful-ly! O how blest, to cease from
Shall the Lord a crown of life a-ward. Blest shall be our lot when
God will bid our tears and grief de-part. O how glad our souls shall
Lay our head up-on His lov-ing breast, O my Shep-herd, take me
Let Thy man-sions un-to me be shared! Take me, Je-sus, to that
mf
mf f mf p
toil and care, Then to en-ter, Then to en-ter heav-en's rest so fair!
struggles cease, When for-ev-er faith re-ceiv-eth its re-ward and praise!
be and blest, When for-ev-er, when for-ev-er peace-ful-ly we rest.
now with Thee, Where for-ev-er, where for-ev-er near Thee I may be!
bless-ed place Where as Sa-lem's cit-i-zen I e'er shall see Thy face!
mf f mf p

268 WHO ARE THEY BEFORE GOD STANDING

Rev. 7, 9-17

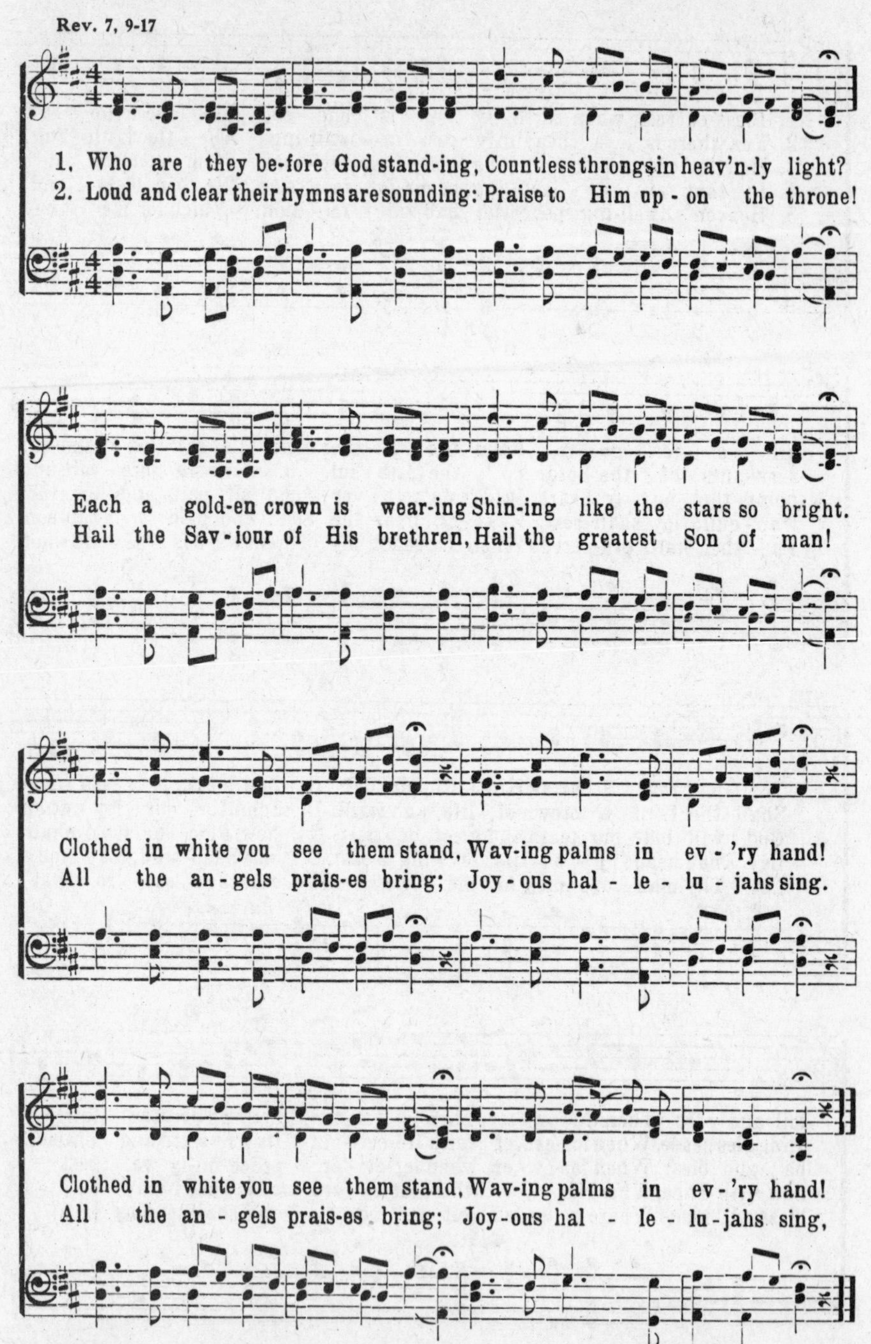
1. Who are they be-fore God stand-ing, Countless throngs in heav'n-ly light?
2. Loud and clear their hymns are sounding: Praise to Him up - on the throne!
Each a gold-en crown is wear-ing Shin-ing like the stars so bright.
Hail the Sav-iour of His brethren, Hail the greatest Son of man!
Clothed in white you see them stand, Wav-ing palms in ev-'ry hand!
All the an-gels prais-es bring; Joy-ous hal - le - lu - jahs sing.
Clothed in white you see them stand, Wav-ing palms in ev-'ry hand!
All the an - gels prais-es bring; Joy-ous hal - le - lu - jahs sing,

WHO ARE THEY BEFORE GOD STANDING

3. Who are they who in such favor
Stand before the face of God?
Who such great reward did merit,
For as angels is their lot?
‖ :In what battle, in what war
Did they this great vict'ry score?: ‖

4. It were they who came victorious
Out of life's deep, troubled sea,
Bearing here the cross in patience,
From all selfish honor free.
‖ :Robes of honor they possess,
Called the great Lamb's righteousness.: ‖

5. It were they who here contended
For the glory of our Lord;
Satan, world and death subduing
Followed not the sinning horde.
‖ :Brave in battle they did stand,
Trusting God's almighty hand.: ‖

6. They are branches of that true vine
Who to us brought help and grace;
And they without fear did venture
Anguish, danger, death to face.
‖ :Now from sorrow, pain and grief
God has granted them relief.: ‖

7. It were they in priestly garments
Who appeared before their God,
Ready day and night for service,
Many sacrifices brought,
‖ :Now in sacred place they stand,
Happy in that Holy Land.: ‖

8. It were they, who, overcoming
Consecrated all to God,
And in love of Christ the Saviour
Found Salvation in His blood,
‖ :They enjoy eternal bliss,
Crowned with God's own righteousness.: ‖

9. As the hart at noontime panteth
For the brooklet clear and cold,
So their souls did sigh while watching,
Living waters to behold.
‖ :Now their thirst is satisfied,
For they rest at Jesus' side.: ‖

10. Now before the throne they're standing,
Serving God by day and night;
Casting still their crowns of glory
Down before the throne of light,
‖ :Where their Mediator stands,
Guarding them with His own hands.: ‖

11. O what words describe the rapture,
When I with that Holy Band
And with radiance brightly gleaming
Shining like the stars I stand?
‖ :Amen, thanks to Thee above,
Praise to Thy eternal love!: ‖

12. O Lord Jesus, look upon me!
Heart and hands to Thee I raise.
Grant that on my pilgrim journey
On Thee I direct my gaze!
‖ :And through conflict, toil and strife
Fit me for eternal life.: ‖

269 TO THAT FAIR CELESTIAL CITY

p
mf
1. To that fair ce-les-tial cit-y Would my spir-it fain de-part. Oft a
2. To that fair ce-les-tial cit-y Would my spir-it fain de-part. There to
3. To that fair ce-les-tial cit-y Would my spir-it fain de-part. There to
long-ing for that man-sion Pass-es o'er my wea-ry heart. There the Saviour's
feast with my dear Mas-ter On His breast to soothe each smart. There to feel in
gath-er with the ransomed Praising God with thankful heart. There awaits for
ho-ly pres-ence Doth il-lu-mi-nate God's king-dom. We be-hold in
His blest pres-ence Love's soft, gen-tle, sooth-ing rap-ture. We be-hold in
ev-'ry vic-tor, On that shore, a crown of hon-or. We be-hold in
heav-en's light Je-sus' countenance so bright, Je-sus' countenance so bright.
f

RESURRECTION

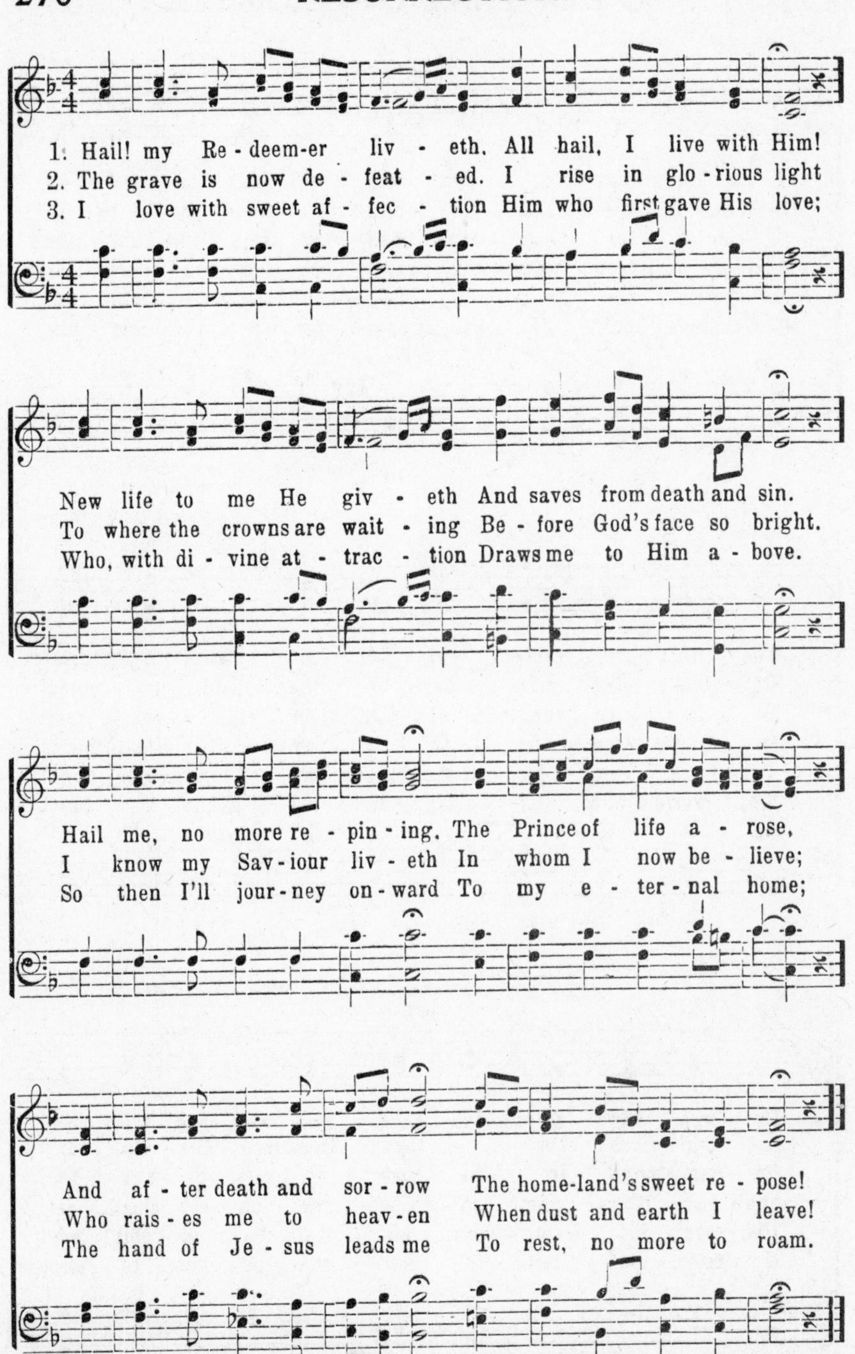

1. Hail! my Re - deem-er liv - eth. All hail, I live with Him!
2. The grave is now de - feat - ed. I rise in glo - rious light
3. I love with sweet af - fec - tion Him who first gave His love;
New life to me He giv - eth And saves from death and sin.
To where the crowns are wait - ing Be - fore God's face so bright.
Who, with di - vine at - trac - tion Draws me to Him a - bove.
Hail me, no more re - pin - ing. The Prince of life a - rose,
I know my Sav - iour liv - eth In whom I now be - lieve;
So then I'll jour - ney on - ward To my e - ter - nal home;
And af - ter death and sor - row The home-land's sweet re - pose!
Who rais - es me to heav - en When dust and earth I leave!
The hand of Je - sus leads me To rest, no more to roam.

271 TO HIM THAT OVERCOMETH

Rev. 1. 2-3
p
mf
1. To him that o - ver - com - eth shall be giv - en
2. Who o - ver - com - eth shall be made par - tak - er
3. Who o - ver - com - eth shall in shin - ing rai - ment
4. Who o - ver - com - eth shall be - come a pil - lar
5. Who o - ver - com - eth, he shall be in - vit - ed
6. Grant me, Lord Je - sus, strength for o - ver - com - ing
f
The fruit from trees of life in Par - a - dise!
Of hid - den man - na, by the Lord pre - pared!
Be - fore the throne of God in glo - ry rest!
In God's own sanc - tu - a - ry, in His house!
To sit up - on the throne at Christ's right hand!
Sin, world and Sa - tan and his gloom - y host!
He who has served the Lord and well has striv - en
A glo - rious her - i - tage from God His Mak - er,
His name shall in the book of life be writ - ten,
Shall have the name in - scribed up - on his shoul - der:
His grief, his sor - rows, all shall be re - quit - ed,
O make me faith - ful, let me be vic - to - rious

TO HIM THAT OVERCOMETH

f
Shall rest from toil, and take from Him the prize!
A ti - tle new shall un - to Him be shared!
Be - fore God's an - gels he shall be con - fessed!
Je - ru - sa - lem, the cit - y God a - vows!
The prom - ised crown a - dorns him in that land!
Thy face to see on yon - der bless - ed coast!
p
God will re - fresh him With heav'n-ly bless - ing! E - ter - nal
He who be - liev - eth And Him re - ceiv - eth Shall win the
To him be giv - en, Who well has striv - en The palms of
A hab - i - ta - tion For ev - 'ry na - tion The Lord shall
On pas - tures ver - nal In life e - ter - nal He'll rest from
There wilt Thou bless me, With joy re - fresh me, There I'll dis-
mf
rap - ture shall be his part! E - ter - nal rap - ture shall be his part!
treas-ure, the morn-ing star, Shall win the treas-ure, the morn-ing star!
vic - t'ry, a just re-ward, The palms of vic - t'ry a just re-ward!
o - pen in Sa-lem's tent, The Lord shall o - pen in Sa - lem's tent!
la - bor, from toil and care, He'll rest from la - bor, from toil and care!
cov - er e - ter - nal rest, There I'll dis - cov - er e - ter - nal rest!

272 HAIL TO THE BRIGHTNESS

THOMAS HASTINGS
LOWELL MASON
1. Hail to the bright-ness of Zi - on's glad morn-ing! Joy to the lands that in dark-ness have lain! Hushed be the ac - cents of sor-row and mourn-ing, Zi - on in tri-umph be - gins her mild reign.
2. Hail to the bright-ness of Zi - on's glad morn-ing, Long by the proph - ets of Is - rael fore - told! Hail to the mil - lions from bond-age re - turn - ing! Gen - tiles and Jews the blest vi - sion be - hold.
3. Lo, in the des - ert rich flow - ers are spring-ing, Streams ev - er co - pious are glid - ing a - long; Loud from the moun-tain - tops ech - oes are ring - ing, Wastes rise in ver-dure and min - gle in song.
4. See, from all lands, from the isles of the o - cean, Praise to Je - ho - vah as - cend - ing on high; Fallen are the en - gines of war and com - mo - tion, Shouts of sal - va - tion are rend-ing the sky.
273 O THAT I WERE WITH JESUS
1. O that I were with Je - sus! O that I could take wings,
2. Where we with joy and won - der Thy coun - te-nance be - hold,
3. There where the host of right - eous Will cel - e - brate in glee,
4. There where the trib - u - la - tion Of earth shall be no more;
5. In tones of heav'nly sweet-ness, Trans-fig-ured with de - light,
6. Our tears which here are fall - ing Will bring mirth like a sea;

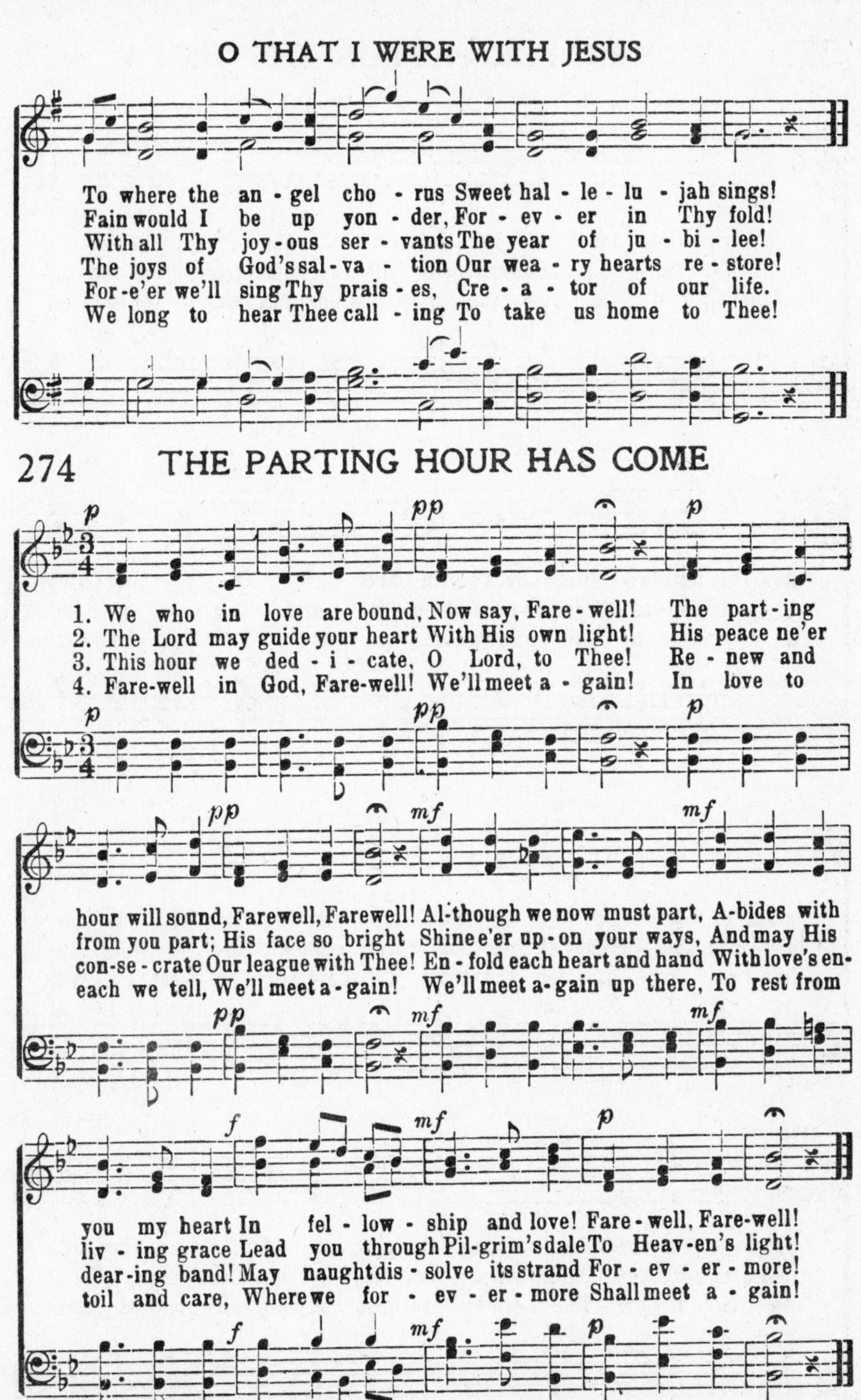
O THAT I WERE WITH JESUS
To where the an - gel cho - rus Sweet hal - le - lu - jah sings!
Fain would I be up yon - der, For - ev - er in Thy fold!
With all Thy joy - ous ser - vants The year of ju - bi - lee!
The joys of God's sal - va - tion Our wea - ry hearts re - store!
For - e'er we'll sing Thy prais - es, Cre - a - tor of our life.
We long to hear Thee call - ing To take us home to Thee!
274 THE PARTING HOUR HAS COME
p
pp
p
1. We who in love are bound, Now say, Fare - well! The part - ing
2. The Lord may guide your heart With His own light! His peace ne'er
3. This hour we ded - i - cate, O Lord, to Thee! Re - new and
4. Fare - well in God, Fare - well! We'll meet a - gain! In love to
pp
mf
mf
hour will sound, Farewell, Farewell! Al - though we now must part, A - bides with
from you part; His face so bright Shine e'er up - on your ways, And may His
con - se - crate Our league with Thee! En - fold each heart and hand With love's en-
each we tell, We'll meet a - gain! We'll meet a - gain up there, To rest from
f
mf
p
you my heart In fel - low - ship and love! Fare - well, Fare - well!
liv - ing grace Lead you through Pil - grim's dale To Heav - en's light!
dear - ing band! May naught dis - solve its strand For - ev - er - more!
toil and care, Where we for - ev - er - more Shall meet a - gain!

275 AWAKEN, FOR PAST IS THE GLOOM

f
1. A - wak - en, for past is the gloom of the night! The Sav-iour
2. No long - er the dark grave can fill us with fright, For Je - sus
3. The light of Je - ho-vah il - lu-mines our way, We walk un-
f
mf
has brought us life, free - dom and light! O let us sing
has freed us from death's gloom - y night! The yoke of our
a - fraid in the bright-ness of day! Then let us be
mf
prais - es in joy - ful ac - cord. Ex - alt - ing the pow - er of
con-science no long - er we feel, And crushed is the foe by the
hap - py, for af - ter the strife The Lord will re - fresh us with
f
ff
Je - sus, the Lord! Ex - alt-ing the pow - er of Je - sus, the Lord!
Con-quer - or's heel! And crushed is the foe by the Con - quer-or's heel!
wa - ters of life! The Lord will re-fresh us with wa - ters of life!
f
ff

276 I MUST TELL JESUS

E. A. H. E. A. HOFFMAN

1. I must tell Je - sus all of my tri - als; I can - not bear these
2. I must tell Je - sus all of my troub - les; He is a kind, com -
3. Tempted and tried I need a great Sav - ior, One who can help my
4. O how the world to e - vil al - lures me! O how my heart is
bur - dens a - lone; In my dis - tress He kind - ly will help me;
pas - sion - ate Friend; If I but ask Him, He will de - liv - er,
bur - dens to bear; I must tell Je - sus, I must tell Je - sus;
tempt - ed to sin! I must tell Je - sus, and He will help me
He ev - er loves and cares for His own.
Make of my troub - les quick - ly an end.
He all my cares and sor - rows will share.
O - ver the world the vic - t'ry to win.
CHORUS
I must tell Je - sus!
I must tell Je - sus! I can - not bear my bur - dens a - lone; I must tell
Je - sus! I must tell Je - sus! Je - sus can help me, Je - sus a - lone.

LOVE FOR JESUS

1. Je - sus, Thou my soul's re - pose, And my Sav - iour who a - rose,
2. Am I sick and pressed with grief, No one near to give re - lief,
3. Am I need - y, faint and tried, Is my sor - row mul - ti - plied,
4. Therefore, Je - sus, I'll a - new Love Thee faith-ful - ly and true.
Ev - 'ry - thing art Thou to me, Shalt my
Je - sus, my Phy - si - cian dear, And my
Je - sus is my strength in - deed, And my
Thou, O Je - sus, Thou shalt be All and
All for - ev - er be, Shalt my All for - ev - er be.
Help - er will be near, And my Help - er will be near.
friend in ev - ery need, And my friend in ev - ery need.
ev - ery - thing to me, All and ev - ery - thing to me.
278
NEARER, MY GOD, TO THEE
Saran F. Adams
Lowell Mason
1. Near - er, my God, to Thee, Near - er to Thee! E'en tho' it be a cross
2. Tho' like the wan - der - er, The sun gone down, Darkness be o - ver me,
3. There let the way appear Steps un - to heav'n; All that Thou sendest me
4. Then, with my waking tho'ts Bright with Thy praise, Out of my ston - y griefs,
5. Or if on joy - ful wing, Cleaving the sky, Sun, moon, and stars forgot,

NEARER, MY GOD, TO THEE

279 JESUS, LOVER OF MY SOUL

CHARLES WESLEY S. B. MARSH

That rais-eth me, Still all my song shall be, Near-er, my God, to Thee,
My rest a stone; Yet in my dreams I'd be, Near-er, my God, to Thee,
In mer-cy giv'n; An-gels to beck-on me Near-er, my God, to Thee,
Beth-el I'll raise; So by my woes to be Near-er, my God, to Thee,
Up-ward I fly, Still all my song shall be Near-er, my God, to Thee,
Near-er, my God, to Thee, Near-er to Thee. A-men.
FINE
1. Je-sus, Lov-er of my soul, Let me to Thy bos-om fly,
While the near-er wa-ters roll, While the tem-pest still is high!
2. Oth-er ref-uge have I none; Hangs my help-less soul on Thee:
Leave, ah, leave me not a-lone, Still sup-port and com-fort me!
3. Thou, O Christ, art all I want; More than all in Thee I find;
Raise the fall-en, cheer the faint, Heal the sick, and lead the blind.
4. Plenteous grace with Thee is found, Grace to cov-er all my sin;
Let the heal-ing streams abound, Make and keep me pure with-in.
D. C.–Safe in-to the ha-ven guide, O re-ceive my soul at last!
D. C.–Cov-er my de-fense-less head With the shad-ow of Thy wing.
D. C.–False and full of sin I am, Thou art full of truth and grace.
D. C.–Spring Thou up with-in my heart, Rise to all e-ter-ni-ty.
D.C.
Hide me, O my Sav-ior, hide, Till the storm of life is past;
All my trust on Thee is stayed, All my help from Thee I bring;
Just and ho-ly is Thy name, I am all un-right-eous-ness;
Thou of life the foun-tain art; Free-ly let me take of Thee;

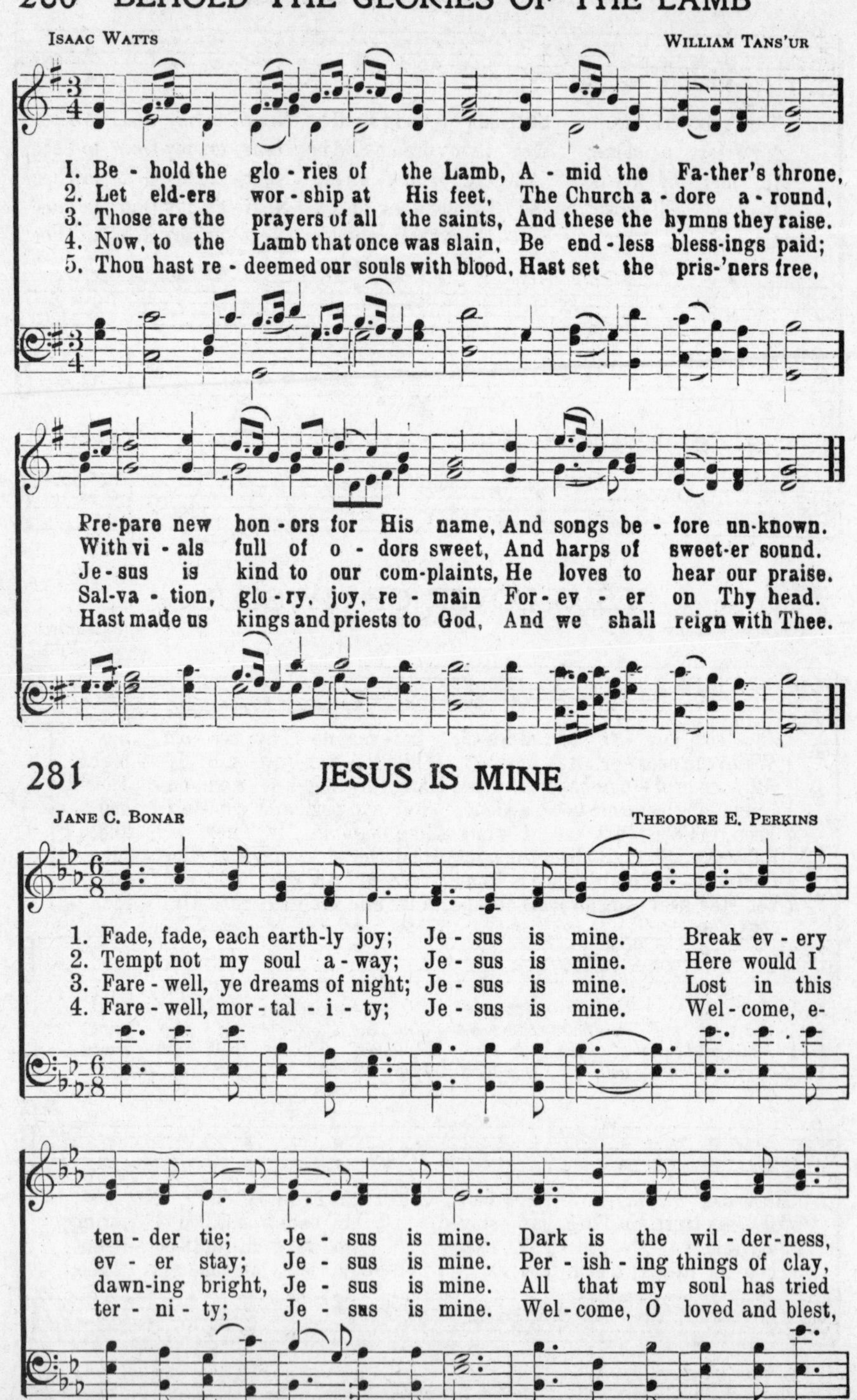
280 BEHOLD THE GLORIES OF THE LAMB
Isaac Watts
William Tans'ur
1. Be - hold the glo - ries of the Lamb, A - mid the Fa-ther's throne,
2. Let eld-ers wor - ship at His feet, The Church a - dore a - round,
3. Those are the prayers of all the saints, And these the hymns they raise.
4. Now, to the Lamb that once was slain, Be end - less bless-ings paid;
5. Thou hast re - deemed our souls with blood, Hast set the pris-'ners free,
Pre-pare new hon - ors for His name, And songs be - fore un-known.
With vi - als full of o - dors sweet, And harps of sweet-er sound.
Je - sus is kind to our com-plaints, He loves to hear our praise.
Sal-va - tion, glo - ry, joy, re - main For - ev - er on Thy head.
Hast made us kings and priests to God, And we shall reign with Thee.
281 JESUS IS MINE
Jane C. Bonar
Theodore E. Perkins
1. Fade, fade, each earth-ly joy; Je - sus is mine. Break ev - ery
2. Tempt not my soul a - way; Je - sus is mine. Here would I
3. Fare - well, ye dreams of night; Je - sus is mine. Lost in this
4. Fare - well, mor - tal - i - ty; Je - sus is mine. Wel - come, e-
ten - der tie; Je - sus is mine. Dark is the wil - der-ness,
ev - er stay; Je - sus is mine. Per - ish - ing things of clay,
dawn-ing bright, Je - sus is mine. All that my soul has tried
ter - ni - ty; Je - sus is mine. Wel - come, O loved and blest,

JESUS IS MINE

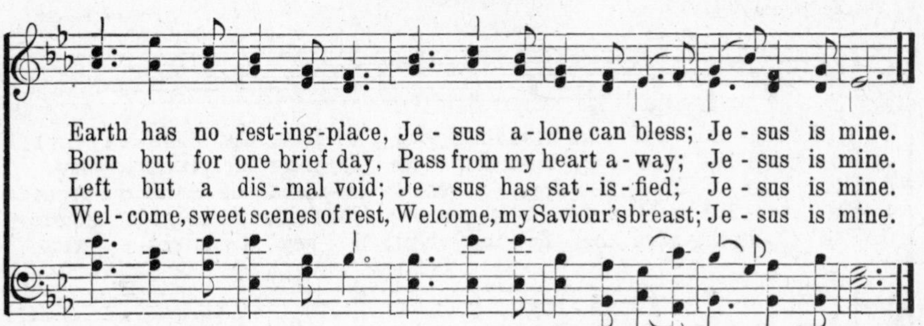

Earth has no rest-ing-place, Je - sus a-lone can bless; Je - sus is mine.
Born but for one brief day, Pass from my heart a-way; Je - sus is mine.
Left but a dis-mal void; Je - sus has sat-is-fied; Je - sus is mine.
Wel-come, sweet scenes of rest, Welcome, my Saviour's breast; Je - sus is mine.

282 WORK, FOR THE NIGHT IS COMING

ANNIE L. COGHILL LOWELL MASON

1. Work, for the night is coming, Work thro' the morning hours; Work while the dew is
2. Work, for the night is coming, Work thro' the sun-ny noon; Fill brightest hours with
3. Work, for the night is coming, Under the sunset skies; While the bright tints are

sparkling, Work 'mid springing flow'rs; Work when the day grows brighter, Work in the
la - bor, Rest comes sure and soon. Give ev-'ry fly-ing min-ute Something to
glow - ing, Work, for daylight flies. Work till the last beam fad-eth, Fadeth to

glow-ing sun; Work, for the night is com - ing, When man's work is done.
keep in store: Work, for the night is com - ing, When man works no more.
shine no more; Work, while the night is dark'ning, When man's work is o'er.

283 WITH SONGS AND HONORS SOUNDING

Isaac Watts — Henry Smart

1. With songs and hon - ors sound-ing loud, Ad-dress the Lord on high;
2. He sends His show'rs of bless-ing down To cheer the plains be - low;
3. His hoar - y frost, His fleec - y snow; De-scend and clothe the ground;
4. He sends His word, and melts the snow; The fields no long - er mourn;
5. The chang-ing wind, the fly - ing cloud, O - bey His might-y word:
O - ver the heav'ns He spreads His cloud, And wa - ters veil the sky.
He makes the grass the moun-tains crown, And corn in val - leys grow.
The liq - uid streams for - bear to flow, In i - cy fet - ters bound.
He calls the warm - er gales to blow, And bids the spring re - turn.
With songs and hon - ors sound-ing loud Praise ye the sov-'reign Lord.

284 THE LORD MY SHEPHERD IS

Isaac Watts, — B. C. Unseld

1. The Lord my Shep - herd is, I shall be well sup - plied;
2. He leads me to the place Where heav'n-ly pas - ture grows,
3. If e'er I go a - stray, He doth my soul re - claim,
4. While He af - fords His aid, I can - not yield to fear;
Since He is mine and I am His, What can I want be - side?
Where liv-ing wa - ters gen - tly pass, And full sal - va - tion flows.
And guides me in His own right way, For His most ho - ly name.
Though I should walk thro' death's dark shade, My Shepherd's with me there.

285 JESUS, ROSE OF SHARON

Ida A. Guirey — Chas. H. Gabriel

1. Je - sus, Rose of Shar - on, bloom with - in my heart; Beau - ties of Thy
2. Je - sus, Rose of Shar - on, sweet - er far to see Than the fair - est
3. Je - sus, Rose of Shar - on, balm for ev-'ry ill, May Thy ten - der
4. Je - sus, Rose of Shar - on, bloom for - ev - er - more; Be Thy glo - ry
truth and ho - li - ness im - part, That wher-e'er I go my life may
flow'rs of earth could ev - er be, Fill my life com - plete - ly, add - ing
mer - cy's healing pow'r dis - til For af - flic - ted souls of wea - ry,
seen on earth from shore to shore, Till the na - tions own Thy Sov'-reign-
shed a-broad Fra-grance of the knowledge of the love of God.
more each day Of Thy grace di - vine and pur - i - ty, I pray.
bur-dened men, Giv - ing need - y mor - tals health and hope a - gain.
ty complete, Lay their hon - ors down and worship at His feet.
REFRAIN.
Je - sus, ... Rose of Shar - on, ...
Bless - ed Je - sus, Rose of Shar - on,
Bloom in ra - diance and in love with - in my heart.

286 O GOD OF WISDOM

Menno M. Brubacher, 1926 — Walter E. Yoder, 1926

1. O God of wis-dom, life and love, Thine is the bless-ed plan
2. These souls be-trothed be-fore Thee stand; Thy bless-ing we im-plore;
3. As they go forth up-on life's way, Sus-tain them by Thy grace;
4. May they with ho-ly lives a-dorn Thy doc-trines, Lord, and be
5. And when Thou, Lord, shalt come a-gain To gath-er home Thine own,

In ho-ly bonds of love to join The twain, cre-a-ted man.
U-nite Thou them in heart and hand, And guide them ev-er-more.
May they Thy ho-ly laws o-bey And live in joy and peace.
A-mid life's sun-shine and its storm True wit-ness-es for Thee.
May they, with du-ty no-bly done, Be blessed be-fore Thy throne.

287 O GOD, OUR HELP IN AGES PAST

Isaac Watts — William Croft

1. O God, our help in a-ges past, Our hope for years to come,
2. Be-fore the hills in or-der stood, Or earth re-ceived her frame,
3. A thous-and a-ges, in Thy sight, Are like an ev-'ning gone;
4. Time, like an ev-er-roll-ing stream, Bears all its sons a-way;
5. O God, our help in a-ges past, Our hope for years to come;

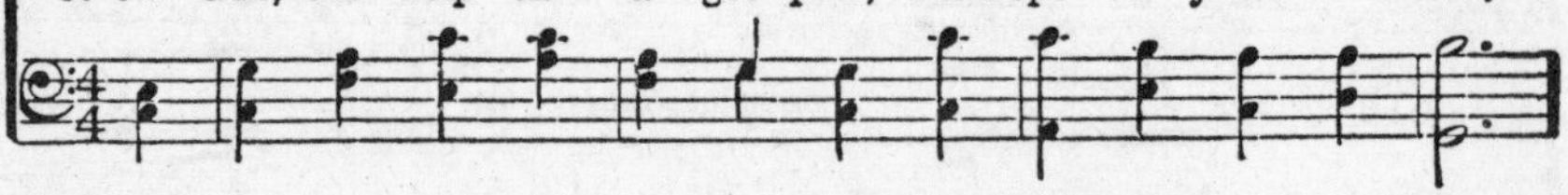

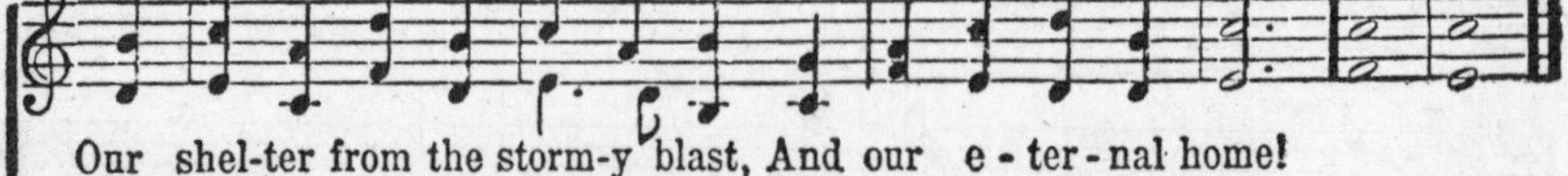

Our shel-ter from the storm-y blast, And our e-ter-nal home!
From ev-er-last-ing Thou art God, To end-less years the same.
Short as the watch that ends the night, Be-fore the ris-ing sun.
They fly, for-got-ten, as a dream Dies at the ope-ning day.
Be Thou our guide while life shall last, And our e-ter-nal home! A-men.

288 BLESSED ASSURANCE

Fanny J. Crosby

Mrs. J. F. Knapp

1. Bless-ed as - sur - ance, Je - sus is mine! O what a fore-taste of
2. Per - fect sub-mis - sion, per-fect de - light, Vi-sions of rap - ture now
3. Per - fect sub-mis - sion, all is at rest, I in my Sav - iour am
glo - ry di - vine! Heir of sal - va - tion, purchase of God, Born of His
burst on my sight! Angels de-scend-ing, bring from a - bove Ech-oes of
hap - py and blest; Watching and waiting, look-ing a - bove, Filled with His
REFRAIN
Spir - it, washed in His blood.
mer - cy, whis-pers of love. This is my sto - ry, this is my
good - ness, lost in His love.
song, Prais - ing my Sav - iour all the day long; This is my
sto - ry, this is my song, Praising my Sav - iour all the day long.

289 THE LOVE OF GOD

F. M. L.*

F. M. Lehman
Arr. by Claudia Lehman Mays

1. The love of God is great-er far Than tongue or pen can ev - er tell;
2. When hoary time shall pass a - way, And earthly thrones and kingdoms fall;
3. Could we with ink the o-cean fill, And were the skies of parchment made;
It goes be - yond the high-est star, And reach-es to the low - est hell.
When men who here re-fuse to pray, On rocks and hills and mountains call;
Were ev-'ry stalk on earth a quill, And ev - 'ry man a scribe by trade;
The guilt - y pair, bowed down with care, God gave His Son to win;
God's love, so sure, shall still en - dure, All meas-ure-less and strong;
To write the love of God a - bove Would drain the o - cean dry;
His err - ing child He rec - on - ciled, And par-doned from his sin.
Re-deem - ing grace to Ad-am's race—The saints' and an - gels' song.
Nor could the scroll con-tain the whole, Tho' stretched from sky to sky.
CHORUS
Oh, love of God, how rich and pure! How meas-ure - less and strong!

THE LOVE OF GOD

It shall for-ev-er-more en-dure— The saints, and an-gels' song.

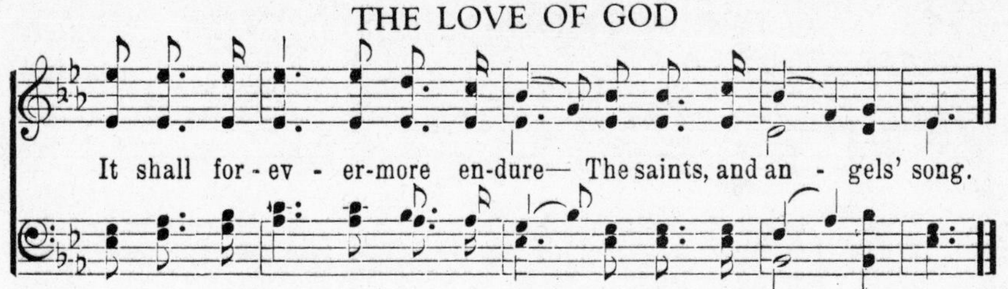

290 REVIVE US AGAIN

Wm. P. Mackay

John J. Husband

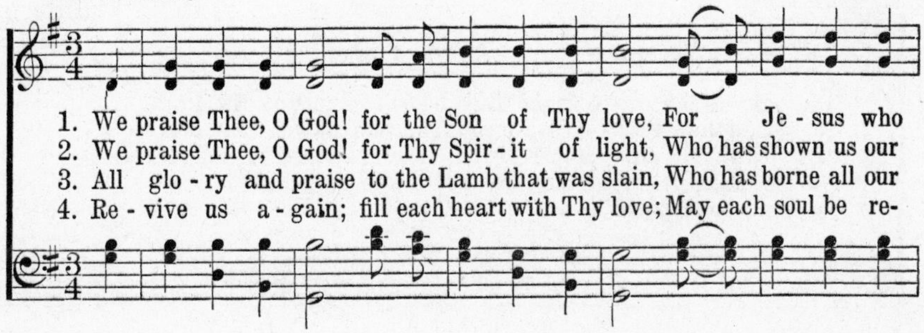

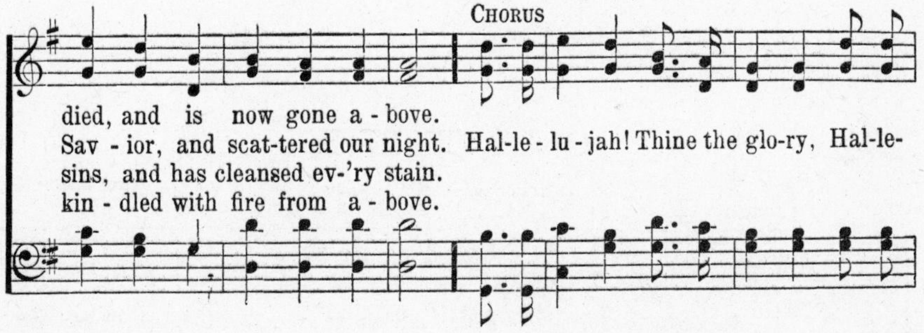

1. We praise Thee, O God! for the Son of Thy love, For Je-sus who
2. We praise Thee, O God! for Thy Spir-it of light, Who has shown us our
3. All glo-ry and praise to the Lamb that was slain, Who has borne all our
4. Re-vive us a-gain; fill each heart with Thy love; May each soul be re-

CHORUS
died, and is now gone a-bove.
Sav-ior, and scat-tered our night. Hal-le-lu-jah! Thine the glo-ry, Hal-le-
sins, and has cleansed ev-'ry stain.
kin-dled with fire from a-bove.

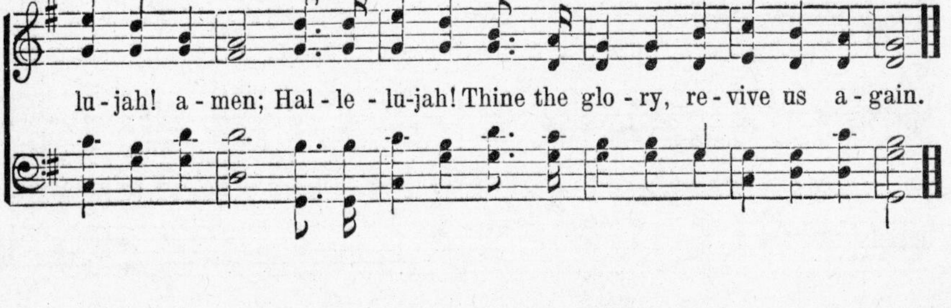

lu-jah! a-men; Hal-le-lu-jah! Thine the glo-ry, re-vive us a-gain.

291 O FOR A THOUSAND TONGUES

Charles Wesley

Carl G. Glaser
Arr. by Lowell Mason

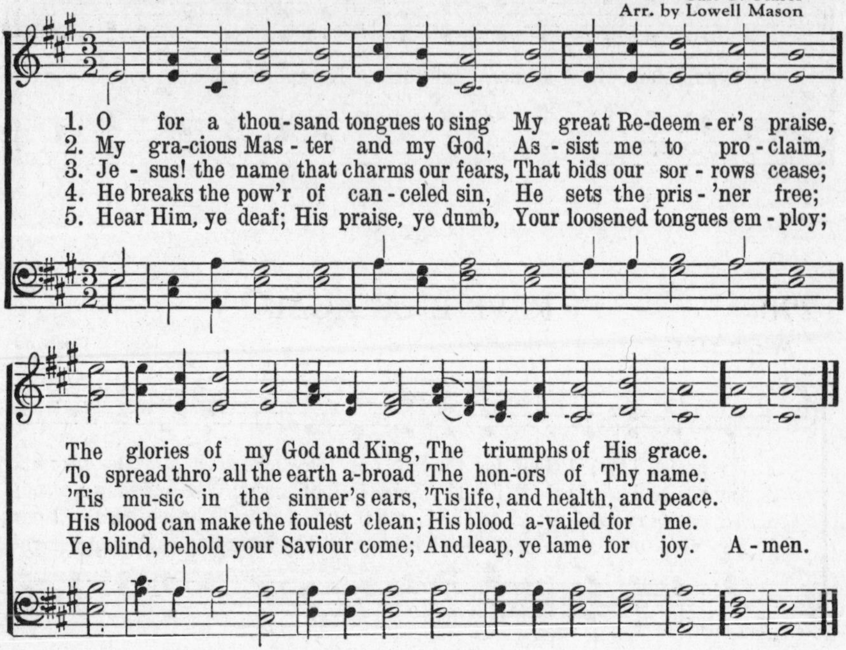

1. O for a thou-sand tongues to sing My great Re-deem-er's praise,
2. My gra-cious Mas-ter and my God, As-sist me to pro-claim,
3. Je-sus! the name that charms our fears, That bids our sor-rows cease;
4. He breaks the pow'r of can-celed sin, He sets the pris-'ner free;
5. Hear Him, ye deaf; His praise, ye dumb, Your loosened tongues em-ploy;
The glories of my God and King, The triumphs of His grace.
To spread thro' all the earth a-broad The hon-ors of Thy name.
'Tis mu-sic in the sinner's ears, 'Tis life, and health, and peace.
His blood can make the foulest clean; His blood a-vailed for me.
Ye blind, behold your Saviour come; And leap, ye lame for joy. A-men.

292 ONLY BELIEVE

P. R.

Paul Rader

CHORUS
On-ly be-lieve, on-ly be-lieve; All things are pos-si-ble, on-ly be-lieve;
On-ly be-lieve, on-ly be-lieve; All things are pos-si-ble, on-ly be-lieve.

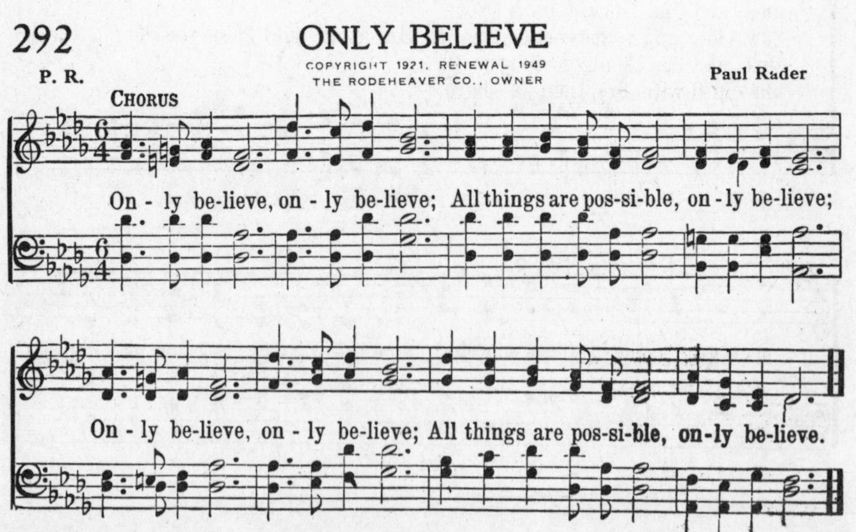

REST FROM YOUR LABORS

M. E.

p Andante
f
Rest from your la - bors on this ho - ly day, And give thanks to God,
Rest from your la - bors on this ho - ly day, And give thanks to God,

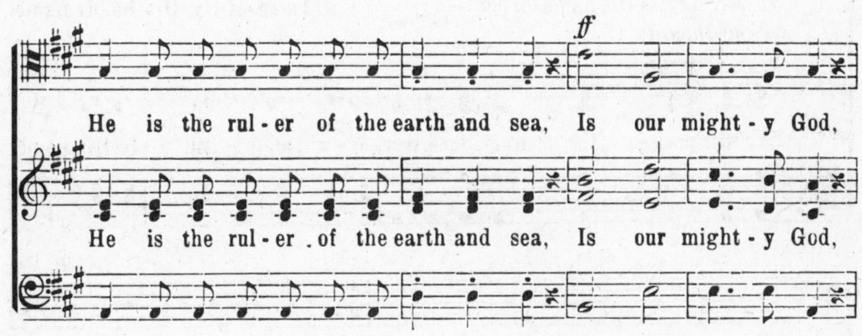
ff
He is the rul - er of the earth and sea, Is our might - y God,
He is the rul - er of the earth and sea, Is our might - y God,

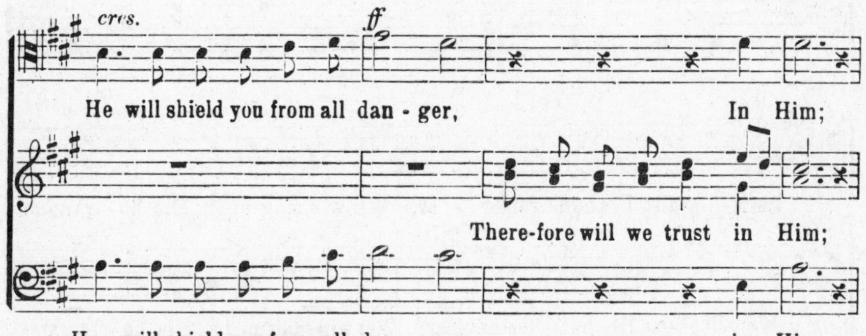
cres.
ff
He will shield you from all dan - ger, In Him;
There-fore will we trust in Him;
He will shield you from all dan - ger, in Him;

REST FROM YOUR LABORS

m
f
Bless - ed be His name for-ev - er, Bless-ed be the name of God.
Bless-ed be the name of God.
Bless - ed be His name for - ev - er,
Soprano obligato
We will praise His name for-ev - er, We will mag-ni-fy His ho-ly name;
Semi-staccato
We will praise His name for-ev-er, We will mag - ni - fy His name;
Repeat pp
Bless - ed be His name for-ev - er, Bless-ed be the name of God,
ff
Bless-ed be His name for-ev-er, Bless the name of God,
Duet.
We will praise His name for-ev - er, We will mag-ni-fy His ho-ly name;
We will praise His name for-ev - er, We will mag-ni-fy His ho - ly name;

COME UNTO ME

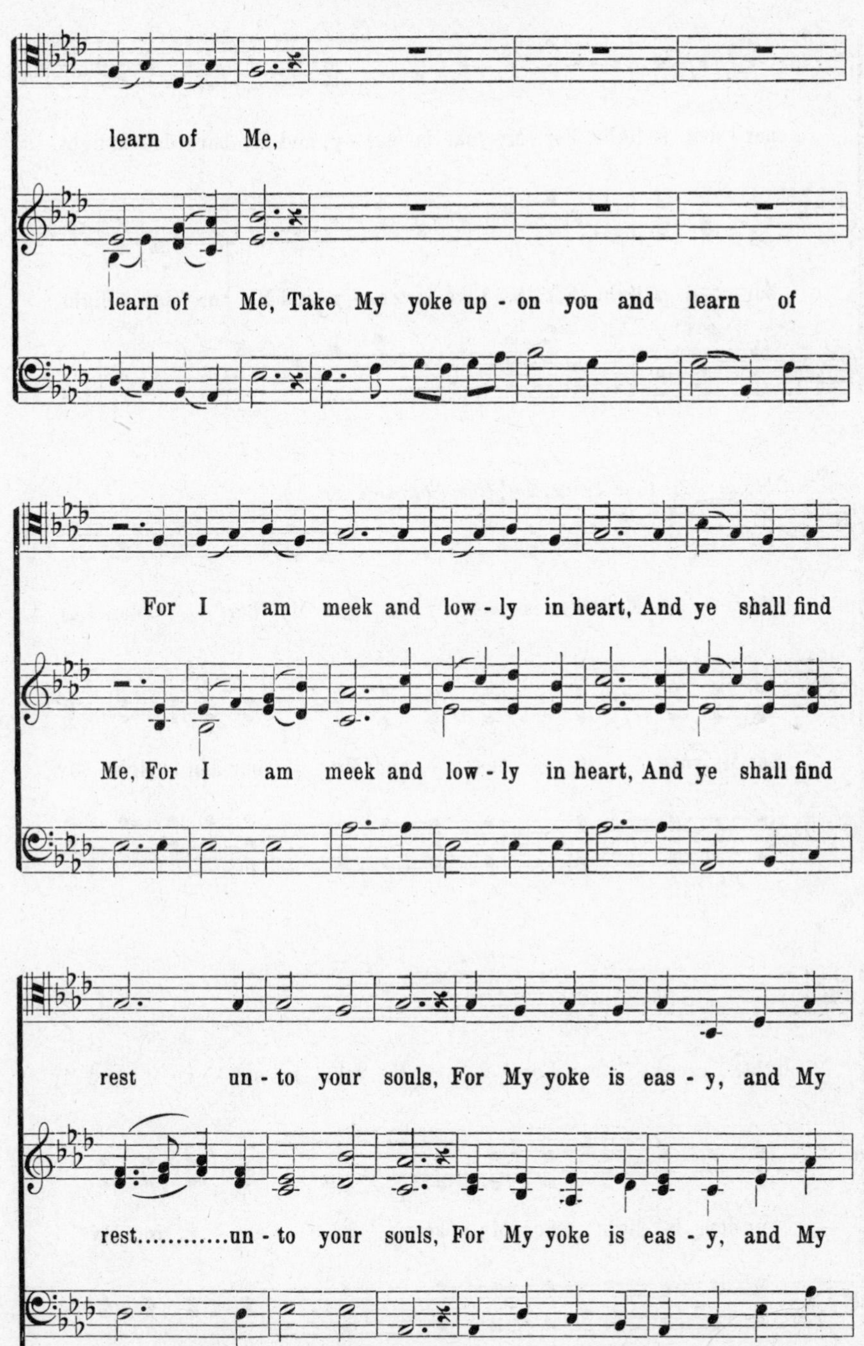
learn of Me,
learn of Me, Take My yoke up - on you and learn of
For I am meek and low - ly in heart, And ye shall find
Me, For I am meek and low - ly in heart, And ye shall find
rest un - to your souls, For My yoke is eas - y, and My
rest............un - to your souls, For My yoke is eas - y, and My

COME UNTO ME

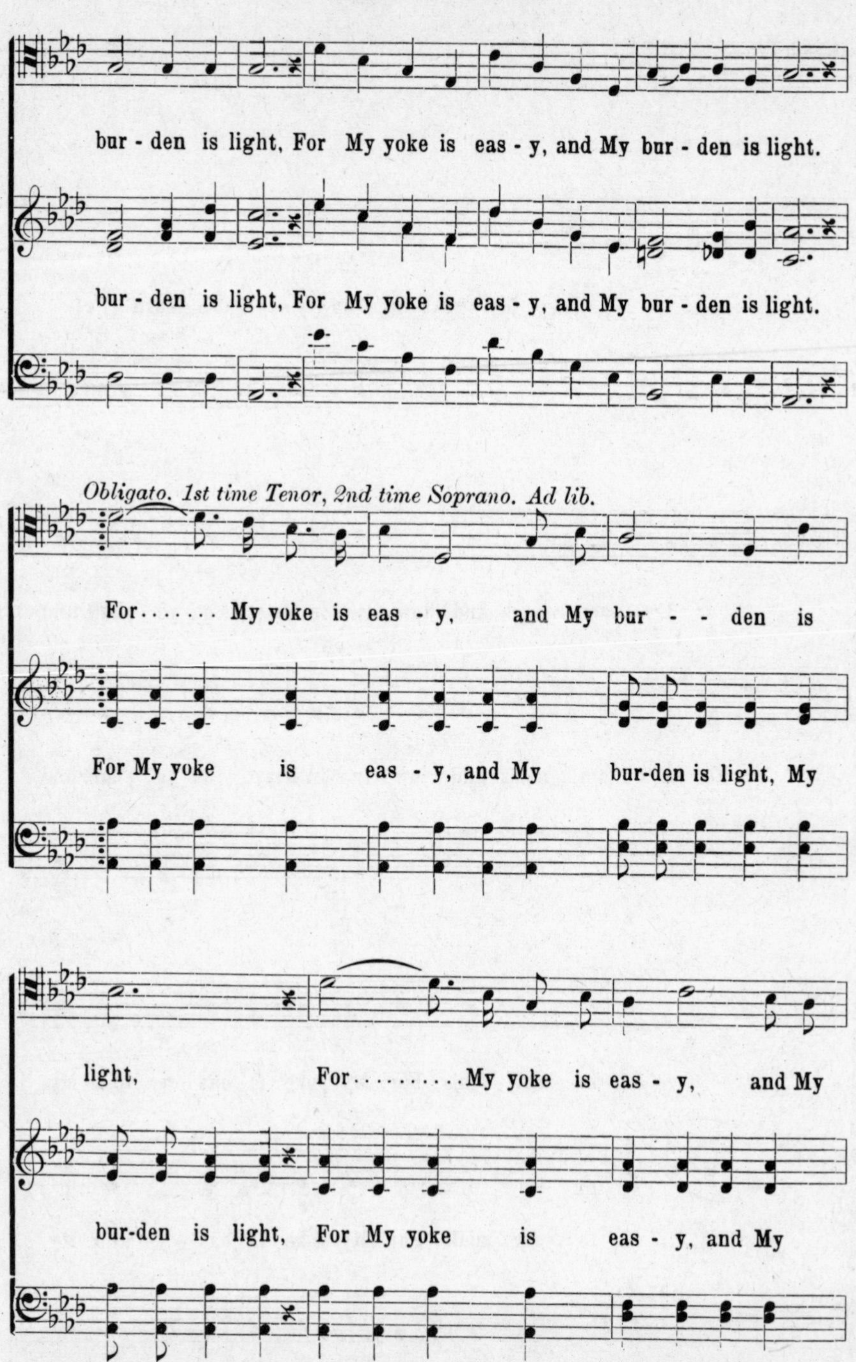
bur - den is light, For My yoke is eas - y, and My bur - den is light.
bur - den is light, For My yoke is eas - y, and My bur - den is light.
Obligato. 1st time Tenor, 2nd time Soprano. Ad lib.
For....... My yoke is eas - y, and My bur - - den is
For My yoke is eas - y, and My bur-den is light, My
light, For..........My yoke is eas - y, and My
bur-den is light, For My yoke is eas - y, and My

COME UNTO ME

bur - den is light. Come un - to Me,
bur-den is light, My bur-den is light. Come un - to
come un - to Me, come un - to Me, And I will give you
Me. un - to Me, come un - to Me, And I will give you
Come un - to Me, un - to Me,
rest, and I will give you rest, I will give you rest,
rest, and I will give you rest, I will give you rest,
p rit.
pp rit.
I will give you rest, I will give you rest.
I will give you rest, I will give you rest.

PSALM 92

mf
It is an ex-cel-lent thing, thanking the Lord, singing praises unto Thy name,
mf
Most Ex - alt - ed! Each morn Thy loving kindness, Each eve Thy faithful promise,
p
Lord, I praise Thee with
mf
Yea, Thy grace and Thy mer - cy de - clar - ing!
mf
joy- - ous sing-ing!
f
Lord, I praise Thee with singing! Lord, I praise Thee with joy-ous sing-ing of Thy a-
f
In the might of Thy hands.......... will I tri-umph!
mf
chievements! I will tri-umph in Thy might!
mf
mf

PSALM 92

In the might of Thy hands will I tri - umph! I love to sing of Thy great a-
chieve-ments and to tri - umph in Thy might! Lord, oh, how are all Thy
ac - tions, Thy a-chieve-ments so great! Lord, oh, how are all Thy ac - tions,
All Thy ac - tions,
Thy a-chieve-ments so great! Thou, O Lord Most Ex - alt - ed! En-
dur-est ev - er - more! Thou, O Lord Most Ex-alt - ed! En-dur - est ev - er-more!

PSALM 92
Oh, how are all Thy ac - tions so great!
O Lord, how are all Thy a-
so great!
So great,.................................... Oh, how
ff
So great, O Lord, all Thy ac-tions, how are they so great.
chieve-ments so great,
ff
So great, all Thy ac-tions, so great, oh, how are they so great.
Yea, it is an ex-cel-lent thing, thank-ing the Lord, Sing-ing
prais-es un-to Thy name, Most Ex-alt - ed! Thy a-
So great!................
chieve-ments are great! Thy a-chieve-ments are great, so great, so great!
are great!
are great! Thy a-chieve-ments are great!..... ......

PSALM 126

p
When the Lord shall re - turn His e - lect from cap - tiv - i - ty,
p
'Twill seem like a won-der - ful dream to us! Our mouth shall be filled with
laugh-ing glee, Our tongue sing His prais - es with ju - bi - lee!
mf
Men shall re-late it, tell - ing the hea-then: "The Lord has done won-drous
mf
The Lord has done won-drous things for us! The
things un-to them! The Lord has done wondrous things!
The Lord has done wondrous
The Lord has

PSALM 126

Lord has done wondrous things for us!
The Lord has done won-der-ful things! In this we glo-ry, in
things for us! Yea,
done wondrous things! In this we,
this we glo-ry. The Lord has done won-drous things for us!
Slowly
Lord, free us then from our bond-age. As brooks of wa-ter Thou dost
p
mf
drain at noon-tide! Aft-er tear-ful sow-ing fol-lows a joy-ful
p
mf
har-vest. Aft-er tear-ful sow-ing fol-lows a joy-ful

PSALM 126

p
harv - est: They ven - ture forth with weep - ing, With pre-cious
p
mf
seed en-trust - ed, And come with re - joic - ing, and come with re-
mf
joic - ing, Their sheaves of vic - t'ry bring - - - ing!
p
Aft - er tear - ful sow - ing fol-lows a joy - ful har - vest,
mf
f
Fol - lows a joy - ful har - vest, a joy - ful har - vest!
f

THE TWENTY-THIRD PSALM

I shall not want, God is my Shep-herd; God is my Shep-herd, I shall

not want; God is my Shep-herd, I shall not want, God is my Shep-herd,

I shall not want, I shall not want! He lead-eth me on ver-dant

pas-tures; He lead-eth me by the still wa-ters; On ver-dant

pas-tures, He lead-eth me!

By the still wa-ters, He lead-eth me!

THE TWENTY-THIRD PSALM

On ver-dant pas-tures, On ver-dant
By the still wa-ters!
pas-tures. He lead-eth me, by the still wa-ters He guid-eth me!
My faint-ing soul He doth re-store, and lead-eth me in right-eous
pathways. He on righteous pathways leadeth me!
He on righteous pathways
To glo-ri-fy His name, To glo-ri-fy His name, To
lead-eth me!

THE TWENTY-THIRD PSALM

glo-ri-fy His name, To glo-ri - fy His name! Though in this vale of
Though
death and gloom I wan-der, my soul shall have no fear,
in this vale of death and gloom
p
For Thou art still with me! Thy rod and staff sup - port - ing, my
Thy rod and staff sup-
f
com - fort e'er shall be! Thy rod and staff sup - port - ing, my
f
port - ing, my com-fort e'er shall be! Thy rod and staff sup-
com-fort e'er shall be! Shall be! Be - fore my foes a ta- - - -
port - ing, my comfort e'er shall be! Be-fore my foes a

THE TWENTY-THIRD PSALM

ble - - - Thou dost here pre - pare a ta - ble's set be-
ta - ble Thou dost here pre-pare a ta-ble's set be-
fore my foes! My cup dost Thou re - plen - ish, With oil dost Thou a-
fore my foes!
f
noint my head, My cup dost Thou re - plen-ish, with oil dost Thou a-
f
noint my head. With oil dost Thou a-noint my head. O-ver - flow-ing
is the cup for me! Thy mer - cy and Thy truth a-bound through-

THE TWENTY-THIRD PSALM

out this pil-grim life; Thy mer-cy and Thy truth a-bound through-
out this pil-grim life; And in the house of God I
e-ver-more shall dwell, And in the house of God I
And in the house of God I
e-ver-more shall dwell, There in the house of God,
e-ver-more shall
In His e-ter-nal House. Thy mer-cy and Thy truth a-bound here

THE TWENTY-THIRD PSALM

in this pil-grim life. Thy mer-cy and Thy truth a-bound here
in this pil-grim life!
And in His ho-ly house I
There in His ho-ly house I
e-ver-more shall dwell!
e-ver-more shall dwell, There in His ho-ly house,
In His e-ter-nal house, His e-ter-nal house!

299 TODAY IS THE LORD'S DAY

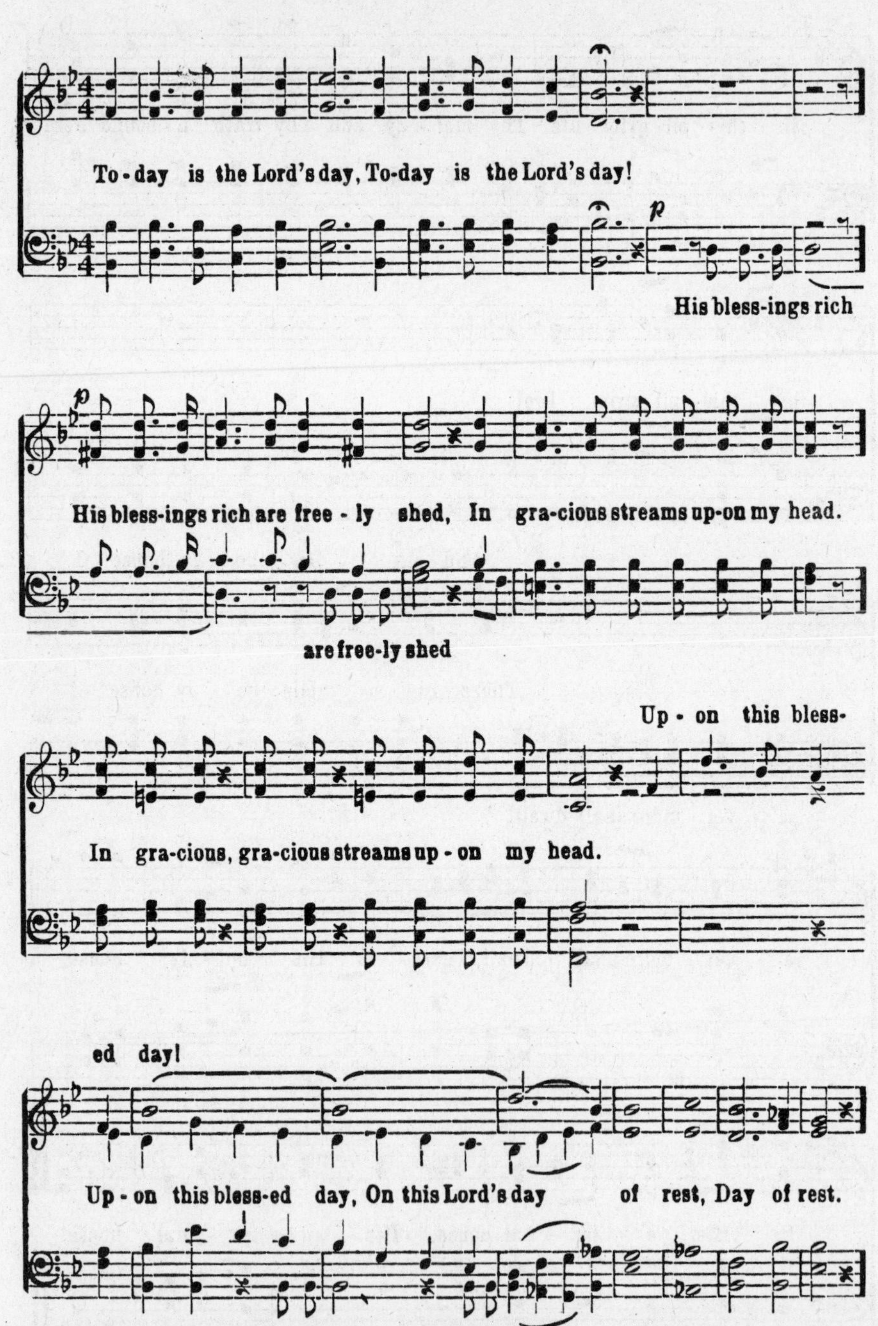
To-day is the Lord's day, To-day is the Lord's day!
His bless-ings rich
His bless-ings rich are free - ly shed, In gra-cious streams up-on my head.
are free-ly shed
Up - on this bless-
In gra-cious, gra-cious streams up - on my head.
ed day!
Up - on this bless-ed day, On this Lord's day of rest, Day of rest.
Up - on this bless-ed day, Welcome day of rest

TODAY IS THE LORD'S DAY

A peace di - vine A heaven-ly rest, De-scends from God in-to my breast up-
A peace di - vine, a heav'n - ly rest!
on this bless-ed day A peace di-vine, A heav'n-ly rest!
A peace di - vine, A heav'n - ly rest!
A peace di-vine, A peace di-vine, a heav'n - ly rest!
The Day-star's gold-en ray Doth in our hearts with glo - ry shine As we par-
take this bread di - vine Up - on this bless-ed day, This bless-ed day of rest.

THERE WERE SHEPHERDS

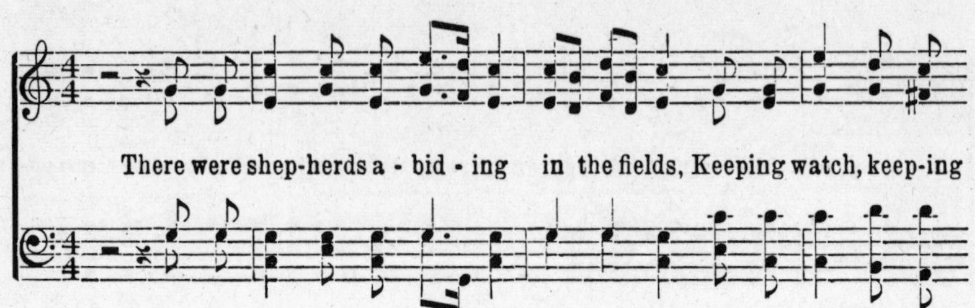
There were shep-herds a - bid - ing in the fields, Keeping watch, keep-ing

watch o'er their flocks by night. And the an - gel of the Lord came up-

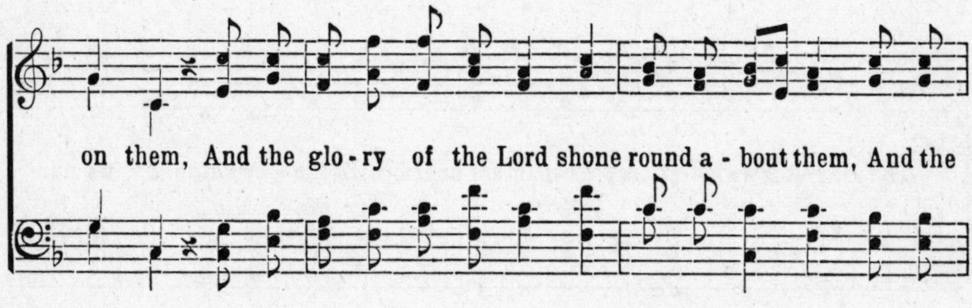
on them, And the glo - ry of the Lord shone round a - bout them, And the

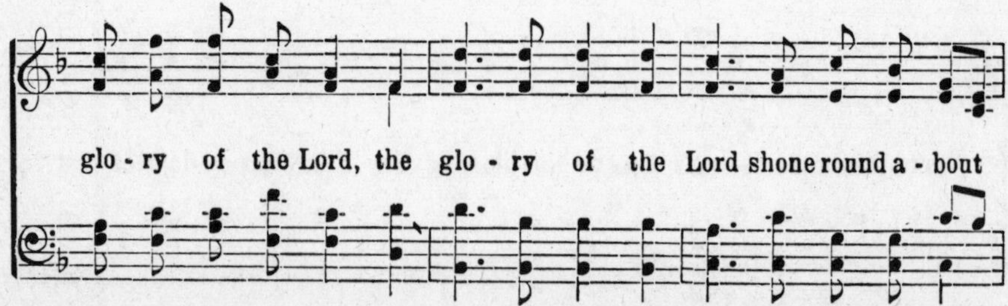
glo - ry of the Lord, the glo - ry of the Lord shone round a - bout

THERE WERE SHEPHERDS

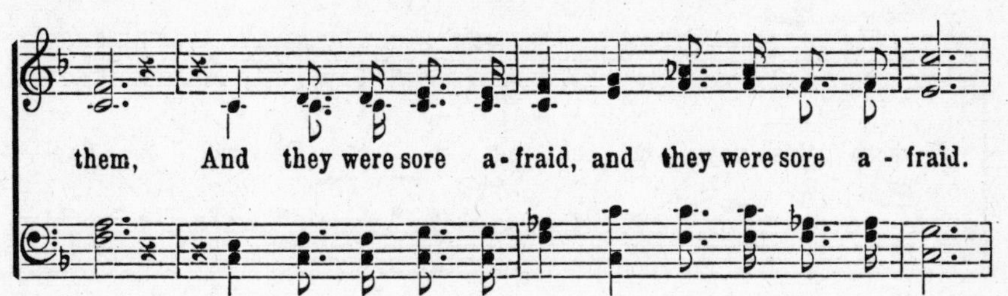
them, And they were sore a-fraid, and they were sore a-fraid.

"Fear ye not, fear ye not, for be-
And the an-gel said un-to them:

hold I bring you good ti-dings of great joy, Which shall be to all

peo-ple, to all peo-ple; For un-to you is

THERE WERE SHEPHERDS

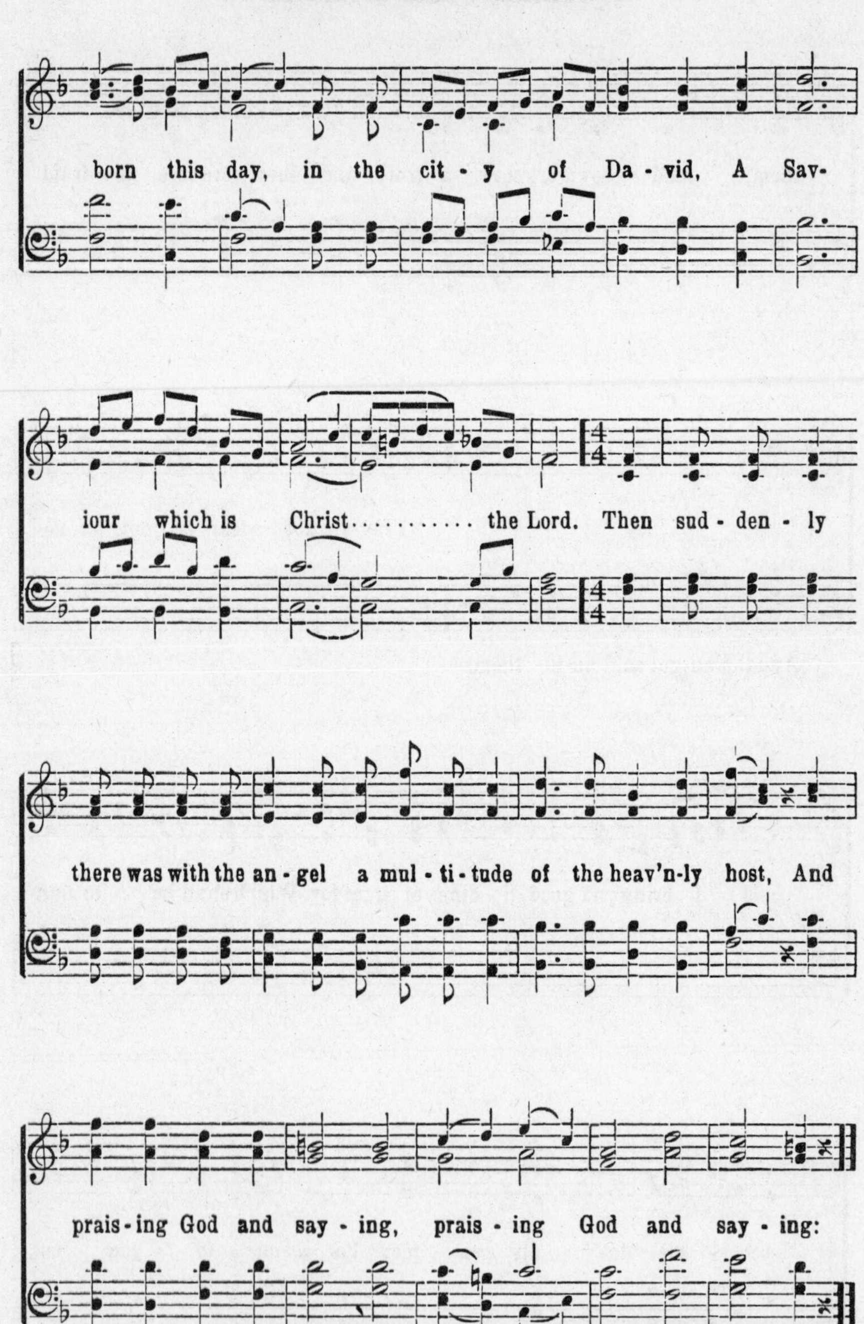
born this day, in the cit - y of Da - vid, A Sav-
iour which is Christ.......... the Lord. Then sud - den - ly
there was with the an - gel a mul - ti - tude of the heav'n-ly host, And
prais - ing God and say - ing, prais - ing God and say - ing:

Finish with "Glory, Glory"

THERE WERE SHEPHERDS

CHORUS
f
Glo - ryl Glo - ry! Glo - ry to God in the high - est!
f
p
mf
On earth peace and con - cord, Un - to man - kind good will and
p
mf
In the
f
fa - vor! Un - to man - kind good will and fa - vor!
f
high - est
In the high - est
mf
f
Glo - ry to God!.................... Glo - ry to
In the high - est!
mf
f

THERE WERE SHEPHERDS

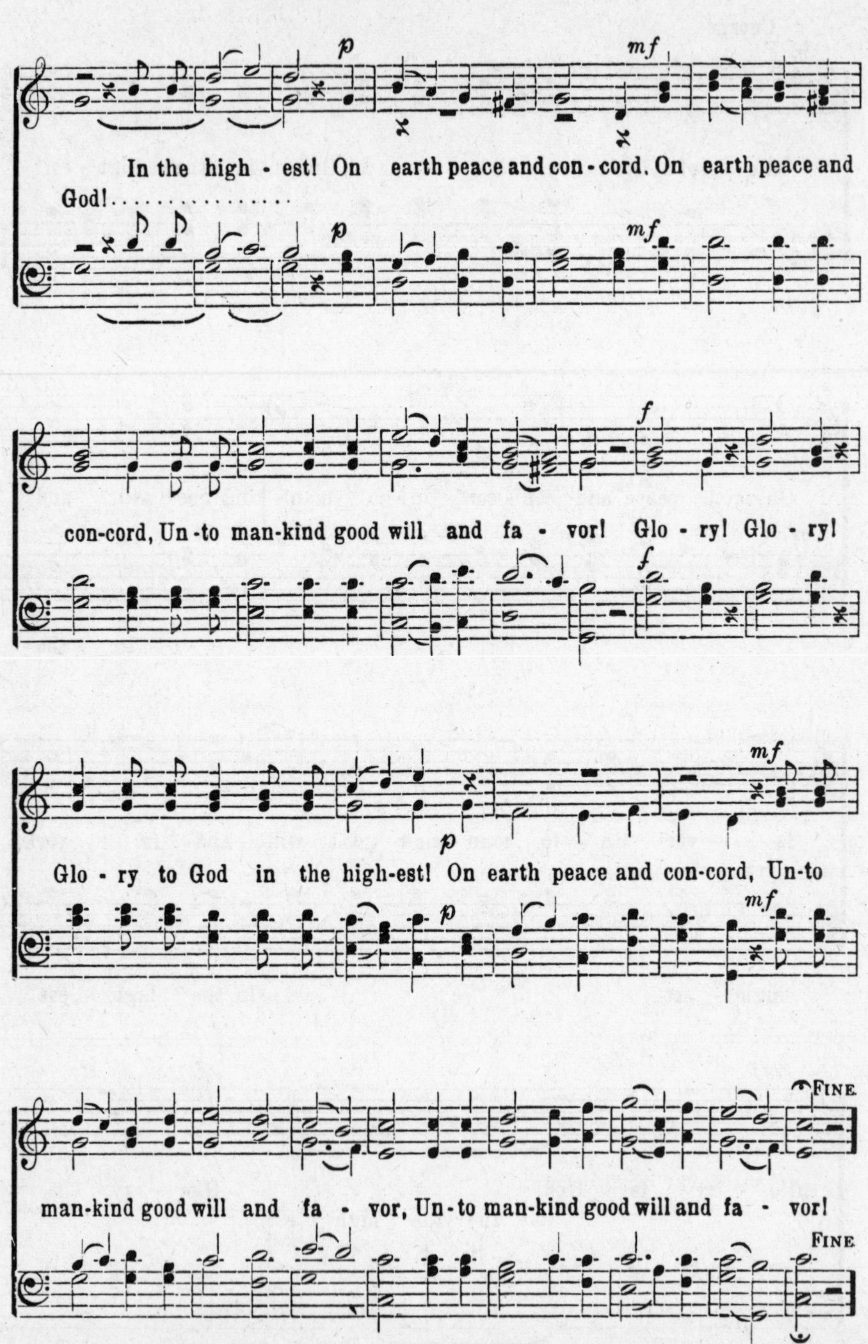
p
mf
In the high - est! On earth peace and con - cord. On earth peace and
God!.................
p
mf
f
con-cord, Un-to man-kind good will and fa - vor! Glo - ry! Glo - ry!
f
mf
p
Glo - ry to God in the high-est! On earth peace and con-cord, Un-to
p
mf
FINE
man-kind good will and fa - vor, Un-to man-kind good will and fa - vor!
FINE

THERE WERE SHEPHERDS

CHORAL
Slowly
p
How shall I, Lord, re - ceive Thee And how Thy grace ex - tol?
p

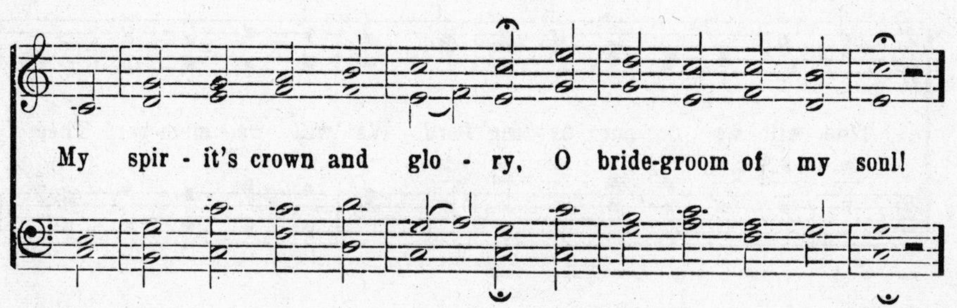
My spir - it's crown and glo - ry, O bride-groom of my soul!

f
Give me the un - der - stand - ing How full of light and grace
f

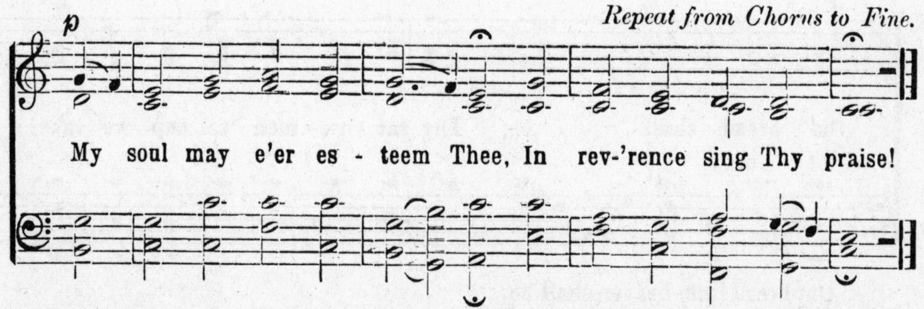
Repeat from Chorus to Fine.
p
My soul may e'er es - teem Thee, In rev-'rence sing Thy praise!

301 WE WILL REMEMBER THEE

James Montgomery M. Y. R

Ac - cor-ding to Thy gra-cious word, In meek hu - mil - i - ty,
This will we do, our dy - ing Lord, We will re - mem-ber Thee,
Thy bod - y bro-ken for our sake, Thy bod - y bro - ken for our sake,
Our bread shall be; Thy sac - ra - men - tal cup we take,
Our bread from heaven shall be;

WE WILL REMEMBER THEE

And thus re-mem-ber Thee. Can we Geth-sem-a-ne for-get?
Or there Thy con-flict see, Thine ag-o-ny and blood-y sweat, And
not re-mem-ber Thee? When to the cross we turn our eyes, And rest on
Cal-va-ry, Oh Lamb of God our sac-ri-fice, We must re-mem-ber Thee.

TOPICAL INDEX

GENERAL INDEX

Titles in CAPITALS – First lines in lower case

GENERAL INDEX

GENERAL INDEX

GENERAL INDEX

RAINBOW LITHOGRAPHING CO.
MUSIC PRINTERS · CHICAGO, ILL.